VOLTA

MAN'S GREATEST LAKE

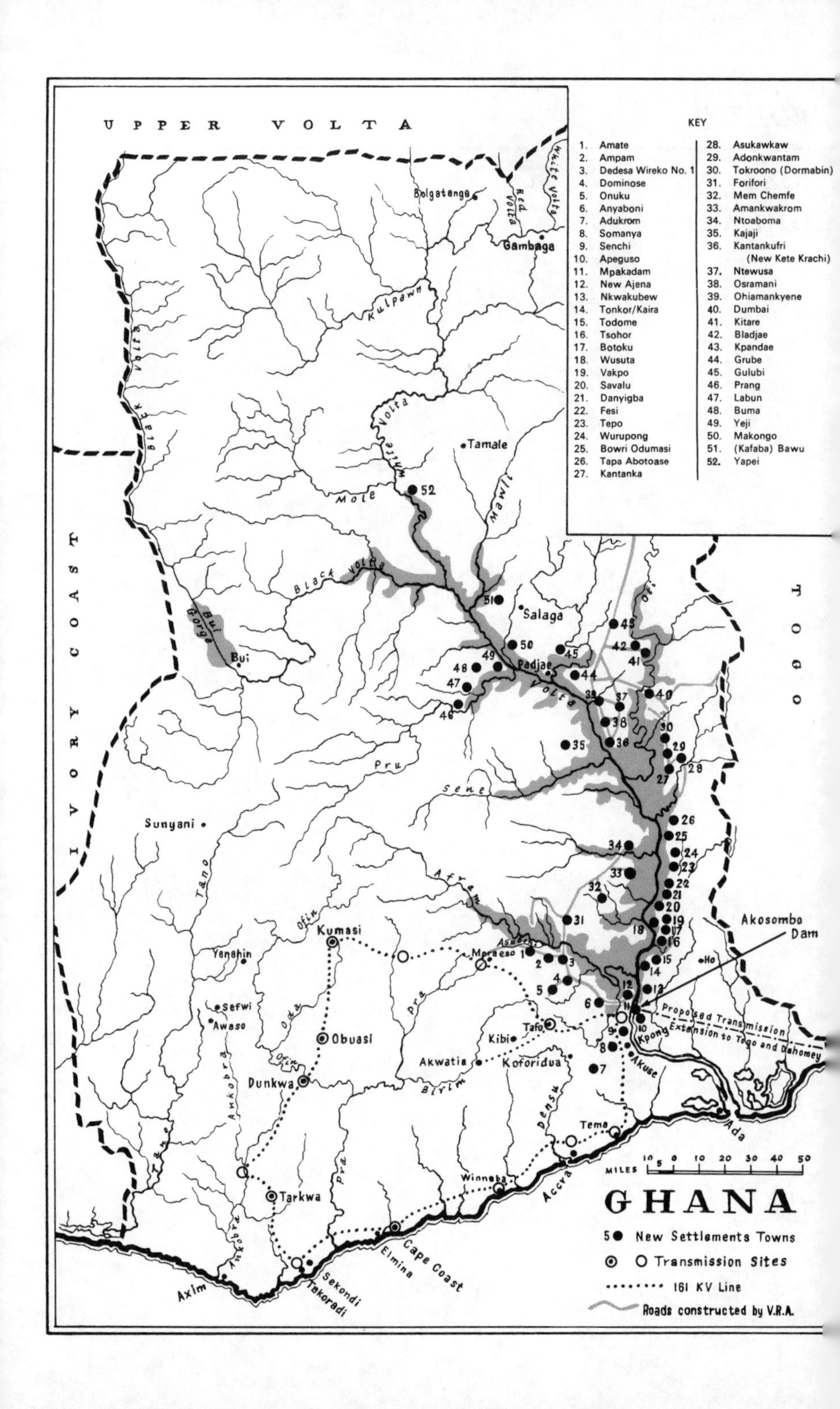
UPPER VOLTA
KEY
1. Amate
2. Ampam
3. Dedesa Wireko No. 1
4. Dominose
5. Onuku
6. Anyaboni
7. Adukrom
8. Somanya
9. Senchi
10. Apeguso
11. Mpakadam
12. New Ajena
13. Nkwakubew
14. Tonkor/Kaira
15. Todome
16. Tsohor
17. Botoku
18. Wusuta
19. Vakpo
20. Savalu
21. Danyigba
22. Fesi
23. Tepo
24. Wurupong
25. Bowri Odumasi
26. Tapa Abotoase
27. Kantanka
28. Asukawkaw
29. Adonkwantam
30. Tokroono (Dormabin)
31. Forifori
32. Mem Chemfe
33. Amankwakrom
34. Ntoaboma
35. Kajaji
36. Kantankufri (New Kete Krachi)
37. Ntewusa
38. Osramani
39. Ohiamankyene
40. Dumbai
41. Kitare
42. Bladjae
43. Kpandae
44. Grube
45. Gulubi
46. Prang
47. Labun
48. Buma
49. Yeji
50. Makongo
51. (Kafaba) Bawu
52. Yapei
IVORY COAST
TOGO
Bolgatanga
Gambaga
Tamale
Salaga
Bui
Padjae
Sunyani
Kumasi
Yenahin
Sefwi
Awaso
Obuasi
Dunkwa
Tarkwa
Axim
Takoradi
Sekondi
Elmina
Cape Coast
Winneba
Accra
Tema
Ada
Akuse
Kpong
Kibi
Tafo
Akwatia
Koforidua
Mpraeso
Ho
Akosombo Dam
Proposed Transmission Extension to Togo and Dahomey
Red Volta
White Volta
Black Volta
Kulpawn
Mole
Mawli
Volta
Oti
Pru
Sene
Afram
Asukawkaw
Ofin
Oda
Pra
Birim
Densu
Tano
Ankobra
Bui Gorge
MILES 10 5 0 10 20 30 40 50
GHANA
New Settlements Towns
Transmission Sites
161 KV Line
Roads constructed by V.R.A.

VOLTA

MAN'S GREATEST LAKE

James Moxon

ANDRE DEUTSCH

FIRST PUBLISHED 1969 BY
ANDRE DEUTSCH LIMITED
105 GREAT RUSSELL STREET
LONDON WC1
PAPERBACK EDITION 1984
NEW AND REVISED PAPERBACK EDITION 1984
COPYRIGHT © 1969 BY JAMES MOXON
ALL RIGHTS RESERVED
PRINTED IN GREAT BRITAIN BY
THE PITMAN PRESS BATH

ISBN 233 97717 1

This book is dedicated to the memory of the two pioneers whose work was the foundation of the Volta River Project.

Sir Albert Kitson 1868–1937

Duncan Rose 1901–66

This edition – which includes Chapters 27–30 – is further dedicated to the memory of Dr Kwame Nkrumah (1911–72), President of the First Republic of Ghana, to whose fiery imagination and determination the Volta River Project owes so much. And to the memory of his friend Edgar F. Kaiser (1908–81), formerly Chairman of Kaiser Corporation – whose active participation in the Project from the outset 'made a difference'.

CONTENTS

LIST OF ILLUSTRATIONS

MAPS

ACKNOWLEDGEMENTS

My first thanks must go to my friend André Deutsch for first persuading me to write this book and then, patiently, waiting for it.

From that time onwards I have fallen and relied upon so many hundreds of people that I could not possibly acknowledge or thank them all individually. Collectively however I must mention in particular the staff of the Volta River Authority with whom I worked with such rapport over a period of several years; of Kaiser in its many guises (I can think of six of its many subsidiaries which have helped me) and of Valco, the aluminium smelter; of Sir William Halcrow and Partners Ltd of London and Bird and Robertson of Johannesburg, Consulting Engineers; of Impregilo, the main contractor for the Akosombo dam, and their many sub-contractors; of the principal supply contractors; of the University of Ghana which has conducted so much research into the project; and of the many agencies of the Ghana Government which have been concerned with this project.

Individually however I must record my thanks in particular to Sir Robert Jackson, who has not only written the Foreword but who has, from many corners of the world, always promptly responded to my calls for advice. I also sincerely thank Mrs Audrey Bishop for early research work and constant assistance, and Mr Joseph Addo-Aryee Abrahams, my secretary, who has painstakingly typed the manuscript (and more) several times over. And finally I owe a debt of gratitude to Mrs Margaret Legum for the irksome task of offering editorial advice. The faults that remain will result from my obstinate refusal at times to take the best advice offered.

James Moxon

FOREWORD

Sir Robert Jackson KCVO CMG OBE

There are now several very large multi-purpose schemes in operation in various parts of the world, but the Volta River Project is probably unique in the extraordinary political setting which surrounded its conception, planning and construction. Its seeds were planted in the closing stages of a British Crown Colony, struggled to life in the early days of the first of the new African States, and are now represented by a great power and growing industrial complex where men of many races can work together, and where public and private capital is joined together in effective partnership.

Like nearly all the great multi-purpose schemes, the Volta River Project has a long history – well described in this book – but the final, critical, fifteen years of the phase which covered its detailed planning, construction, and the start of operations, are bound up at all points with the lively history of the last years of the Gold Coast, and the turbulent birth of modern Ghana. Indeed, on many occasions, the VRP – as it was always known – was the dominant political factor in Ghana, and this was particularly the case when the country felt the full force of the power struggle between the Western and Eastern powers on the African continent. This became intense after the breakdown of the negotiations between the Government of the UAR with the American and British Governments to construct the High Dam at Aswan, and the conclusion of an agreement with the USSR to build the project. At one time both American and Russian engineers were investigating different aspects of the Volta River – against a background of great political activity – and it is a tribute to their professional integrity that they came to the same conclusions. Some observers may deduce from this experience that more engineers should enter politics.

On several occasions between 1958 and 1961 (it was at the end of that year that agreement was finally achieved) the scheme came perilously close to disaster. More often than not, these very dangerous incidents had their roots in the different – and sometimes contradictory – policies adopted by Dr Nkrumah in his dealings with the Western and Eastern powers. Yet, West Africa has a unique skill in practising 'brinkmanship' – West Africans and their governments seem able to go to the very edge of the precipice, and yet some combination of intuition, common sense and good luck always turns them back from disaster, and normal life is resumed. Certainly, the history of the VRP demonstrates, on several occasions, how everything appeared to be lost and yet, eventually, success was achieved and the scheme brought to life.

Inevitably, the history of the Volta scheme and Dr Nkrumah's administration of Ghana are closely interwoven. Only time will put the events of 1951 to 1966 into proper perspective, but this book tells the story in detail, and each reader will be able to judge for himself the contribution to the project made by the former President. The story is long, complex, and involved – but never without interest. Fortunately, it has a happy ending for Ghana, for the scheme is now in operation; it could easily have been otherwise. One interesting view could be taken by someone opposed to any form of planning, and that is that if the British and Gold Coast Governments had decided, about 1952, to go ahead with the project without any detailed planning it would undoubtedly have been a success, having regard to the great increase in the world demand for aluminium (and, consequently, for cheap power). The only snag in this argument is that no government, at that time, would have been prepared to take the political risks involved – the disaster of the groundnuts scheme in Tanganyika then dominated all thinking about great development schemes throughout the Commonwealth.

Several men played key roles in the Volta scheme in its present form. Mr Edgar Kaiser and Mr Chad Calhoun worked endlessly to create American official and private support for the project, the Rt Hon. Harold Macmillan and the Rt Hon. Duncan Sandys did all they could on behalf of the British Government, and then, in the last analysis, President Kennedy made the final decisions that permitted the various Western governments and companies to come to agreement with the Government of Ghana. It is fitting that his name should be recorded for all time at the dam site at Akosombo, and the people of Ghana – like millions of people in other lands – will forever remain in his debt.

Again, when thinking of the Volta scheme and individuals who played a special role, the outstanding work of Dr G. Lodigiani should always be remembered. To him, and to his firm, must be given the main credit for building the dam and power complex in record time, and at a cost nearly twenty per cent under the official estimates. Dr Lodigiani has certainly left his mark on the continent of Africa – already four great dams at Kariba, Akosombo, Rosaires, and Kainji have risen under his brilliant direction.

At the present time, the Government of Ghana is faced with a major financial problem. I have no doubt that that problem will be resolved successfully, and that the great natural talents of the Ghanaians will develop and flourish, and make their State – as I have always believed it would be – the showpiece of Africa. In resolving the present financial difficulty, the smelter (the Volta Aluminium Company) is coming into operation at a most fortunate time, and its earnings of foreign currency should make an important contribution to the country's economy, as well as providing employment for several thousand Ghanaians. The mining industry is already consuming appreciable amounts of power, and I have no doubt that the coming years will show substantial increases in consumption both for industrial and domestic purposes.

This book about the Volta scheme also tells of the many other benefits that will flow from its full development – the big fishing industry which will certainly come from the lake, the possibilities for profitable water transportation, the development of irrigation, and of increased agricultural production. Some of this work will profit from experience in other countries; in turn, the new experience in Ghana may well have valuable lessons for other states. Personally, I have been delighted to be associated with the Volta Project, on the one hand as a Member of the board of the Authority, and, on the other, as Senior Consultant to the United Nations Development Programme which has been working with the Government of Ghana for many years on several aspects of the scheme. I attach the highest importance to this 'knitting' of experience with big projects all over the world, and it is something which each individual state can contribute to the constructive work of the United Nations.

For many years to come, the consumption of power by VALCO (the Volta Aluminium Company) will be the primary economic justification for the Volta scheme. The agreement between the Volta River Authority and the company covers a period of thirty years, from 1967 onwards. What are the prospects of success, having regard to the endless and unpredictable political forces which will continue to bear on the relations of African states with the outside world, and to the never-ending debate on the role of public and private capital, especially in the developing countries? The first thing that can be said is that the Master Agreement, which records all the commitments and understandings between all the parties concerned with the VRP, represents the best thinking that could be brought to bear on the project, and takes into account experience with other great projects (including the Suez Canal and the Anglo-Iranian Oil Company) in other parts of the world. The Government of Ghana was advised by international experts of high repute, the other governments and VALCO were represented by men of great experience, and the International Bank for Reconstruction and Development (the World Bank) contributed its unique experience in these matters, as well as investing substantially in the project. From my personal experience, I know that these negotiations were conducted in a spirit of reasonableness and goodwill, and that there was always the common objective of creating a Master Agreement which would be fair to all concerned. Nevertheless, if past history is a guide, that Master Agreement is bound to be attacked at some stage or another in the future; when that happens much will depend on the honesty and reasonableness of the men then responsible for the project. If, by good fortune, they possess those qualities they will need to keep in mind the conditions under which the Master Agreement was developed in 1961, and they will also need to take into account any new circumstances which have developed subsequently – changes in science and technology, for example. However, whatever the future may hold, nothing can now change the fact that Ghana has developed most successfully one of its most precious natural resources, the waters of the Volta, and that from now on it will have at its disposal some of the cheapest power in the world.

Finally, I would draw attention to the special experience gained in the resettlement of some 80,000 people who were forced to leave the area inundated by the new lake. Although (unfortunately, in my view) it was not possible to adhere to the basic principle of 'self help' recommended by the Preparatory Commission, much excellent work was accomplished in this operation, and lessons learnt which could be invaluable for governments in other parts of the world faced with similar problems. The papers of a symposium held to discuss this operation will be published shortly, and I remain hopeful that other books will be written dealing exclusively with this aspect of the VRP.

Throughout the entire period involved with the Volta scheme, Mr James Moxon was in a special position to observe every political and other development connected with the project. I have read his book with the greatest interest. To the best of my memory, it is an accurate record of developments in which I participated personally, and I recommend it with confidence to anyone interested in the politics of modern Africa, and in large scale development under most delicate political and economic conditions. I wish the book every success, just as I hope that the Volta Project itself will bring not only material benefit to the people of Ghana, but will also serve as an example of how great projects may be brought to life as a result of honest co-operation between governments and people in the developing and in the industrialized nations of the world.

R.G.A.J.

AUTHOR'S NOTE

Throughout the text of this book appropriate abbreviations have been used to name the aluminium producing companies and the other authorities referred to. Alphabetically they are:

ALCAN – Alcan Aluminium Ltd
ALCOA – Aluminum Company of America
BACO – British Aluminium Co. Ltd
OLIN – Olin Mathieson Inc.
TVA – Tennessee Valley Authority
VALCO – Volta Aluminium Co. Ltd
VRA – Volta River Authority
WAFAL – West African Aluminium Co. Ltd

In the case of Alcan, the name of the international parent company at the time of the Volta River Project negotiations was Aluminium Ltd. Alcan was the abbreviation then normally used for the Canadian subsidiary, Aluminium Ltd of Canada. In 1965, however, the abbreviation Alcan was adopted for use by the parent company and it is used throughout this book with that connotation even though, strictly speaking, its use prior to 1965 was restricted to the Canadian subsidiary.

Though this is not a technical book in any sense certain technical processes have been described and, of necessity, technical terms used. Though these are explained in the text, a brief list of such terms is included here in order to enable the lay reader to familiarize himself with them. They are:

BLANKET. The impervious clay outer cover of a rockfill cofferdam.

BLONDINS. Towers supporting a steel cable for constructional use.

COFFERDAM. Type of dam used by contractors to enclose a dry working area.

DEWATERING. The process of pumping dry the river bed between the cofferdams.

FILTER. Layers of graded sand sandwiched between the rock shell and the clay core in a rockfill dam.

FLUME. Channel through which flood water passes.

GABION. Rectangular cage made from heavy steel wire and rock-filled.

GANTRY. Overhead crane travelling on rails.

GRIZZLY. Screen used for grading rock sizes.

GROUT. Process of pumping liquid cement under pressure into rock to form impervious seal.

INTAKE CHANNEL. Point from which water enters the penstocks.

PENSTOCK. Steel tube through which water flows into turbine.

RIP-RAP. 10-12 ton boulders used, inter alia, for 'finishing' the face of the dam.

ROCKFILL. Type of dam in which main component is rock enclosing, for example, a clay core.

ROTOR. That part of generator which revolves.

SADDLE DAM. Subsidiary dam designed to block adjacent valley.

SCROLL CASE. The steel tube, like a snail's shell, which feeds the water from the penstock into the turbine.

SPILLWAY. Concrete and steel structure designed to discharge surplus and flood water from the lake.

STATOR. That part of generator which stands fixed.

TAILRACE. Point at which water is discharged from the turbines.

TRANSITION. Graded rock placed on the surface of the cofferdam to carry the clay blanket.

WICKET GATES. The steel shutters that control the amount of water entering the turbine.

Part One

1

THE RIVER VOLTA

The River Volta is very far from being all Ghana's. Indeed its waters spring from no less than six West African states and almost two thirds of its 150,000 square mile basin is outside Ghana – in Upper Volta, Togo and Dahomey and to a lesser extent in the Ivory Coast and Mali. But the 61,000 square miles of it that lie within the boundaries of Ghana is the crucial part; it is there that the combined waters of the White, Black and Red Volta together with the Oti join forces to form that massive flow that, with the construction of the Akosombo dam had, in a matter of two years, filled a lake the size of Lancashire and, by the time that Lake Volta had fully filled in 1968, had doubled its area to the size of Kent, Surrey and Sussex combined. The lake now covers 3,275 square miles – the largest man-made lake in the world in area, though with a capacity of some 120 million acre feet of water, fourth in terms of volume, admitting precedence to Kariba, Bratsk (USSR), and Aswan.

The main stream of the Volta, which is about 1,000 miles in length, rises in the Kong Mountains about 25 miles out of the Upper Volta town of Bobo-Dioulasso, and after flowing first north-east and then due south for some 320 miles as the Black Volta it enters Ghana. It continues due south down Ghana's western boundary for a further 200 miles before it passes through a narrow gorge at Bui where a second hydro-electric project may in due course be sited. From Bui, after a southwards curve, the Black Volta winds north-east and east again until it joins the White Volta (another Upper Volta offspring) and together they combine to flow southwards for the remaining 300 miles to the sea.

For its part the White Volta starts life only a few miles across the hills that separate it from one of the watersheds of the Black Volta but, combining with its sister river the Red Volta to form a pincer movement around the capital city of Ougadougou (Upper Volta), it then flows across the Ghana border to join the senior triplet, the Black Volta.

One other major tributary is the Oti which, though comprising only some 18 per cent of the total catchment area of the Volta Basin, nevertheless contributes between 30 and 40 per cent of the annual flow of water. One reason for this is that the Oti, as the Pandjori, rises in the heart of Dahomey's rainy Atakora Mountains. Tumbling down from the hills first northwards and then west and then south the Oti, as it now becomes, flows across the north of Togo and then down its Ghana border imbibing vast quantities from the streams of the Togo Mountains before proceeding southwards in loops and contortions for a distance of 200 miles to join the Volta at a point which is now about half way up the lake.

Akosombo dam is situated within the river's only gorge – other than Bui – 68 miles from its mouth, at the point where the river cleaves the Akwapim-Togo range of hills. This is the first time that a river system of such a size has been artificially controlled so near its estuary and the consequent economic advantages are obvious.

In spite of the variety of its sources the Volta conforms to a remarkably regular timetable of rise and fall. But the extent of these is always uncertain, and following the precedent of the Zambesi during the construction of the Kariba dam in 1958, the Volta chose to have its peak flow for a hundred years or more in the most crucial year of the Akosombo dam's construction – 1963. Precise records of river levels on the Volta have been kept only since 1929. The River is always at its lowest in March each year and at its highest at the end of September or early October. The lowest flow so far recorded for any year was in March 1942 when as little as 420 cubic feet per second (cusecs) was recorded as against an average for March of a little over 1,000 cusecs. The 1963 record was 501,500 cusecs, compared with an average peak of 183,000. And if comparison is needed, half a million cusecs of water would fill the Dome of St Paul's Cathedral in three-fifths of a second or Lake Windermere in under six hours.

Not a great deal is known of the early history of the Volta. Together with the Rivers Senegal and Niger it must have done much over thousands of years to help erode away some of the lush vegetation and fertile soil that is believed once to have covered the Southern Sahara. Nowadays it is the yellow sand of this area that heavily colours the river during the annual swollen flow from June till November.

The story appears to begin some 300 to 500 million years ago when, so we are assured, the sandstone and shale rocks which constitute the bed of the Basin were formed. Half a million years ago we find Man (though barely recognizable as such) inhabiting the Volta Basin – naked, without fire, with a few stone implements and with no dwellings other than caves. By three thousand years ago, a much more recognizable Man had appeared – with fire, spears, arrows, axes and hoes (still tipped with stone), small villages or round huts, perhaps cattle and yams. Another thousand years – about the time Christ was born – invaders came, introducing iron and settling in villages along the Volta fishing with hooks and harpoons and hunting with arrows, and making clay figures of men and animals. Other groups appeared, one with massive hoes for tilling the soil and another (on the Black Volta) with strange roundish perforated stones – no doubt of the utmost contemporary importance but for what practical purpose no one now knows.

It is very probable that until the eleventh, or even the twelfth century what is now Ghana was inhabited here and there, and particularly in the forest area, by small tribal groups – possibly pygmies similar to those who still survive to this day in the Ituri forest of the Congo. Subsequently several completely separate migrant groups from widely separate parts of West Africa appear to have converged on the area.

Probably the first to arrive, about the thirteenth century (some say earlier), came from the north-west, from the direction of the western Sahara or Mauretania, and were Guans – an early wave of the broader Akan grouping. They probably originated from North Africa and may have had some connection with the medieval empire of Ghana which became 'lost' in the vastness of the continent a century or two earlier. They appear to have come down the Volta and to have established communities –

still surviving – at a number of centres on either bank of the river, and ultimately to have reached the sea coast. They have a spoken language of their own which they still use – though nowadays they tend to be absorbed into the greater Twi-speaking Akan group.

The main body of Akans, who comprise the Fantis, the Nzimas, the Ashantis, the Akims, the Kwahus and several other groups, appear to have arrived in waves from a similar direction a century or so later. The Fantis and the Nzimas perhaps followed the course of the more westerly Tano and Ankobra rivers to the coastal belt between the forest and the sea, whilst the Ashantis, Akims and neighbouring groups seem to have penetrated the forest to the west of the Volta and settled there.

These waves of migration were probably more or less complete by the fifteenth century when two separate groups of completely different origin to these appear to have arrived from the east. Tradition has it that the first to arrive, the Ga-Adangme-Krobo group, started their westerly trek from somewhere in the Niger Delta, and they still recall how they passed through Dahomey and Togo and eventually crossed the Volta before settling on the triangular Accra plains that are bordered by the Volta on the east, the sea to the south, and the hills and the forest to the north and west. The second group, the Ewes, appear to have come from the same general direction and, halting awhile in what is now Togo, they then spread out along the eastern bank of the Volta in what is now part of Ghana and part of Togo.

At approximately the same time the founders of the Mamprussis and the Dagombas of northern Ghana seem to have migrated westwards from the direction of Hausaland and Lake Chad and so arrived from the north-east. Finally, as late as the seventeenth century it seems, a further wave from the north-west arrived – again from the direction of ancient Ghana – and dominated the northern outposts of the Akans in the savannah country to the north of the forest, to form the modern state of Gonja in northern Ghana.

What happened to the pygmies – if ever they were there – no one knows. But to this day every Ghanaian believes in the 'little folk' or *mmoatia*, with their mischievous Huckleberry ways and their tiny feet pointing backwards.

It was the rivers, then, and the Volta in particular, that led the Akans from the southern Sahara to their lush and fertile homesteads of today in the forests, mountains and valleys of southern Ghana. It was the Volta and its open plains that absorbed the westward immigration of the Ga-Adangmes and the Ewes, each of which chose to settle on opposite banks of the great river. And it was the open savannahs that link the White, Red and Black Voltas which enticed the horsemen of the northern kingdoms to settle amongst the tributaries that merge into the mainstream of the Volta.

Of course they all had different names for it – names which in their own areas survive to this day. *Volta* however is the name that was given to it by the fifteenth-century Portuguese explorers and it is the name that has stuck. It is in fact the Portuguese word for 'meander' which suggests that in their search for the great inland sources of gold they must have penetrated far into the interior, for it is there, rather than in its majestic sweep to the sea that the river can properly be said to meander.

It appears that for years after trading on the Gold Coast had become a routine affair, the Volta still remained the select hunting ground of the adventurous few – no doubt Portuguese first, then Dutch – who were prepared to face its dangers. Barbot, a French Huguenot domiciled in England, who made several voyages down the coast between 1678 and 1682, was evidently teasing the Dutch authorities when he described how they had first warned him seriously not to take his yacht into the Volta estuary but later, possibly after a round or two of schnapps, admitted that they themselves sent sloops up the river for slaves and cloth from as far away as Abyssinia and Nubia, and could then accurately describe the 'falls and clifts' which made the river difficult to navigate in the vicinity of what we now know as the Akosombo gorge.

By the end of the sixteenth century, however, the influence of the Portuguese had waned in West Africa. But nonetheless Portuguese continued to be the lingua franca until well after 1800, and words of Portuguese origin are still in everyday use in Ghana today. A 'palaver' – correctly a meeting or conference with the ruling chief – is also a popular word in pidgin English to describe any undue fuss. 'Palaver sauce' is a popular Ghanaian dish. A 'dash' in Ghana is a tip, a present, or even a bribe and derives from the Portuguese *das* 'to give'. Everyone knows what a 'piccin' is. When the Duke of Windsor visited the Gold Coast as Prince of Wales in 1926 he was everywhere called 'King-piccin'. A 'Patakey man' is or used to be any 'white man' who was, by his swarthy appearance, obviously not an Englishman or of Northern European extraction. Latterly other categories of 'white man' have been recognized, for Africans are very quick to pigeon-hole types as they think appropriate. Soon after the Second World War a large contract was awarded in Ghana to the firm of George Wimpey Ltd of London to build the first part of the University of Ghana at Legon. It was not long before any white man of the works-foreman category became a 'wimpey'.

It was in the year 1733 that the river gorge at Akosombo was next invaded, becoming the home of a tribe of retreating warriors who had been one of the most historically successful of the Akan sub-groups – the Akwamus. After ruling a large part of the Guinea coast with imperial control for some two hundred years the Akwamus reached the zenith of their power in 1677 with the capture of Accra, which at that time was the trading stronghold of Dutch, British and Danish merchants.

It had all been on account of Akotia's foreskin. Young Akotia was an Akwamu prince and had been sent by the king to the Accra court to learn European trading methods and something of the languages. The Accras, after their fashion, had the young prince circumcized, which was not only contrary to Akwamu custom but would certainly debar him from the Akwamu succession, for under Akan custom a chief must be bodily perfect in every respect. The Akwamus demanded the return of Akotia's foreskin 'with a fetish priest to replace it in its proper place'. The Accras appear to have been unable to satisfy the demand and in the war which followed they were completely overrun.

Their decline began once the Akwamu ruler had achieved absolute power upon siting his frontiers as an effective and rapacious customs barrier between the coastal merchants on the one side and the rich producers of gold, ivory and slaves on the other. Corrupted by power and wealth the Akwamus fell prey to their powerful neighbours, the Akims, and finally after ignominious defeat took refuge in the wooded but strategically safe Akosombo gorge on the Volta River.

Today on the opposite bank of the river, the west bank, live the Krobo people who have a wholly different history. They were among those, the non-Akans, who came to Ghana several centuries ago from the east. For reasons of defence – mostly against the predatory Akans – they and their neighbours established themselves on the sugar-loaf style mountains that rise sharply from the Accra plains. Of these the Krobo Mountain is the most famous, with its history of grisly ritual and blood-curdling customs that were unquestionably bound up with the problem of maintaining a growing community within the confines of a limited space.

In 1896, with the worst fears of Ashanti marauding past, the greatest of the Krobo kings, Sir Emmanuel Mate Kole,[1] brought his people down from their fortified mountains and thereby stimulated the formation of the most successful farming community in the whole of Ghana. They expanded quickly across what is now the southern shore of Lake Volta, and established themselves with their prolific road-head market towns – such as Assessewa – as the market gardeners of southern Ghana. Sir Emmanuel's son, Nene Azzu Mate Kole, has been their ruler since his father died in 1938. One of the early Achimota[2] boys, 'Fred' Mate Kole has brought to his people the benefits of education applied intelligently to a farming community. And recently, as a member of the board of the Volta River Authority, he has had a considerable influence on the practical solutions that have been reached to the many problems of resettling the inundated farming communities, many of whom are his own subjects.

[1] Queen Victoria knighted him for his great services.

[2] The Prince of Wales College, Achimota, is Ghana's most famous secondary school.

2

EMPIRE DAYS

The rumbustious days of piracy on the Volta extended well into the nineteenth century. Undoubtedly the most colourful figure of the still flourishing slave and smuggling trade (for smuggling quickly followed on the heels of slavery) was an African, Geraldo da Lema, who was, without doubt, an incorrigible adventurer and freebooter, and a thorough-going rogue. He had been the domestic slave of a Brazilian slave trader, Cesar Cerquvia Lema, who died in 1862, whereupon the young adventurer assumed his master's fortune, his wife and his name. Within three years he was in trouble with the Chief of Ada, the combined river and sea port for the Volta, and was driven from the town. Furious, he raised a private army of three or four thousand and prepared to attack Ada but two British warships, the *Dart* and the *Lee*, were lying off the mouth of the Volta and da Lema was obliged to withdraw. Frustrated, he marched his irregulars up the east bank of the river and sacked and destroyed Kpong the prosperous Krobo river port, fifty miles upstream from Ada. The influential Accra traders, all of whom had branches at Kpong, were up in arms and the British with a powerful army marched to the Volta and engaged da Lema's mercenaries in a battle in which eighty Accras and the Chief of Ada were killed. This round, it appears, had gone to da Lema. Indeed three years later in 1868 we find Captain Glover, of subsequent Ashanti war fame, offering a reward of £200 for da Lema's capture, for the smouldering war between the Adas and the Anlos (da Lema's people) from across the river was now being fanned into new activity. The goal was the control of the Volta River trade. This time, however, history was made, for the Colonial Steamer *Eyo*, with the British Governor from Cape Coast on board, actually crossed the dreaded Ada bar and entered the Volta River – the first steamer ever to do so. So surprised and alarmed were the Anlos to see the vessel plying up the river that they promptly came to terms and signed a treaty on board the *Eyo*, guaranteeing freedom of trade on the Volta.

This, however, did nothing to prevent Geraldo da Lema from pursuing his lucrative contraband trade with Anlo and up-country merchants in cheap spirits (turpentine flavoured with burnt sugar and called 'Hamburg Rum'), gunpowder and guns for the Ashantis, and other goods. It seems that, in spite of the price on his head, he visited Accra and Cape Coast on several occasions reckoning, correctly, that the British had their hands full enough with the current Ashanti wars to have forgotten, temporarily, about him.

It was at this moment that Ada suddenly sprang into world news with the unconventional arrival by sea in a Thames pleasure launch of none other than Sir Henry M. Stanley, still enjoying the experience of having been popularly hailed 'Man of the Year' for unearthing David Livingstone, some months earlier, on the shores of Lake Tanganyika.

Britain, now ruling the whole length of the Gold Coast, had, in the face of fierce public controversy at home, decided that nothing less than an expeditionary force of British troops would resolve the recurrent threats to the security of the coastal trade from powerful and restless Ashanti. One of Britain's most popular young generals, Sir Garnet Wolseley, fresh from success in Canada, was appointed to command the campaign, and at the same time one of West Africa's most colourful figures, Governor John Glover of Lagos (Captain Glover RN), had been given instructions to support Wolseley's frontal attack on Kumasi with a flanking movement from the Volta.

It was the Wolseley campaign that, to the General's annoyance, brought an avalanche of leading newspaper correspondents to Cape Coast, his headquarters, whilst it was 'Golibar', as Glover's well trained Hausa and Yoruba troops from Lagos called him, who brought Stanley to Ada. Stanley's employers, the *New York Herald*, had equipped their ace correspondent with a 35-foot steam launch, believing naïvely that Wolseley's forces could use the River Pra as their approach route to Ashanti. Though the vessel was of no use for that particular purpose Stanley had the idea, during a temporary lull in preparations at Cape Coast, of visiting Captain Glover's base camp at Ada, of which everyone on the Coast had heard so much, but about which no one – not even the General – knew anything in detail.

And so, on what appears to have been a madcap journey, but which marks the essential difference between the lobby correspondent and the best type of on-the-spot reporter, Stanley, accompanied by another famous writer of the day, G. A. Henty, crossed the surf at Elmina where his launch, the *Dauntless*, was anchored. Clinging to the coast and at night navigating more by the sound of the surf breaking on the shore than by any other means, they reached Ada 140 miles away the following evening. On the return journey a day or two later they were less fortunate. At night, at the utter mercy of a tornado which fortunately for them had spent itself whilst they were at Ada, they suffered a complete engine breakdown and the following morning were obliged to hitch a lift back to Cape Coast on a passing steamer. The *Dauntless* they left on board, to be delivered back to its moorings at Henley-on-Thames.

Stanley was tremendously impressed by Glover, who was clearly a kindred spirit. His original aim had been to take his army of Hausas and Yorubas far up the Volta in an armada of assorted steam vessels and to attack the Ashanti capital from the rear. While Governor at Lagos he had explored far up the Niger, attempting to open a new trade route to the north-west. He had failed, wrecking his steamer on a rock. Now, it seemed, there was an opportunity to try on the Volta what he had failed to do on the Niger. And he had authority to do so. Wolseley's subsequent appointment however had interfered with his plans, which he had had to modify to fit in with the general campaign. His new role was to make use of the steamers only as far as Akuse (he could never have got them further upstream in any event because of the rapids) and to establish base camps on the west bank of the river. Then he was to harass the Ashantis' allies, the Akwamus and the Anlos, on the east bank to prevent them from counter-attacking across the river while he and the friendly allies from the coastal area west of the river were

The untouched river gorge at Akosombo, pre-1960

Sir Albert Kitson, the geologist who first discovered bauxite in Ghana and in 1915 noted Akosombo as a future hydro-electric dam site

Duncan Rose, the South African mining engineer, who first investigated on the ground the hydro-electric potential of the Volta

The nineteenth-century mission house at Kpong where both Kitson and later Rose stayed during their Volta investigations

carrying out their flanking movement on Kumasi, the Ashanti capital. By any standards it was a complicated programme to execute in a little over four weeks but, considering that except for his Lagos troops he was leading not regular soldiers but a variety of royal armies led by their own kings, it is remarkable that it got off the ground at all. Pressed however by Wolseley, who was leading white troops and was therefore in a hurry, he moved quickly, and together with his second-in-command accomplished both tasks on schedule.

No wonder Stanley felt, perhaps for the first and last time, that he had met his equal. He describes Glover, then only forty-three, the first morning they met, down at the river side at Ada Foah superintending personally the loading of his 250-ton flagship *The Lady of the Lake.* This vessel, which Glover had brought out specially for the campaign (it could carry up to 500 troops), had started its life as a pleasure steamer on Loch Earne in Ireland. Now it was mounted with rocket tubes, as were also Glover's other three armed steam launches. It was quite a fleet for the Volta in 1873.

Stanley fell to wondering what would happen to the whole expedition if 'this ready-handed, ready-witted, energetic commander and supervisor fell sick and be incapacitated from duty'. Though he had excellent men under him, as the Africans summed it up, 'English officers very good, Sah, but they no Gobner Golibar.' In point of fact, after Glover had been obliged to leave the Volta for the main march on Kumasi, the campaign that continued against the Anlos was, though punitive, barely conclusive.

Stanley and Henty, before returning to Cape Coast, were fortunate enough to be able to travel some twenty-five miles upstream on *The Lady of the Lake* to a point where Glover had two large camps of coastal allies. Obviously deeply impressed by the visitors the officer in charge, Captain Reginald Sartorius of the 6th Bengal Cavalry, lobbed a few rockets over the river into the Anlo camp on the opposite bank to the delight of the allied forces who were already a little frustrated at having to wait for fighting to begin. Inevitably the explorer in Stanley emerges. 'The Volta needs exploring', he says, 'because we are ignorant of its source and course above Kpong and very few ordinary stay-at-home people', he adds in a flourish of one-upmanship, 'know anything of its mouth.'

Close on Stanley's heels however was a young Frenchman, M. J. Bonnat, who between 1875 and 1876 kept a day-to-day diary of just the expedition that the great explorer of Africa would have loved to undertake. Bonnat had tried trading on the Niger but had moved to the Gold Coast and was in fact opening up new territory just east of the Volta when he was captured by the Ashantis in 1869. Both he and his fellow captives, the Swiss Ramseyer missionary family and Kuhne, a Swiss trader, had spent four years in Ashanti as political hostages and had only recently been released at the close of the Wolseley campaign. Bonnat however, who had got on particularly well with his captors, had emerged with a remarkable six-year trading monopoly agreement on the middle Volta with additional powers as 'Governor' of the area for and on behalf of the Ashanti King.

His description of his three-month trading expedition up the river with his flotilla of five canoes, laden with Ada salt and imported goods and manned by a crew-cum-private-army of twenty-seven, makes fascinating reading, particularly as the whole area was just beginning to recover from a devastating period of Ashanti depredation which had only recently been halted.

Fluent in the Ashanti language and at the same time a firm believer in 'showing the flag' – whether the French tricolor (run together from odds and ends of his wardrobe), the Union Jack, or both, whichever seemed appropriate in the circumstances – Bonnat successfully shows himself cutting a commanding figure further and further inland and in the face of more and more powerful chiefs. Travelling with him was another Ada trader, Robert Bannerman – a member of a well-known Accra family founded by an early nineteenth-century Scots patriarch – with, if anything, an even more imposing floating supermarket than Bonnat's, and between them they seem to have overcome any prejudices that the traditional river barons may have had against them. At Krachi for example they successfully portaged their heavy canoes over and round the Volta's most frightening cataracts and at the same time were permitted to penetrate what had hitherto been the river's most jealously guarded trade check-point – where the immensely powerful Krachi Dente Fetish (which we shall meet again later on) took advantage of the cataracts to enforce a very profitable customs barrier.

But it was not Bonnat who was destined to pursue the Volta trade, for misunderstandings arose, perhaps not surprisingly, from his unusual Ashanti connections and he returned to the Gold Coast in an entirely new role in which he was to acquire considerable fame. For it was Bonnat who introduced to the Gold Coast the first deepcast gold mining and thus set in motion an industry which has produced, amongst other lesser ones, the world's richest gold mine in the Ashanti Goldfields operation at Obuasi.

Meanwhile, in da Lema territory, a new British drive in 1878 to check smuggling led to an attempt on the life of the District Commissioner. The trouble was checked but no punishment was carried out and da Lema remained at large. In 1885 however, after a further attempt at disposing of a new District Commissioner, da Lema was cornered and arrested. The Commissioner was obliged to have the prisoner marched along the hundred miles of coast to Accra and, in spite of an Anlo attempt to rescue him, they reached the capital and he was tried and convicted. Soon after leaving Accra on the return journey an enormous force of Anlos fell on the party and rescued their hero. It appears however that he was recaptured later and duly served his sentence. He died in 1904, a blind old man, having tripped over some children, fallen over a balustrade and broken several bones.

Da Lema may have been a scoundrel, but it is doubtful if most of his European counterparts were any better. Ellis, the late nineteenth-century historian of the Gold Coast, who as a young man had been the first of da Lema's two District Commissioner targets, says that 'the morality of the average European trader on the west coast of Africa will not bear inspection even at long range, though I have met exceptions to this rule'. These were the days of the POR – an early attempt to give a convenient tag to the class of European traders known along the coast as Palm Oil Ruffians. They were in fact the generation between the wholesale slave-traders of earlier days and the scrupulous twentieth-century merchant with his economics degree.

There are still in Ghana today European traders who came

there before the First World War and worked both with and against many survivals of this category of late nineteenth-century merchant. Equally there are many Ghanaians living today who started life on their pay-roll. Alexandre Dumas, grandson of the author of *The Three Musketeers*, son of Dumas Fils and a great West African trader in his own right, was one of these merchants.

As a boy in Marseilles, it seems, he intended to enter the church and was sent as a young novitiate to a Roman Catholic seminary in Brazil. But the blood of the Dumases was hot and young Dumas was obliged to renounce his vows. His great-great-grandfather before him, le Marquis Alexandre Davy de la Pailleterie, had married a girl of African descent whilst in Martinique and the child of that marriage ran away from home at the age of fourteen and, using his mother's surname, Dumas, joined the French army. He rose to be one of Napoleon Bonaparte's leading generals and was described by him in 1796, after the Austrian campaign, as the 'Horatius Coclès of the Tyrol'. The famous author was his son. At first our young Dumas went to fight for the French in Indo-China and on discharge, lured by the tropics, accepted a post as a trading factor with a Marseilles firm trading in Dahomey. He was quick to realize that for a smart young man there was a future in West African trade and as soon as he could free himself from the articles of his employers, he set up his own firm, not in Dahomey but in the promising trading centre of Ada at the mouth of the Volta. Already there were British, German and Swiss factories at Ada doing thriving business and there appeared to be plenty of room for a French one as well.

Since the *Eyo* had crossed the Ada bar in 1868, followed by Glover's fleet, the Ada merchants had not been slow to see the tremendous possibilities for steam vessels on the Volta, at least for the first 65 miles as far as Akuse. Between Akuse and Kpong there were shallow rapids that were quite out of the question for a steam vessel in the low river season and very dangerous, albeit just navigable, when the river was in spate. Above Kpong at Senchi there were more and equally difficult rapids. One by one each of the major Ada business houses, including Dumas, invested in a river steamer and there followed a period of successful river trading between Ada and Akuse – and beyond by canoe and head loading. Ada was and still is blessed with a very large and profitable supply of sea salt from the lagoons to the west of the town that are (or rather were until 1964) seasonally flooded by the Volta. This salt has for centuries found its way up the Volta and for hundreds of miles into the interior. This was an ideal staple cargo for the new steam launches.

Paul Hutter,[1] whose first contact with the salt trade was in 1896 when he was the Swiss agent at Ada, used to tell how in those days a 90-lb bag of Ada salt sold for one shilling, and how up-river in Krachi the system of barter was salt for guinea corn, Moshi blankets and shea-butter (a valuable vegetable fat). In those days gold and silver coins, which had already become common in the south, were scarce in the north and trade was conducted either by barter or for cowrie shells.[2]

But the principal up-river cargoes for the new steam launches – apart from their passenger service – were of course the popular lines of imported goods. 'Dumas prints' imported from France are still remembered as the most popular cotton goods of the period – both for design and colour. Indeed the name is still in general use for the best quality prints. Rum came from Cuba and from Martinique and was known as puncheon rum, imported in the barrel and sold for a penny a tot. Years ago I bought for a few shillings at a riverside village a dirt-encrusted one-gallon copper rum measure – beautiful when polished – which was then being used for paraffin. Made in Paris, it was very likely a Dumas import.

At the turn of the century Dumas married a very attractive African girl from the most famous of all the Ada trading families, the Ocanseys, dealers in slaves and salt in the nineteenth century and earlier and promoters of cinemas and newspapers in the twentieth century. Mrs Dumas was herself a successful salt trader – when she was not visiting France with her husband –

[1] A famous Gold Coast trader who in old age became a hermit and lived alone near Krachi. See also p. 170 below.

[2] The New Ghana decimal currency introduced in 1965 is based on the principal of cowrie values. Varying from time to time, a fixed number of cowries in the old days was worth one *pesewa* (one penny). Today a hundred *pesewas* are worth one *cedi* (10 shillings or US $1.20).

and included Timbuktu amongst the places she regularly visited. There were two daughters of the marriage, both of whom were educated in France. The younger, Marie-Josèphe, who was still at school in France when her father died in Marseilles in 1919 during the influenza epidemic, still lives at her father's seaside trading premises at Ada. Now she runs a small village shop which also caters for fishermen, and at the back, overlooking the sea, you can sit and drink a bottle of ice-cold beer and talk of the past. With her charming French accent she talks of returning to France one day. Business at Ada is dead now. But her elder married sister had carried on the Dumas tradition with a son who, after his mother's death when he was still young, was brought up by Marie-Josèphe and, as his Napoleonic ancestor had done before him, took Dumas as his surname. He has one son and three daughters; one of whom, Mary Dumas, is my god-daughter.

A book that I can always dip into with never-failing pleasure is Alexandre Dumas's *Dictionary of Cuisine*, and abridged English translation of which, in an American paperback edition, I found in Paris a few years ago. Dumas himself considered that of all his five hundred-odd books this was his masterpiece, and this is barely surprising as a more scholarly treatise on the history of everything to do with gourmandize cannot exist. Some of his confessions are remarkable as, for example: 'In fifty or sixty years of my life I drank nothing but water, and no Grand Lafite or Chambertin ever gave a wine lover more pleasure than I have had from a glass of fresh spring water.' It is an amazing statement from a man who was once known as 'King of Paris, who embraced life with the passionate strength of his enormous arms and lived on the lavish scale befitting his fantastic income'. But the man is always full of surprises. His recipe for poached eggs is one of them: 'Have 15 poached eggs drained and placed on a platter. At the same time have 12 ducks, almost done, roasted on the spit. Take the ducks off the spit, cut them to the bone, drain off their juices, season juice with salt and coarse pepper. Reheat but do not boil, and pour over the poached eggs.' He has a recipe for Elephant's Feet given to him by the celebrated Duglerez chef to the Rothschilds, which includes half a bottle of Madeira and fifty green peppers and sounds superb. He does not approve of eating eagles but has enjoyed donkey. Like most Frenchmen (and many others) he enjoys snails and frogs' legs. Of Kedgeree he says, 'A dish of Indian origin, now commonly served in England, which seems to have become an Indian dependency.' Dumas wrote the Dictionary last of all whilst, as an ageing man in his late sixties, he lived with his son, Dumas Fils. Seven years before he died Alexandre Dumas of Ada was born and his grandfather's greatest joy was to play with his small grandson and to have him around the house. It is barely surprising that, when I once mentioned the *Dictionary of Cuisine* to Marie-Josèphe at Ada she remarked, 'Oh, they were all like that, including my father. They loved their food.'

A sad postscript to this nostalgic link between the greatest of the salons of nineteenth-century Paris and the windswept, palm-fringed, sun-drenched beaches of Ada concerns the disposal of Dumas's property after the death of his elder daughter in 1927. Though his widow was still alive and apparently prospering, all the movable property was put up for sale, and his collection of family books and records, his furniture, his piano, all were sold off by auction so that when Marie-Josèphe arrived from France in 1933 it was to an empty house.

3

ROUTE TO THE NORTH

Although it was undoubtedly the advent of relatively peaceful trading conditions to the Volta that had given the Ada business houses the incentive to invest in river steamers before the end of the nineteenth century, it is encouraging to note that the Government of the Gold Coast was not lagging far behind in its endeavour to open up the country with plans for river transport and for modern harbours and railways.

In August, 1895, Joseph Chamberlain, Britain's Colonial Secretary, authorized a London firm of Civil Engineers to undertake a survey of the constantly shifting Ada sand bar and of several dangerous sandbanks on the lower stretches of the river itself. He asked them also to advise on the siting of two deep-sea harbours.

It was exactly two years before the consulting engineers were able to submit their report (their chief engineer had had to be invalided home – 'he is injudicious in the use of wines etc.', the doctor wrote, 'and I think he takes them at hours when they are not beneficial – before sunset' – and this had led to delays) but the report was a good one. It recommended Takoradi Bay as the site for a deep-water harbour. Though this was not to be started for another twenty-five years, it was never questioned as the best possible site. In the east of the country it recommended a breakwater, and a jetty with steam cranes, for Accra. This was put in hand almost at once and served, with remarkable success for sixty years until Tema Harbour was opened in 1962.

Ada came worst out of the report. It was true, they said, that for £150,000 it would be possible to make the necessary improvements to Ada and the river, but they were set instead on a proposal to connect Kpong by railway to Accra. This line was surveyed but never built.

The next idea for the Volta was a revival of Glover's dream of an inland steamer route to the north. For this purpose the services were obtained of a Commander D. Paget Jones RN, who had been doing a similar survey of the Niger and had years of experience on such major waterways as the Euphrates, the Irrawaddy, the Ganges and the Indus. Today he would qualify as a United Nations technical expert. Equipped for the task with sextant, compass, binoculars, chart paper, something called *Nories' Epitome and Tables* and camping equipment, Commander Paget Jones arrived in the Gold Coast in 1899 as the river was subsiding from its annual flood and quickly got to work. Anxious to be helpful, but clearly knowing little of actual conditions on the river above Kpong, the Governor's office in Accra had, as an afterthought, asked the District Commissioner at Ada to obtain estimates for hiring a river steamer for the Commander's use. Telegrams flashed to and fro revealing that, of the four to be hired, Alexandre Dumas was able to supply the winning tender which included the services of an English engineer who received a salary of £20 per month.

Wasting no time in Accra, the Commander is quickly to be found on the banks of the Volta at no other place than Akosombo itself. Writing from Chiasi – now the main dormitory suburb of Akosombo – and making no mention whatever of steam launches he says, 'I passed yesterday through the Senchi rapids by the route usually taken by canoes at this time of year, a very circuitous one, and one which would be quite impassable for any other description of boat; in fact the custom house canoe was capsized there yesterday but I have every reason to believe that in the main stream there is a deeper and better channel.' Clearly the experience of being punted along the river bank was a new and professionally irritating one for him as he adds, 'Actual soundings were impossible to obtain as the canoes could not stem the current except close to the bank.'

A month later he had reached Nsunua 130 miles north on the British bank of the river which in those days, except in the south, formed the frontier between German Togo on the east bank and the Gold Coast on the west. In fact the German Commissioner at Kete Krachi (opposite Nsunua) proved to be most helpful and gave the Commander some very useful information about the river's behaviour which he clearly had not been able to secure elsewhere. This was that the exact time each year of the highest flood hardly ever varied but was always between September 15th and 20th.[1] The actual variation in height could be as much as twenty-nine feet.

Continuing north the Commander went up the White Volta as far as its confluence with the River Nasia – about half-way between Tamale and the northern border – by which time the river had become barely navigable even for canoes, whereupon he returned south again.

Back in Accra he presented a report in which he was able to recommend the purchase of a 90-foot stern wheel steamer with, if necessary, two flats for towing, the whole able to carry 120 tons of cargo per trip. This was for the lower stretch from Kpong to Nsunua (130 miles) at which point there was a wholly impassable cataract. A one and a half mile road or monorail was to provide access to the upper stretch. For this – the 200 miles between Nsunua and Daboya – the most northerly point recommended for steam vessels – he proposed two 60-foot stern wheel steamers, each with a flat for towing, capable between them of carrying the same 120 tons of cargo. He made it clear that these steamers would be able to operate only for some four months in the year when the river was in spate, but that this would still allow for seven round trips a year.

He then sat down with the Director of Public Works to prepare an estimate of cost, which proved to be in the region of £50,000 in capital outlay and about £11,000 in recurrent expenditure allowing for fairly heavy capital depreciation. This gave them a figure of a little more than £15 per ton for cargo and they cautiously added, 'If the Government purpose to go in for trading and can obtain cargo for the return journey, then of course the cost per ton will be reduced.'

But it appears that the Government did not purpose to go in for trading or indeed to lay out £50,000. Commander Paget Jones returned to London to hear that the scheme had been abandoned.

The Governor, however, had not yet closed the file. This was

[1] In fact it is sometimes as late as the first week of October.

that most disastrous of all governors, Sir Frederic Hodgson, who committed the all-time blunder in this same year, 1900, of trying to seize and sit upon the sacred Stool of Ashanti. Happily, he failed, though not before causing a great upheaval for it had been prophesied that if the Stool were ever captured the Ashanti nation would collapse and never rise again.

Before leaving for Kumasi to tackle the turbulent Ashantis, Hodgson found himself with other worries. It seems that Paget Jones, though meticulous in checking his equipment, was unaccountably short of one pair of binoculars. It was no use his explaining that he would gladly refund the cost of them rather than have a fuss. It was necessary for His Excellency to have a full report of the exact circumstances of the loss so that he could apprise the Secretary of State of the irregularity. And, rather as if he had an envious eye for them himself, he asked in a carefully written minute to the Chief Secretary, 'What does the Director of Public Works propose to do with the bath, buckets and lamps?' Preserving the well-trained stiff upper lip the Chief Secretary replied that their disposal awaited 'further instructions'. Satisfied, at least on that score, His Excellency found it necessary to recommend to the Secretary of State for the Colonies that 'unless some satisfactory explanation can be obtained' of the loss, Commander Paget Jones should be called upon to refund the cost of the missing item, to wit £6 8s od.

Having signed his despatch, His Excellency then gave written directions to his Chief Secretary that 'these papers should be attached to those which will be found in my room to the left of my desk'. The following day His Excellency and Lady Hodgson were swinging gently in their hammocks on the first of their fourteen-day journey to Kumasi. Mr Chamberlain, in London, seems to have had a *tête-à-tête* with the unfortunate Jones who, whilst wholly admitting the loss, submitted that in fact he had 'lost several of his own personal effects through the upsetting of canoes while he was engaged in the service of the Government'. And it is altogether to Mr Chamberlain's credit that he turned down flat the Governor's suggestion and added 'unless you press the matter I do not propose that anything further should be said to him on the subject'. By the time the Governor had returned to Accra, a further letter from Mr Chamberlain made it unnecessary for His Excellency to give the matter another thought. In Ghanaian royal terms, he had been 'destooled'.[1]

In retrospect it is clear that Commander Paget Jones's proposals for a mechanized waterway to the north were doomed before ever they were presented. For one thing, the basic economic figure of £15 per ton for freight, though cheap by comparison with head-loading costs (which were almost four times heavier), was no cheaper than canoe rates. Moreover, by the turn of the century the Gold Coast had, in many respects, flashed past the Golden Age of the railway and was now on the brink of the age of motorized road transport. By 1900 the cocoa industry had taken root and cocoa was a crop that was going to demand the development of a network of motor roads rather than of railways.

Meanwhile, with the opening up of the north, canoe transport on the Volta flourished as never before and came to be used for a while in conjunction with both hand- and bullock-drawn vehicles. In 1901 the Volta River Transport Scheme was started. By means of a 16-foot road from the Volta at Padjae northwards through Salaga to Gambaga, it gave direct access, by the combination of canoe and vehicle, from the sea at Ada to the very north of the north. This alone was calculated to reduce the freight rate from the coast to Gambaga from £120 to £40 a ton.

By 1907 the pressure of river transport on the infamous Kete-Krachi 'bottleneck' – a mile or more of the most dangerous and impassable rapids – led to the construction of Commander Paget Jones's proposed monorail. Though perhaps lacking some of the speed and refinements associated with the contemporary Japanese version, it was nevertheless a tremendous boon to canoemen, who could now 'trolley' their fully-laden canoes around the rapids instead of the arduous portaging of the past. In the following year when for the first time European firms opened up trade in Tamale all their goods were shipped by canoe from Ada. The river was now at its busiest.

But it was a relatively short-lived boom. With the Kumasi-Tamale road (including the Yeji Ferry over the Volta) open to

[1] The Governor's dismissal was the sequel to a three month siege of the Kumasi Fort by the Ashantis during which Hodgson and his wife and a garrison of 1,000 suffered great privation and a number of lives were lost.

through motor traffic in 1921 it was inevitable that the bulk supply route linked to the railway should gain the upper hand. By 1926 a determined effort on the part of the railways and of private transport operators had tended to put river transport, as a competitive venture, out of business.

During the war years it came into its own again and the Ada fleet of sailing wherries which plied up the river as far as Akuse was one of the colourful sights of the river.

The Volta had what was possibly its first bona-fide tourist in the year 1911. Mary Gaunt was an adventurous Australian widow of indeterminate years but of a most determined countenance, who had apparently dreamed of West Africa ever since she had read of it as a child in the outback, behind Geelong. Indeed when she came to London to make her living as a writer it was of West Africa that she wrote, losing no opportunity to gather second-hand background material when she could. Finally she saved enough money to be able to afford a six-month visit to the continent of which she dreamed. She was armed with introductions both from the Colonial Office and from the head offices of leading merchant houses but, it seems, with precious little else other than a steel uniform chest full of evening dresses and her elder brother's naval camping kit and medicine chest (which she claims she never used except to give cascara sagrada tablets to a hammock bearer who was in fact stricken with pneumonia). She set sail for West Africa, having a quick look in turn at the Gambia, Sierra Leone and Liberia. But the Gold Coast was her real destination and, having overshot the beginning of it by fifty miles, she put ashore at Axim, the first sea port. There she hired carriers and hammock bearers to take her back the fifty miles to the French border so that she could honestly claim that she had started at the beginning.

After her trail to the frontier and back, she travelled alternately by sea and land from Axim to Accra, where she spent a month, not resting but sight-seeing as much as she could. Then she moved to the Volta. To be different she force-marched her carriers by full moon across the Accra Plains and right past the foot of the terrifying Krobo Mountain. At this point, seeing a single light on the supposedly abandoned hill, her carriers broke into a gallop that landed her at Akuse two hours earlier than expected so that her host had to be weaned from his bed at four o'clock in the morning. Surprisingly, he gave her a gracious welcome and took her upstairs, and first gave her whisky-and-soda because it was so late and then tea and fruit because it was so early.

From Akuse Mary Gaunt decided to strike north and persuaded the astounded agents (to whom she had a never-ending folio of introductions) that she wanted a canoe and crew to 'pull' her as far as Labolabo, whence she would strike east into German territory. No one remembered to warn her that being 'pulled' up the Kpong and Senchi rapids would be dangerous. Probably they did not dare. 'The Senchi rapids', she writes, 'raise the river thirty-four feet in a furlong or two, and the water, white and foaming, boils over the brown rocks like the water churned up in the wake of a great ocean steamer. I could not believe we were going up there when we faced them, but the expert canoe-men with shout and song defying the river, poled and pulled and pushed the canoe up to another quiet reach and when they had reached calm water flung themselves down and smoked and chattered and looked back over the way we had come.' Later she was told that many bags of cotton had gone to the bottom in these rapids and that many barrels of palm oil had been dashed to pieces against the rocks. 'I had one great advantage,' she continues, 'I did not realize the danger till we were right in it, and then it was pressing, it absorbed every thought till we were in smooth water again, with the men lying panting at the bottom of the canoe, so that I really had no time to be afraid till it was all over. Frankly, I don't think I could enter upon such a journey again so calmly, but I am glad I have gone once, for it was such a wonderful and enchanting river. Some day they dream the great waterway will be used to reach Tamale, a ten day's journey farther north, but money must be spent before that happy end is arrived at.'

But if the rapids did not frighten Mary Gaunt, the Customs men did. And not because she was a smuggler either. Without batting an eyelid she will force-march by night over uncharted territory, clamber over a mountain top in the midday sun because it is too steep for her hammock men, face rapids and even the Ada bar in the teeth of a hurricane, and take it all in her stride. But throughout her book she reveals a terror of being raped, not by her carriers or servants and not by her many and various hosts but by the Customs officers who man the preventive stations along the river frontier between British and German territory. She returns to it again and again. She admits that there is no rational explanation for her fear. 'I may have wronged them', she says, 'for they were quite civil, but I was afraid. Again and again they made me remember that I was a woman alone and very helpless. They insulted me by making me fear them. Nothing would have induced me to stay two nights at one of these stations.'

She goes on to explain that at Ajena, where this fearful worry took hold of her, she had to have her camp bed put up on the verandah, because she found the room too stuffy. She was a confirmed fresh-air fiend and was for ever opening windows. 'The moonlit river', she conceded, 'was glorious to look upon, but I was anything but happy in my own mind; I wondered if I wanted help if my canoe men, who were very decent, respectable fellows, would come to my help. I wonder still.'

She tortured herself needlessly. The truth is that Mary Gaunt was, even then, over fifty years ago, much safer from assault on the Volta than she would have been on a Thames punt.

The last glimpse we have of this amazing woman on the Volta is at Ada, which she insisted upon visiting *en route* from Lome, the capital of German Togo, to Accra. This meant disembarking from one vessel and awaiting another and twice crossing the perilous Ada surf and bar. She heads her chapter 'Facing Death' but, bearing in mind her prejudices, it might well have been a fate worse than death. Coming ashore she was lowered from the ship into a canoe. 'Then', she writes, 'the Customs-house officer edged his way close beside me and stretching out his hand put it on my arm. I did not like it so I promptly shook it off and as promptly the boat was apparently flung crash against a stone wall. She had really hit the beach and I went over backwards and head first into the bottom of the boat. The man's help had been kindly meant; he would have held me in my place. But there is no time for apologies when a surf boat reaches the beach. Before I had realized what was happening two Kroo boys had dived to the bottom of the boat, seized me without any ceremony whatever, and raced me up on to the shore where they put me down in the blazing sun of an African afternoon without even a helmet or an umbrella to protect my head. At least I had landed in safety and the thing was now to find the Commissioner and see what he would do for me.' How long-suffering were those Commissioners.

But her arrival was nothing to her departure. Hearing that it would be a 'bad bar' Mrs Gaunt joined the captain on the bridge of the lighter with her camera. 'I thought I might as well see all there was to see,' and besides she wanted to take some photographs. Soon they were at the bar and 'we seemed to be heading for a wild waste of boiling water worse than anything I had ever conceived of. But I fear I must have been too upset to draw the slides for I got no photographs'. But now they were in trouble. Wave after wave rose up like mountains and crashed across the vessel. Again and again the two men at the wheel were flung off, their clothes being ripped off them as if they had been shells. The captain took over. Mary Gaunt clung on, refusing to go below. 'I thought if I were to be drowned I would rather be drowned in the open. Crash, crash, crash came the tons of water; there was a ripping of broken wood and a human wail that told me that crew and passengers had realized their danger. . . . Then suddenly the ship seemed to give a leap forward and instead of the waves crashing on to us we were riding over them.' The Captain seized her by the arm. 'We're all right now,' he said, 'but, my God, you will never be nearer to it.'

Then she saw the havoc. 'The bulwarks were swept away. The boats were smashed. The galley was swept overboard and, transformation scene, every solitary creature on board that little ship, with the exception of the Captain and me, was stark. Customs-house officers were stripped, clerks who had come to tally cargo in all the glory of immaculate shirts and high starched collars were nude and the men who worked the ship had got rid of their few rags as superfluous. Everyone had made ready to face the surf.' Everyone that is, but Mary Gaunt and the Captain. She heard soon afterwards that among the casualties was her brother's naval medicine chest. 'Oh well,' she said, remarkably mildly, 'it's gone and there is nothing more to be said.'

4

A DAM AT AKONSOMO

With the Volta 'discovered' by Mary Gaunt, another Australian, Albert Kitson, entered the scene. From the day of his first arrival in 1913 he set about opening up vital new prospects for the mineral wealth of the country, and more than fifty years later the Ghanaian head of the Geological Survey Department remarked that 'the spirit of Kitson is still ablaze today in the department's activities'.

Albert – later Sir Albert – Kitson had been appointed by the Colonial Office to establish a new department with the purpose of discovering what mineral wealth, in addition to gold, lay concealed beneath the forests and mountain tops of the still little known interior of the Gold Coast. He found the first traces of bauxite a hundred miles inland within a year of his arrival, and at a time when geologists in far more accessible countries were still walking over bauxite without recognizing it. Later he found the rich industrial diamond deposits at Akwatia, which are still being vigorously worked, and the iron ore deposits at Shieni, now conveniently close to Lake Volta. Probably no other geologist has so many exploited geological discoveries to his name.

On April 24, 1915 he was engaged on a rapid canoe voyage down the Volta, as part of a counrtywide survey. 'I noticed on entering the narrow gorge below Ajena,' he recorded, 'that it was an ideal place for a dam. At the time there was no opportunity to make measurements but, during a geological traverse made along the Volta, this place – Akonsomo [*sic*], 2.5 miles below Ajena – was examined hurriedly, and a measurement made of the river at about half a mile above the gorge. There it proved to be 200 yards wide, with depths, at 10 feet intervals, across the middle 140 yards, of 60 to 90 feet.' He was also able to calculate that the volume of water passing through the gorge was 1,634 cubic feet per second on one day and that on the following day the river had risen about one foot. He conjectured what a huge increase in the volume of river water there must be 'when for fully 5 months of the year it is 10 feet deeper than when measured, and during several weeks, 20 feet deeper'.

Indeed, writing ten years later in an official bulletin outlining the mineral and water-power resources of the Gold Coast, Kitson, using the most conservative of calculations, estimated that a 100-foot dam at 'Akonsomo' would generate 180,000 horse-power or 134,000 kilowatts, which is a little less than the output of one of the four generators now installed at Akosombo. He envisaged the consequent lake being at least extensive enough to provide water transport down the Afram stretch for the movement of the bauxite deposits, estimated at some 4 million tons, that had been located on the Kwahu plateau. These appeared to be the most accessible of many other known deposits of bauxite in the country, calculated then as amounting to more than 60 million tons[1], sufficient to manufacture some 12 million tons of aluminium. It was this juxtaposition of raw bauxite and potential water power that pointed to the possibility of an economic project.

During his leave in 1917 and while the war in France was still on, Kitson took the opportunity of visiting bauxite mines in the South of France,[2] as well as a hydro-electric project in Scotland, so as to understand clearly the technical problems involved in all stages of aluminium production. Armed with the necessary data he returned to the Gold Coast and prepared a detailed proposal for the use of Volta hydro-electric power to process bauxite into aluminium, and in 1924 additional proposals were added to canalize the Lower Volta and irrigate the Accra Plains. This might have emerged as one of Governor Guggisberg's greatest triumphs. But he was already committed to such

[1] Ghana's reserves of workable bauxite are today calculated as being in excess of 200,000,000 tons – sufficient to supply the Tema smelter, at its maximum planned rate of production for more than 250 years.

[2] Bauxite is named after the Provence village of Les Baux where it was first mined.

memorable development projects as Takoradi Harbour, Achimota College and Korle Bu Hospital as well as a widespread motor road construction programme for the movement of cocoa, and consequently the project remained in its drawer.

The other bauxite product that Kitson recommended was high alumina cement (*ciment fondu*) all the ingredients of which were available either on the Kwahu plateau or, in the case of limestone, a few miles away on the Afram at Asuboni. At the time his proposal came to nothing. But in 1964, just as these Afram limestone deposits were threatened with flooding by the actual rise of Lake Volta, it was decided to recover as much of the limestone as could be removed before it was inundated. A total of 5,000 tons was removed and was used at the steelworks at Tema.

Kitson's proposals for harnessing the Volta were not confined to Akosombo. He pointed also to the suitability of constructing a 100- or 200-foot dam on the Black Volta at Boie (Bui), of which we shall hear more later. He saw this as the means of electrifying a future railway to the north. He also had proposals for using power from the coastal rivers, the Tano, the Pra and its tributary the Ofin, and from several plateau rivers such as the Pawmpawm and the Asuboni. Some, at least, of these early proposals are still very much alive as possible additional sources of power for the future. And his suggestions for a 440-mile national transmission line for Volta power to service Cape Coast, Sekondi, Tarkwa, Dunkwa, Sefwi, Obuasi, Kumasi and the Kwahu area are only in minor detail different from those that have now been installed.[1]

Kitson was a perfect example of the pioneering Empire builder. Born in India and educated in Australia he had geological experience in many parts of the world. His carefully kept logbooks of every trip he made, on foot, by bicycle, canoe and horseback into every corner of the Gold Coast, provide a fascinating collection of geological data coupled with a wealth of human observation. Three nights before he 'discovered' Akosombo he was sleeping at the old riverside frontier station of Mpeasem across the river from Anum. 'This evening and tonight are both lovely,' he wrote. 'There is moonlight, a clear

[1] See front end-paper (1).

sky, it is starry (Southern Cross very good) with mild, cool zephyrs. A band was playing in the village on the opposite bank various airs "Marching thro' Georgia", "God save the King", "Work for the night is coming", "Where there's love at home" etc. After three hours with 2 or 3 repetitions of the national anthem they finished with it and then they or the other villages started firing guns with heavy charges. I could see the flashes plainly and then, about two seconds later, heard the reports. One (at 11.45 p.m.) has just gone off. With sound travelling at 1,142 feet per second it would make the village between $\frac{1}{3}$ and $\frac{1}{2}$ mile away.'

His river trip ended at Kpong where he stayed for a few days at the disused Provincial Commissioner's house, a handsome two-storied Swiss-style building, the property of the Basel Mission. 'But', he wrote, 'it has a very unpleasant smell as the roof is infested with bats, and two monkeys are caged in one of the lower rooms and have been in the habit of running about the place.'

By an interesting coincidence this is the same house that Duncan Rose occupied during his survey of the Volta between 1939 and 1949 which was to bring the Volta River Project one stage nearer reality. Duncan Rose – tall, handsome, weather-beaten South African pioneer – seemed to have stepped straight out of the memorable pre-war advertisement for Barney's tobacco, which had usually been carried to some lonely outpost for several hundreds of miles on the heads of bearers.

A Yorkshireman by birth, Rose had emigrated to South Africa soon after graduating at Cambridge. During the 1930s he had been one of the early enthusiasts of aluminium as the metal of the century, and at one time had bauxite interests in Nyasaland. He is said to have first been fired with the idea of a hydro-electric aluminium scheme for the Gold Coast by Kitson's 1925 bulletin, which he came across in the public library in Johannesburg in November 1938. Sensing that war was imminent he could see the advantage to the Commonwealth of a sterling source of aluminium. Within four months he had paid an exploratory visit to the Gold Coast and returned to Johannesburg to report back to his first financing partner, T. W. Charles. Together they interested the Anglo-Transvaal Consolidated

Investment Co., a leading South African mining finance house, which agreed to sponsor a full-scale investigation of the combined bauxite and power potential of the scheme. Their next move was to form the African Aluminium Syndicate in which they were joined by Christopher St John Bird, a partner in a Johannesburg firm of consulting engineers. By May 1939 St John Bird was in the Gold Coast preparing a preliminary report whilst Rose himself was also back in the country negotiating concessions.

During his first visit in February, Duncan Rose had already presented to the Gold Coast Government what he described as 'tentative proposals' for a hydro-electric scheme. At this stage his proposed dam was only 120 feet high and the resultant lake a mere 30 miles long by 2½ miles wide with an area of 80 square miles. Even so he was quick to point out that payment of heavy compensation to the people affected by the flooding might jeopardize the whole scheme and he adds that the lake itself would be of great public value for water transport. He talked of a possible aluminium smelter at Koforidua and of using surplus electric power to electrify the Accra to Kumasi railway line. At this stage he was thinking in terms of a £2½–3½ million scheme.[1]

St John Bird, however, was every inch the cautious and painstaking consulting engineer and produced for the Syndicate, after his initial three-week visit, a remarkably detailed report, considering the prevailing pioneering conditions. What he could not gather for himself he secured from existing sources and, though there remained all the necessary geological and other groundwork to be done, he estimated that a dam of some 250 feet high was necessary, impounding a lake of not 80 but of 800 square miles and that the cost would be nearer £6½ million than Rose's provisional estimate.

These more formidable figures did not, however, shake Rose's faith in the project. Indeed, so determined was he to button up the scheme to the advantage of his Syndicate, and so anxious to exclude any possible competitors, that he now took steps to secure options over the vital area (the seven-mile gorge in which any dam would have to be sited).

[1] See front end-paper (2).

As the riverside chiefs tell the story today, they were summoned to an urgent meeting at Senchi Ferry at which the District Commissioner introduced them to Duncan Rose. To everyone's surprise, including the DC's, Rose after a few words of explanation produced prepared option agreements in respect of 15 square miles of both river banks and asked the chiefs to sign them for a cash consideration of £30. Detecting no doubt a certain lack of enthusiasm on the part of the chiefs, Rose somewhat impatiently altered the figure to £60, but the chief's only reaction was to make a formal reply that this was a matter concerning which they would have to consult their solicitors.

As it happens the options were signed at a subsequent meeting in return for an agreed sum of £300 each and a rental of £300 per annum, and Rose must have realized that he was dealing with astute landowners who had no illusions about the value of their land.

At this stage however the Second World War broke out, and the Syndicate had to suspend physical operations. Duncan Rose himself left for England to manage a munitions factory. But it seems unlikely that his thoughts were fully fastened on conveyor belts, for during that same period he was vigorously pushing his aluminium scheme both in government and in business circles. Through his lawyer in Accra he got his option agreements in respect of the 15 square miles of possible dam sites renewed and ultimately validated by the courts in 1944. His bauxite concessions had been commandeered and were actually being worked by the British War Office for export to Canada and Britain as an essential wartime raw material.

But the strain of being away from the scene of operations was too great, and in 1943 Rose was permitted to leave his war job for South Africa in order to prepare for resuming investigations on the Coast. First of all he had to plan a campaign for the investigations, which were this time to be on a generous scale with the latest type of equipment including the newest echo-sounding devices and a staff of up to fifteen Europeans and a hundred Africans. It was late 1944 before Rose was back in Accra and in 1945 he made Kpong the headquarters of the newly formed company – West African Aluminium Ltd (Wafal), which took over from the pre-war Syndicate. One indication of the interest and new confidence shown in these post-war investigations is that in March of 1946 Unilever, in the form of its West Coast subsidiary, the United Africa Company, acquired a financial interest in Wafal.

It was in April of that year that I was posted to Akuse as District Commissioner of the Volta River District. So far as the Government was concerned the Wafal investigations were being treated as top-secret and the only file on them in my office was securely locked in my safe. On the ground, however, the situation was more relaxed. Rose himself would call at the office most weeks for his gelignite permits – and woe betide the office staff if they were not ready – and there was always activity on and around the river, with the South African team adding to the life of the neighbourhood and, very likely, to their own experience. Rose and Bird, however, kept mostly to themselves during the week in their severe Basel Mission headquarters, and it was only at weekends that they appeared socially at the Seaview Hotel in Accra, where they would meet friends and discuss progress.

The Seaview was then Accra's only hotel (it still survives) and had numbered among its guests in the past Sir Henry Stanley and G. A. Henty, who broke their adventurous sea voyage from Cape Coast to Ada there in 1873. Built round an open courtyard, it is in the style of fortified merchants' premises of the eighteenth and nineteenth centuries, and is said to have had extensive dungeons for storing slaves in the old days. It had great character and was the only congenial place where black and white could, and did, meet together in relaxed surroundings. When, after Independence, the London *Times* correspondent decided that, in his own interests, he must break with tradition and no longer stay at Government House during his visits to Accra it was to the Seaview that he went rather than to the plush new 100-room air-conditioned palace that had since made its appearance. And Jim Bailey, millionaire owner of *Drum* magazine and a chain of Johannesburg newspapers, stays at the Seaview when in Accra on the basis that he prefers a good bad hotel to a bad good one.

Meanwhile Christopher Bird, backed when necessary by a

number of international experts, was making fair progress on the technical aspects of the proposed dam, the deep sea harbour at Ada, and the opening up of the river in between. But Duncan Rose now came up against serious legal difficulties on the land acquisition side.

The first serious setback was the discovery in 1946 that it would be impossible for the courts to validate any of the numerous options that he was holding or negotiating to cover the vast area to be inundated by the lake. More detailed survey work had now determined that this would be in the region of 1,100–1,200 square miles; much of this area was admittedly low lying and uninhabited but equally a great part of it was both inhabited and cultivated and it included hundreds of villages and several small and medium-size towns. As the law stood then, any option which had the effect of moving people from their habitations was *ultra vires* and could not be validated. The three concessions covering the future dam site, which had already been validated, were not considered to be affected. But it was clear that, if the scheme was to proceed, the law would have to be amended, at the same time providing adequate safeguards for the inhabitants in the form of compensation.

The Government, which appears by this time to have become kindly disposed towards the scheme, undertook to explore the possibility of amendment, and Rose agreed to postpone his validation applications while this was being done.

It is of special interest at the present time, when Ghana is an independent Republic within the Commonwealth, to look back at this particular point of time. Duncan Rose had, between 1939 and 1946, by his phenomenal single-mindedness and personal belief in this scheme, not only secured all the current financial support that he needed both in South Africa and in Britain (Unilever), but had also largely convinced the Gold Coast Government, which at first had been suspicious and cautious, that this was a scheme that, whilst profitable to his company, was also of indirect value to the country as a whole and therefore, within certain limits, worth supporting. Indeed Duncan Rose had clearly attached great importance to securing goodwill at Government level.

What he had failed to do, and what he had probably never

seriously thought it necessary to do, was to secure the same amount of support for his scheme from the chiefs, the politicians and the people of the Gold Coast. He had already antagonized the chiefs in the dam site area at the time of the option agreements, and if ever he had needed support at a political level it was now, for in 1946 the Gold Coast secured a new constitution with a clear African majority in the legislature.

If, then, some Government sympathy lay with Duncan Rose's imaginative scheme and its overall possibilities, its instincts warned it, in these new circumstances, to move with particular care in relation to any changes in the laws that concerned simultaneously the needs of foreign investors and the basic rights of the people. Certainly the time had passed when the Government alone could initiate such a change.

By 1947 Duncan Rose had, it seems, reconciled himself to the need for putting through amending legislation as a private bill, and this he was able to do through the Special Member representing mining interests.

In June of that year I had an interesting letter from Nene Azzu Mate Kole, the Krobo Paramount Chief, whilst I was on leave in England. 'We had a very interesting session of the Leg Co. Old Duncan Rose's concession leases could not be validated in court due to the fact that the amendment which he sought to the concession laws did not pass. It was opposed by us all. I think except Government steps in to pass a special ordinance making the whole scheme a national one and providing against this uncertainty of state boundaries, which is certain to bring never-ending litigation should a concession be granted in these areas, no private company can have a hope to do the job. You see the land factor is too great and only Government can and has the means of settling that.'

And that is what the Government did, at least in part. Late in 1948 the British and Gold Coast Governments jointly decided that not only should the feasibility of an aluminium industry be officially examined but also that the whole potential of the Volta Basin should be explored. This 'writing on the wall' might have thrown a lesser enthusiast; but to Duncan Rose the scheme had already proved itself and he was now ready to look for a customer sufficiently interested in large-scale aluminium production to consider his enterprise worthy of immediate development.

It is not generally known that – quite apart from the commercial and official interest now evident in the Volta River Scheme – a purely African study circle known as the Focus Group, comprising a few young engineers, writers and sociologists, many of them leaders today, had been excited at the opportunities the scheme offered the country, and had prepared as a result of their discussions a searching pamphlet entitled 'Power from the Volta', balancing the social against the technical and economic points of view. Apparently they had been divided about whether to publish it privately or present it officially to the Government. It seems a pity that modesty prevailed and that it was not read more widely at that time.

In September 1949 the Bird Report made its appearance. The 'integrated aluminium scheme', as it was called, was in essence confirmation of what Albert Kitson had outlined some twenty-five years earlier. Bird's dam however was to span the river at Ajena Island, where it would be practicable to build it in two separate sections. It was to be higher than Kitson envisaged, having a crest some 210 feet above river level; and consequently it would create a larger lake, which itself would make communication with the bauxite producing areas even easier. With Rose's two separate bauxite concessions – one at Yenahin in Ashanti and the second at Mpraeso in Kwahu – they planned a single port on the Afram extension of the lake. This would be the terminus jointly of a 100-mile private railway from the Yenahin deposits and of an 18-mile aerial ropeway from the Mpraeso workings. The alumina refining plant and the smelter were to be adjacent to the power house on the west bank of the river at Ajena, where the bauxite-receiving jetties were to be. And then they planned to improve the 72 miles of river between Ajena and the sea at Ada so that, by use of locks and deeper channels, 500-ton barges could operate between the factory site and the new port at Ada, carrying the necessary chemicals and imported materials upstream and the manufactured aluminium ingots down to the sea. At Ada the plan was to have a small but compact and economical harbour accessible both to the river and to the sea.

So tidy was the scheme and with such possibilities that in June 1949 Aluminium Ltd of Canada, which had already acquired extensive bauxite concessions of its own in the Gold Coast, took a quarter interest in West African Aluminium Ltd, thus broadening the latter's base considerably. Duncan Rose had found just the customer he was looking for.

The Wafal-Alcan marriage led to a further development. The following year, the British Aluminium Company Ltd on the one hand and Alcan on the other both found themselves ready to develop an integrated aluminium industry within the sterling area – British Aluminium's interests being in North Borneo and Alcan's interests being in the Gold Coast. The companies agreed that there was neither the capital available nor, probably, sufficient demand for aluminium to justify both schemes; so they decided jointly to examine both of them and to decide on the more favourable.

The most important finding of the Joint Mission was that the Gold Coast scheme was, on balance, the sounder and the more economic of the two. For a capital outlay of £37½ million they estimated, together with a 5 per cent allocation for annual running costs, that they could manufacture 210,000 tons of aluminium per annum and leave a surplus of 50,000kw of electric power for public use. This was March 1951.

But there was one qualifying clause; on account of the one unknown factor, the stability of local conditions, neither British Aluminium nor Alcan could see such a scheme being financed without wholehearted support from both the British and the Gold Coast Governments.

For events were moving fast in the Gold Coast. Whilst the British Aluminium and Alcan Joint Mission was in the Gold Coast making its investigation, Kwame Nkrumah was serving a two-year prison sentence in James Fort, following a political demonstration arising from his Positive Action campaign which had involved some fatalities. But before their report could be published the same Kwame Nkrumah's Convention People's Party had swept the polls at the February 1951 general elections and he had been released from prison and called upon by the Governor to form a Government. He was now Leader of Government Business, soon to be restyled Prime Minister.

5

REGIONAL PLANNING

It will be recalled that towards the end of 1948 – before Wafal had completed its investigations – the British and Gold Coast Governments had agreed that a full-scale examination should be carried out of the whole potential of the Volta Basin, which naturally included any aluminium or other industrial projects.

This decision was an early instance, in a British colony at least, of the application of the principle of regional planning to a whole area rather than pursuing a policy of piecemeal development. It was of course also closely associated with aluminium prospects in general. The immediate post-war slump in the aluminium industry had brought about the partial reduction of bauxite mining in the Gold Coast for export and in 1946 the prospects of resumption were gloomy. By 1947 however the market was beginning to pick up again and British Aluminium decided to resume normal export of their bauxite deposits at Awaso in the west of the country. Indeed the optimists in the industry were already prepared to wager that within a year or two the growing demand would justify not merely the export of bauxite to existing smelters but new smelters themselves.

This optimism for the aluminium market, coupled with good prospects for other uses for the river and its tributaries, combined to offer just the right ingredients for a regional planning exercise. Clearly the need for co-ordinating new roads, bridges, railways and harbours not only to serve one particular industry but to develop the whole of the eastern part of the country was also within the scope of such an investigation, and there was Kitson's secondary proposal for a further hydro-electric project on the Black Volta at Bui still awaiting investigation.

But if there were admirable social and physical reasons for developing the natural resources of the country there were strong political reasons as well. The Second World War had come and gone and the economy of the Gold Coast, dependent as it is on cocoa, had passed through some devastating years. Due to shipping difficulties little cocoa had been shipped during the war. As shipping subsequently became available the cocoa price soared and a form of cash prosperity followed, whilst the state of post-war markets in consumer goods – notably textiles – failed to keep pace with the new prosperity. There followed a period of intense 'hunger' for things to buy, with no sort of prospect to the consumer either of easier supplies or of an early return to something like pre-war prices. An effective nationwide trade boycott followed and lasted for six weeks during which time trading in imported goods virtually came to a standstill. Eventually, with government intervention and a promise of strict price control, the boycott was called off but, perhaps because of delays in enforcing the control, the public considered itself cheated and on February 28 and 29, 1948 widespread looting and arson of overseas stores took place in Accra and quickly spread to other towns. The situation had been aggravated by the discontent of many Gold Coast ex-servicemen with their post-war circumstances. They became a very obvious and potent element in the Gold Coast's rapidly growing independence movement. February 28, 1948 was the turning point. It began with a march of ex-servicemen which got out of hand, and ended in police firing and the death of three men.

A Commission of Inquiry into the disturbances – apart from criticizing the Gold Coast Government for having done too little to keep the public abreast of post-war conditions – made far-reaching recommendations designed to speed independence for the Gold Coast. An all-African commission of some forty people, drawn from all parts of the country, was required to draw up the framework of a new constitution. In 1951 the Gold Coast was to have its first general elections, when Dr Kwame Nkrumah's Convention Peoples' Party was to lead the government during an initial period of internal self-government, prior to complete independence in 1957.

This political history was clearly at the back of the minds both of the Gold Coast and the British Governments when the plan to develop the Volta Basin in relation to the economy of the country as a whole was launched. At this time the Gold Coast was already firmly committed to self-government in the foreseeable future and it was clear that the development of the country's natural resources should be carefully co-ordinated in the national political interest.

So the services were secured of a leading London firm of consulting engineers, Sir William Halcrow and Partners, and by June 1949 one of the partners, Mr Peter Scott, was already in the Gold Coast on a preliminary investigation. By autumn Halcrows had received comprehensive terms of reference which required them 'to carry out a full investigation of the potential value of the River Volta to the economy of the Gold Coast' and set out the necessary details under the headings of power, irrigation, navigation and transport.

1950 opened with the arrival in the Gold Coast of the Volta River Panel – the name given to the body of experts appointed by the Consulting Engineers and the Government to carry out the survey. Led by Mr E. V. Richards, an experienced engineer from the staff of the consultants, the panel also included an irrigation engineer, an electrical engineer, two additional engineers, a geologist, a soil scientist and an authority on local land tenure and water rights. The panel worked on the ground for four months. It soon became evident to them that the terms of reference were so wide that it would be necessary to employ a full-time staff in the Gold Coast in order to continue the investigations. Under some pressure from the Government, however, they agreed to publish an interim report in July of 1950.

Three conclusions immediately emerged. The first was the confirmation that without an aluminium smelter as the major consumer of electricity it would be uneconomic to build a dam and manufacture hydro-electric power. The smelter was the key to the whole project. The second concerned the siting of the new seaport to serve the project. Halcrows quickly rejected Wafal's proposal of Ada because neither geographically nor economically was it suitably sited to replace the old-fashioned facilities of Accra as the major seaport for the east of Ghana. It was all right for Wafal's limited purposes but not for any other. They considered that the best all-round site for practical purposes was Tema, 16 miles east of Accra and 50 miles from the dam site. This was just the lead the Government was looking for. When Tema's superiority had been decided, no time was lost in starting the transformation of the small mud and thatch fishermen's village into the harbour and industrial city of 250,000 people that was proposed.[1]

Halcrows' third important interim proposal concerned the irrigation of the Accra plains lying to the south of the dam site. During the course of the previous two or three years there had been visits to the Gold Coast from representatives of both the Empire Cotton Growing Corporation and the British West African Rice Mission and in each case controlled experiments had been recommended. Irrigation as an idea, however, was something new to West Africa and there was little, if any, demand for it or understanding of it. It was a matter of urgency therefore for a small controlled pilot scheme to be established, and they recommended that this should be done near to Kpong and that a comprehensive soil survey should also be initiated to cover the whole area of the Accra plains.

But these were only the priorities and there still remained a vast amount of detailed work to be done before a comprehensive regional plan for the Volta Basin could emerge.

There was the actual dam site itself, for example. In order to avoid repeating all or most of St John Bird's detailed geophysical investigations between 1939 and 1949 the Gold Coast Government came to an arrangement with Wafal that the latter would make the Bird Report available to Halcrows in return for an assurance that Wafal would be the first company to be approached if the manufacture of aluminium in the Gold Coast were to be allocated to private enterprise. Just how these negotiations were conducted at the London end makes a fascinating vignette of Establishment wheels in motion. With an exchange of letters between a top desk at the Colonial Office and the head of Wafal's firm of financial advisers in the City on the basis of 'My dear Tommy' and 'My dear Bill' the report was made available with-

[1] In 1968 the population was some 85,000.

out either side embarrassing the other with binding commitments.

As it turned out the Bird Report was perhaps weakest on the subject of the geological substrata of Ajena Island, where the dam site was proposed. This was largely because Wafal's expert in this field, South Africa's distinguished geologist Dr A. L. du Toit, had died soon after his initial visit to the Gold Coast and before his detailed work was complete. Anticipating a possible decision against Ajena Island Halcrows started to explore all the alternative sites in the seven-mile gorge and in fact examined seven in number. These included Akosombo, Kitson's first choice, which they found suitable but technically difficult owing to the extreme depth of the river (over 200 feet at points) at this narrow bend.

Of the other sites that at Misikrom, another deep gorge just north of Ajena Island (Akosombo was two miles south), was undoubtedly the best. Geologically it passed all the tests. In size and probably in cost it approximated the Ajena Island dam (in each case the length of the crest of these dams would have been twice that of Akosombo, which is 2,200 feet) and it was handsomely abutted on either bank by a massive hill.

Whilst Halcrows therefore were tending to concentrate on Misikrom, Alcan and British Aluminium's Joint Mission, which was following up the Bird Report, decided to carry on the geological investigations left incomplete by Dr du Toit. They entrusted this to another eminent consultant engineering geologist, Mr Frank E. Fahlquist, who advised that the Ajena Island site was entirely adequate for a dam and strongly recommended the rockfill rather than the concrete barrage type as being the more suitable.

When Halcrows' full report was published then in August 1951 there was a perfectly logical choice of dam sites, two miles apart, with little to choose physically or economically between them. Realizing that there would be some interim period of gestation (though barely contemplating a full ten years) they recommended that a Special Commissioner should be appointed exclusively to handle, with an appropriate staff, this broad portfolio of development, which had been renamed 'The Volta River Project'.

Perhaps the biggest question of all, however, was who should

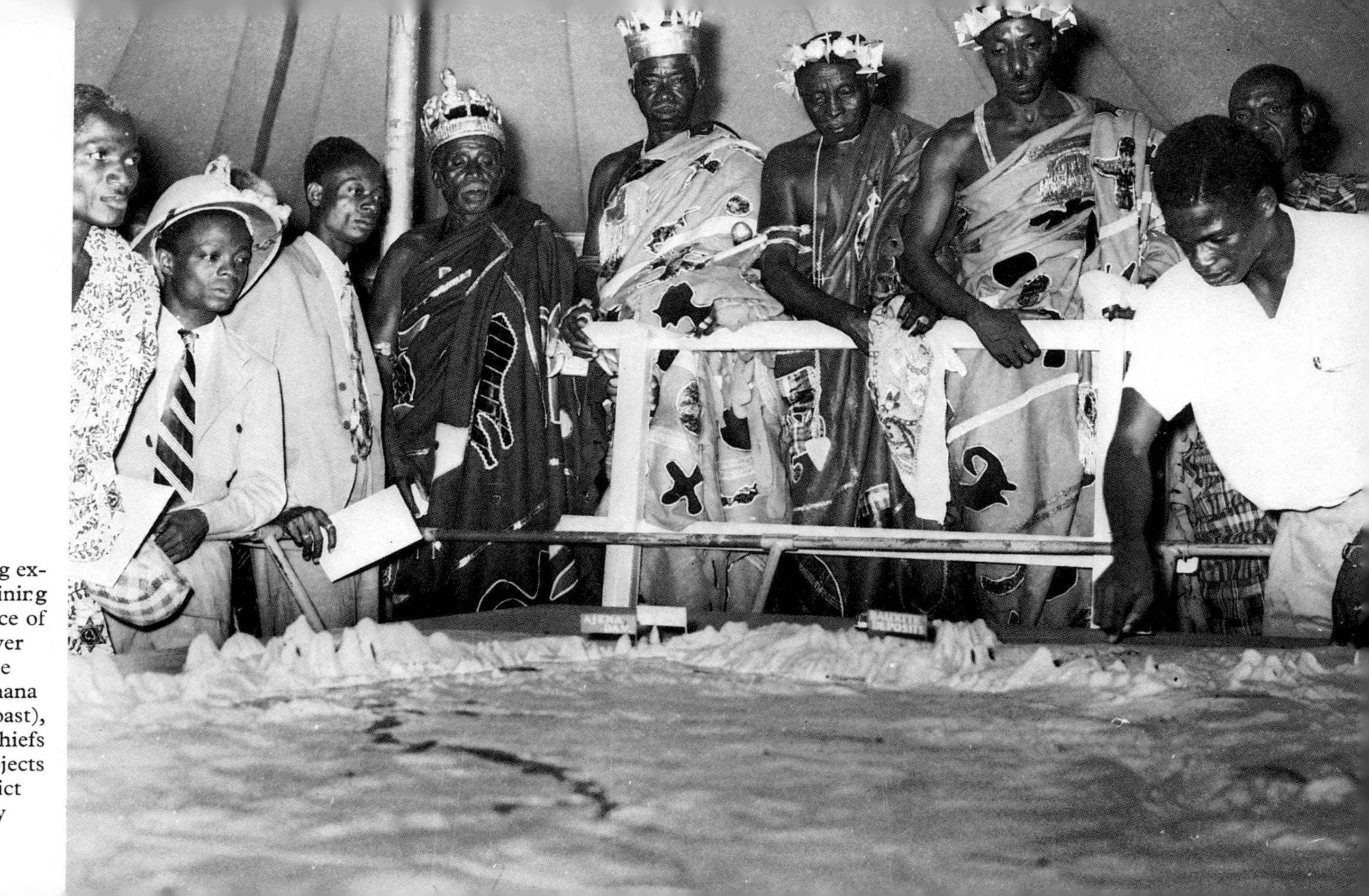

The travelling exhibition explaining the significance of the Volta River Project to the people of Ghana (then Gold Coast), was seen by chiefs and their subjects in every district of the country

The Adomi Bridge spans the Volta at the southern end of the Akosombo gorge. The dam is visible in the background

own the dam. Halcrows' answer made the point that, because of the size of the project, it would be necessary for the Government, and not a private company or syndicate, to control it from the outset. The dam therefore should be publicly and not privately owned. But, insofar as the actual manufacture of aluminium was concerned and the processing of raw bauxite into alumina powder, this was accepted as being a highly technical and specialized industry which it would be preferable to have under private ownership.

At the same time they had now formulated firm views as to the site for the smelter. Gone was Wafal's dam site smelter at Ajena, and gone (at least for the present) was the Joint Mission's smelter at Kpong. After careful calculation Halcrows decided that the smelter and alumina plant should both be at Tema. This recommendation in its turn made others on the siting of new roads and railways easier. With the rejection of the dam site aluminium factory there was no longer any advantage in carrying the raw bauxite by lake and it followed therefore that it should travel by rail.

However, the new proposals allowed for a fairly large margin of electricity to be generated at the dam site powerhouse, over and above the requirements of the aluminium smelter (the principal customer). Kitson had calculated that, if the gold mines in the west and the principal towns of Ashanti and the south were to be served with Volta power, some 440 miles of transmission lines would be necessary. Halcrows agreed, with slight modifications, costing it at about £5½ million.

Looking to the broader development of the river's resources, the consultants produced some useful, though barely startling, proposals for irrigation experiments. The engineers had found little if any data on which to base positive calculations and had to be content with setting the machinery in motion for proper surveys to be made. These would be long-term proposals, and it was thought that a possible use for a further hydro-electric scheme at Bui on the Black Volta might be to generate sufficient power for feeding into the grid to compensate for power lost at the main powerhouse if Lake Volta water was to be spared in any quantity for irrigating by gravity the Accra Plains.

A major step forward had now been taken. With the emergence of the Volta River Project, there was a clear-cut concept of a multi-purpose development plan based on the needs of the region as a whole, and this put the scheme on a much healthier footing.[1]

[1] See back end-paper (3).

6

A PAUSE FOR THOUGHT

With Halcrows' report out in August 1951 the two Governments and the two aluminium companies quickly got together to work out the remaining problems. So far these had in the main been engineering and technical ones, but now the project was no longer the sole concern of the planning engineers: if it were to get off the ground at all, it had to be adopted by the hard-bitten world of international finance with all its related political, strategic and economic influences.

The first of several meetings took place in London in October and November 1951 as a result of which a Memorandum of Conclusions was drawn up. Alcan led for the manufacturers. They made the point that in their philosophy private enterprise, such as should own and run the aluminium smelter, did not and could not marry or mix its capital with government or public-owned funds. The Gold Coast Government however took the stand that in a newly emerging country where there was no tradition or experience of a money market based on privately invested capital, the Government itself had some obligation to the local investors of the future to hold in trust on their behalf a limited percentage of equity shares in any industrial venture as important as the smelter. Eventually it was agreed that, though Alcan made no concession to its majority claim of 60 per cent of the capital, the Gold Coast Government 'as trustees of Gold Coast nationals' should have the right to acquire 10 per cent of the equity capital. And when the Gold Coast Government made the point that, as years passed, the desire for local participation might well exceed the 10 per cent thus set aside, Alcan conceded that if after the smelter had been operating for twenty-five years there proved to be this demand, they would undertake to offer for sale to private Gold Coast nationals at a reasonable price the equivalent amount of stock as had at that time actually passed into the hands of private Gold Coast investors from the 10 per cent block held originally in trust for them. In other words they would play ball if the Gold Coast Government would also play ball, and in this way they underlined the great importance they attached to the principle of private enterprise.

Meanwhile some important decisions had been taken. Still in his first year in office as leader of the Government, Dr Nkrumah, who had at once recognized the vital importance to the balanced development of the country of the Volta River Project in all its aspects, announced in Parliament on December 19, 1951 that, irrespective of the eventual outcome of the Project as a whole, his Government had decided to proceed with the construction of Tema Harbour to serve the interests of the east of the country. The services of Halcrows had again been retained as consultants on the harbour.

The following May Halcrows announced that after nine months of further survey at the two possible dam sites they had now finally found in favour of the Ajena Island site and were redesigning the dam as a rockfill one with an impervious clay core. In fact so quickly had events moved during these few months that by mid-1952 the Gold Coast Government began to ask itself whether the whole scheme should not be deferred for two or three years until it had had time to ensure that the necessary amount of reserve labour and administrative machinery was available to take such a complex project in hand. Their reservations were shared by the other parties. The project was too big to be handled except on the basis of complete certainty.

So with the full agreement of all concerned, the British Government presented to Parliament in November 1952 a white paper in which the whole scheme was clearly set forth. With it was the recommendation that, in view of the many issues involved and the importance of the scheme, a Special Commissioner should be appointed to head a Preparatory Commission which would be required to tie up all the loose ends. The terms of reference included tying in the Project with all the other Gold Coast plans for development in relation to local resources; close liaison with the aluminium companies; the planning of a future Volta River Authority; the preparation of revised time-tables and estimates, and the drafting of a master agreement.

What then was the 'scheme' presented in the white paper? Although sited in the Gold Coast and planned for the general benefit of that country, the scheme was justified to the British Parliament as first and foremost a means for Britain to escape from the dollar-based monopoly of the post-war aluminium producers from whom she had to procure more than four-fifths of her supplies. It was argued that by 1975 the world would be using four to five times as much aluminium as in 1950.[1] With her very limited resources of hydro-electric capacity Britain had already reached an effective limit in aluminium production and, as we have seen, the Joint Mission had selected the Gold Coast as the manufacturing base with the most potential in the Commonwealth area.

Ajena had now been selected as the site for the power station. The dam to be built there would form what would probably be the world's largest man-made lake with an area of over 2,000 square miles (very different from Rose's early guess of 80 square miles). The ultimate capacity of the power station would be 564,000 kw but this would not be fully installed in the first instance as the capacity of the smelter – the prime consumer – would grow in stages. The combined cost of the dam and power station would be £54 million.

In spite of the preference of Halcrows for Tema as the smelter site the aluminium manufacturers had moved it back to Kpong – partly, it seems, to avoid congesting Tema. The smelter was to have an initial capacity of 80,000 tons and an ultimate capacity of 210,000 tons of aluminium a year, the aim being to reach the full capacity within 20 years. The ultimate cost of the smelter would be £64 million.

Then there was the network of roads and railways, to bring the raw bauxite from Yenahin and Mpraeso, and an £11 million harbour at Tema. Together with the cost of seeing to the needs of the people affected by the lake and other public works this total, including the harbour, would be £26 million.

[1] In fact figures show that in 1965 the world was already using four times as much aluminium as in 1950.

Here then was a grand total of £144 million for the scheme, with the immediate need for £100 million for the initial target of 80,000 tons of aluminium per annum.

The Gold Coast Government was to finance all the public works from its own resources, plus a share in the power project and, as already explained, a 10 per cent share, in trust for the public in the smelter. This would amount in all to some £40–£45 million, according to the amount of smelter shares held.

The British Government's share was to be £57 million – the greater part of the cost of the power plant, in the form of a loan repayable over 80 years – and a non-equity holding of some £11 million in the smelter.

The Aluminium Companies would have the major holding in the smelter, amounting to £43–£48 million. Their supply of electricity would be guaranteed by a 60-year contract.

Of the aluminium produced, 75 per cent was to be offered to United Kingdom buyers for a period of 30 years at normal ruling prices.

This then was the scheme that was to be analysed by the Gold Coast's new Preparatory Commission. The Special Commissioner was Commander R. G. A. Jackson, who was no stranger to dams and multi-purpose power projects. He had already been closely associated with the planning of one of the greatest of them all – the Snowy Mountains Project in his native Australia – and had subsequently advised both the Indian and Pakistani Governments on development schemes of this nature.

As a result of wide administrative experience in the Royal Navy during the war, and in the Treasury and the United Nations later, Jackson well understood the need for good public relations and welcomed an early opportunity to meet the local press at the home of the Minister of Commerce and Industry, Mr K. A. Gbedemah.[1]

[1] Later Minister of Finance, Gbedemah was one of the two Ministers particularly charged with responsibility for liaison with the Preparatory Commission and subsequently with the extremely complicated international financial negotiations that ultimately made the Volta River Project possible. Mr George Woods, later President of the World Bank, who in 1958 was invited in his then private capacity to advise the Kaiser Corporation on the complex problems of financing the Project, said that Gbedemah, more than anyone else, sold him the Volta River Project. So when Gbedemah amongst others was carpeted by

One particular devotee of the art of descriptive prose evidently decided to do full justice to the press 'outdooring'[1] of Commander Jackson. He wrote:

'Ah, here is the Press Gang I said to myself as I entered the bright hall of the Hon. Mr Gbedemah. He is the Minister of Commerce, of course. The Press Gang, if you don't know, is an endearing term for journalists when they get together for mischief. And that is when they are out to ask too many questions. They often do.

'Throughout the atmosphere was pleasant. It was easy to pick out the host, for he was the only gentleman in that everlasting dress of a white coat. J. Moxon was also in white, but of the Saturday-afternoon-off-to-the-Oval type.

'But I was looking out for the Commander Jackson, of whom there had been much talk. And there he stood, quite tall and slim. A man of many parts, including faultless dressing. His tie matched with his breast-pocket handkerchief.

'With a medium-sized head and a comparatively small face which may look harsh when he stops talking, Commander Jackson is a man of the world. He had the fashion of illuminating his talk with smiles, which make him charming and a human. He is a listener too, and not merely a talker.

'But when he starts to talk, you will have no mind of interrupting, as you might miss a treat. The gentleman's repertoire of facts and figures on economics generally, to say nothing of aluminium and allied material in particular is fabulously enormous. You will readily understand why they selected him for the job. At one time I felt his head might crack with all the relevant knowledge he had stored up.

'Of course, all the time we were drinking – drinking and eating tidbits and talking, as Commander Jackson told us of his world experiences with rare wit. He is prolific in that.

'Those who liked to talk, talked. Questions were asked, mixed up with a few home truths. But all were nicely said and

---

Nkrumah in his now-famous dawn broadcast of April 8, 1961 (Ian Smith copied the technique) and chose to go into exile, Ghana lost the services of a very able negotiator. Gbedemah returned to Ghana as a private citizen after the February 1966 coup.

[1] In Ghana a child is 'outdoored' on the eighth day after birth and also named.

received, and about 8.30 we found ourselves saying goodnight to our pleasant host.'

It is more than likely that, as the racy reporter flippantly says, 'a few home truths' were discussed. For at the time of Commander Jackson's arrival in the Gold Coast, public opinion within the country was brisk and critical and took nothing for granted. A statement by the Gold Coast Government, introducing the British Government's white paper, made it clear that, whilst this document outlined the scheme as provisionally agreed between the parties, no one was in fact committed at this stage and that, after the Preparatory Commission had completed its task, the Legislative Assembly would debate the whole issue so the country as a whole could have its say in the final decision.

The process of democratic analysis had already got off to a good start for, quite apart from parliamentary debate, other more informal forces were at work examining the Project. In 1948 the country had acquired a new institution of higher learning: the University College of the Gold Coast, affiliated in the first instance to the University of London.[1] Its Department of Extra Mural Studies was under the stimulating direction of a young Englishman, David Kimble. It was the policy of Kimble and his like-minded regional assistants to encourage the countrywide formation of branches of the People's Educational Association (PEA) which lost little time in organizing local discussion groups, lectures and conferences with emphasis on topical and controversial subjects. Kimble chose his topics carefully, and as often as not they were subjects which had never before been publicly aired in the Gold Coast. It was possible to read candid newspaper reports of some PEA discussion on a subject which, so far as the 'Secretariat wallahs' were aware, had never gone beyond the covers of their SECRET files.

The topic that caused near apoplexy among civil servants was the suggestion that the Gold Coast should aim at holding at least a majority share in the Volta River Project so as 'to eliminate the probable danger of an Anglo-Gold Coast-Canadian

[1] The University of Ghana became autonomous in 1960 after twelve years of close association with London University.

dispute'. Such a suggestion reported in the press, they seemed to think, might frighten away the other participants in the project. Yet, when the Legislative Assembly debated the subject the following month, members spoke not on this theme alone; some feared that under the scheme the British Government might be able to buy aluminium cheaply from the Gold Coast and sell it at a profit to other customers. Though the very suggestion must have deeply sorrowed many loyal government supporters, the fact that it was made in Parliament and was privileged made it respectable.

Far from alarming the aluminium companies, however, these public reservations prompted the manufacturers to make sure that the project was fully understood. It was decided for example that a representative party of citizens drawn from all over the country should visit the aluminium interests in Canada and see for themselves exactly what was involved in damming a large river, in generating electricity from water and in manufacturing aluminium from bauxite. One of Commander Jackson's first tasks was to arrange this, and within a few weeks a Gold Coast National Committee had been formed not only to visit Canada and Britain but also to act as a continuing body on behalf of the public interest, to liaise with the Preparatory Commission and ultimately to offer advice.

A plan of campaign was then worked out: a special Publicity Section was to be formed within the Preparatory Commission in order to explain the Volta River Project – first, to the people of the Gold Coast and secondly, overseas. Two overseas experts were hired: a journalist and a photographer. They were to feed the newspapers with articles and pictures, and also to mount a fully mobile travelling exhibition which was to tour all the principal towns in the country. This exhibition showed by the use of models, dioramas, maps, photographs, diagrams, films, posters and captions in seven different languages exactly what the Project was intended to achieve.

This travelling circus – for this is what it resembled, with its marquees and lorries and mobile generators, its loudspeakers and cinema vans, its bunting and its atmosphere of jaunty excitement – proved to be a great success, and in the two years that it operated probably did more to attune the people of the Gold

Coast to the purposes of the Volta River Project than any other form of publicity. As a result of this sort of public relations during the 1950s the public came to be very well informed, and this was an important factor in the development of the Gold Coast as an independent country.

Commander Jackson himself kept in close touch with public feeling about the Volta River Project and recognized people's particular concern about matters of land ownership and inheritance. His job was made easier and more effective by his close friendship with Nkrumah and by the presence of his gifted wife, the eminent economist Barbara Ward. Author of what *Time* magazine calls 'Lyndon's other Bible' (*The Rich Nations and the Poor Nations*) Barbara Ward had reorganized her own complicated public life on her arrival in Accra in 1953, and had made her home both a social and intellectual meeting-place and a centre of ordinary good friendship – qualities that readily appealed to the Prime Minister. And the rapport established between the Jacksons and Nkrumah was a factor in the eventual success of the Project that should not be underestimated.

7

COMMISSIONS AND REPORTS

The Nkrumah-Jackson team lost no time in setting the workings of the Preparatory Commission in motion. Prime Minister Nkrumah's first concern was with the instinctive local fear, expressed both inside and outside Parliament, that the Gold Coast, with her relative inexperience in the art of international bargaining, was not going to derive the best possible terms from the partnership. That she should was the crux of the whole project, and the Prime Minister regarded it as essential that the country's strongest bargaining position should be explored and understood so that the final agreements would be prepared on the basis of complete equality.

Nkrumah was also worried at the comparatively low surplus of electric current (only 50,000kw) that would remain for the use of other industries, when the full needs of the aluminium smelter (514,000kw) had been met. He felt that basically this was still 'an aluminium scheme', and that as the Gold Coast had for years found itself handicapped by its total reliance on the cocoa industry it would be unwise to channel all the country's resources into another single product – aluminium. He therefore readily accepted Jackson's proposal that the best technical advice on increasing the power potential of the Volta should be sought – possibly from the United States Government, in view of their experience with such projects, and perhaps within the terms of their Point Four Programme. And they had agreed that the Technical Assistance Board of the United Nations might be able to advise on the diversification of industry within the Volta Basin.

Sufficient progress had been made by the Preparatory Commission six months after it had started operations for the Prime Minister to call a Press Conference to report 'nothing dramatic or spectacular but a record of steady, solid progress'. The Commission itself, he said, had already proved its value in maintaining close relations with the other participants in the project and in attracting the services of a number of visiting experts. These included Dr Arthur E. Morgan, first Chairman of the Tennessee Valley Authority (TVA) who had declared the Project 'sound and desirable'. He had added that 'the studies and preparations for it have a degree of completeness and thoroughness which are unusual outside the well industrialized countries . . . and compare favourably with the better planned projects in those countries'. The Prime Minister then mentioned that another TVA expert, Professor H. G. Lewis, an Afro-American sociologist of great distinction, was shortly to advise the Preparatory Commission on labour and sociological aspects. Finally he spoke at some length on the question of international financing. Many people in the Gold Coast could not grasp the normal necessity, in a scheme of this magnitude, for borrowing a large proportion of the capital cost of the project on the international money market, believing that borrowing was shameful and implied undue poverty. The Prime Minister reassured them that international borrowing implied the opposite of insolvency since it was only on the strength of a country's good name and economic prospects that others would invest money in it.

In programming its investigation the Preparatory Commission divided the Project into five parts: the bauxite mines; railways and other communications; the dam and power station, and problems related to the lake; the alumina factory and smelter; and the new seaport at Tema. The Commission clearly had less direct responsibility for the actual operation of the private sector of bauxite mining, alumina reduction and aluminium smelting than for railway communications and the dam and powerhouse which were the Government's special responsibilities. Nevertheless, because of this division of responsibility, it was all the more important that the work of the Preparatory Commission and of the work of Aluminium Ltd (representing the interests of the producers) should be closely integrated.

Aluminium Ltd, under the leadership of its President, Nathaniel V. Davis, had indeed entered into the spirit of the whole project, not least in the field of Human Factors (as the Preparatory Commission came to term all those matters related to the people who would ultimately be working on the construction or the operation of the Project). These included such essential considerations as health, housing and food supplies, as well as recruitment, training, and conditions of service. Davis himself had been a regular visitor to the Gold Coast ever since his company had decided to take an active financial share in Wafal in 1949, and he had taken a leading part in the various talks in London, Montreal and Accra. Then during the second half of 1953 Alcan decided to acquire a controlling interest in Wafal, which still held its validated concessions covering certain bauxite deposits, the dam site and some land at Ada, with the additional right to acquire 100 per cent interests if they so desired; and thus in November 1953 Duncan Rose, St John Bird and their associates ceased to be principals in Wafal.

Recognizing the division of responsibilities between the Preparatory Commission and Alcan for the detailed investigations into the various areas of the Project, Alcan now sent to Accra a full time representative, Dr R. Grimes-Graeme, to co-ordinate all their activities and to maintain on-the-spot liaison with the Preparatory Commission.

Once the machinery for technical investigation was at work, Commander Jackson found time to do some extensive travelling in order to liaise personally, as the Prime Minister had wished, with representatives of the United Nations, the United States Government, the TVA and Alcan itself in Canada. Only first-hand visits of this kind could keep the planners of comparable ventures abreast of rapidly developing new techniques – particularly in the all-important field of mammoth-scale rock and earth movement, the economics of which would be a vital factor in the proposed Volta Dam.

During one of Jackson's periodic visits to Montreal the much heralded 'Rubicon' talks were first seriously discussed. It was planned that the two governments and the aluminium companies concerned would meet together and, on the evidence of their joint investigations, decide whether they were prepared to go ahead with the scheme. Commander Jackson thought that by the end of 1954 all the technical reports could be ready and circulated in draft. These could be followed by the economic and financial reports in February of 1955 and the draft of the final report the following month. This would give a clear three months for the welter of facts and figures and proposals and background matter to be fully digested; the Rubicon talks might then take place in July 1955.

1954, meanwhile was a vital year for the Commission. Advisers came and went, and gave the Commission a chance to break a little interim publicity and to show that account was being taken of every aspect of the life of the people. Pictures appeared in the papers, for example, of two anxious-looking gentlemen paddling in a river-bed, which helped to persuade the country that the necessary research was being made into relevant matters of public health. River-blindness, a disease carried by the simulium fly which breeds along the banks of streams, has long been a scourge in the valleys of the Volta and its tributaries and the researchers felt that the formation of the comparatively static Lake Volta, combined with preventive measures, would improve the situation. The visiting experts in this field were the late Dr Andrew Topping, Dean of the London School of Hygiene and Tropical Medicine and Professor George Macdonald, Director of the Ross Institute. To study the fishing potential of the proposed lake came Professor Worthington, Secretary-General of the Scientific Council for Africa South of the Sahara. Major-General G. N. Russell, Chairman of the Road Services of the British Transport Commission, visited the country to make a close survey of all the railway and communications problems. Dr O. H. Koenigsberger, of the London School of Hygiene and Tropical Medicine, joined the Commission to advise on housing and town-planning questions, and Professor W. Arthur Lewis, Stanley Jevons Professor of Political Economy at Manchester University (later Vice-Chancellor of the University of the West Indies) prepared the all-important report on the economic and financial implications of the scheme.

At the same time local experts were also playing an important role. A detailed survey of the whole area to be flooded by the lake, of its towns and villages, of their inhabitants, and of the habits of the migrant Ewe fishermen who formed a high proportion of those who would have to be settled, was carried out by Maurice Hewson, an experienced District Commissioner. Simultaneously, valuable research into the probable economic effect of the dam on the lives of the people living on or near the Volta, between the dam and the sea, was being conducted by Mrs Rowena Lawson from the University's Faculty of Economics.

Another cause of anxiety both to the Preparatory Commission and to Alcan was the evaporation potential of the lake. This may appear to be a matter of only marginal importance but to a hydro-electric engineer endeavouring to gauge the pressure of water available for turning the turbines it was a vital factor and one in respect of which there was little if any relevant factual data. It is true that statistics had been kept by the Meteorological Department for evaporation on reservoirs and specially constructed tanks but it was now established that Lake Volta, at its greatest, would be between 3,275 and 3,500 square miles in area (though capable of dropping to 2,310 square miles at its lowest limit) which as the largest artificial lake in the world, would put its evaporation potential well outside the scope of routine calculating factors. Consequently considerable research was conducted into this on an international basis by the late Mr H. O. Walker, the Gold Coast's own Director of Meteorological Services, and Dr H. I. Penman of Rothamsted Experimental Station in England, who had recently evolved an independent method of estimating evaporation losses. Between them they came to the conclusion that evaporation would account for a loss of 65 inches a year (considerable when the total annual variation in the level of the lake is only likely to be some 12 feet) whilst Alcan's own research put the estimated loss at 60 inches a year. In calculating the amount of power that could be developed, taking into account both evaporation and rainfall, Halcrows used the figure of 55 inches for evaporation – so even experts were faced at times with problems where their theoretical solutions differed considerably.

Two other important milestones marked 1954. The first was the letting of the Tema Harbour contract in July to a consortium of two British civil engineering firms – those of Sir Lindsay Parkinson and Sir John Howard, who have since operated in

Ghana as Parkinson Howard Ltd. The second, in December, was the award of the contract for a bridge across the Volta, a few miles below the dam site, to the well-known bridge-building firm of Dorman Long Ltd. This beautiful 820-foot single-span steel arch bridge was another of Halcrows' proposals for developing the Volta Basin. For years vehicles had been queuing daily for the slow-moving Senchi Ferry, and when the bridge was completed in 1956 this serious bottleneck for motor-traffic to and from the prosperous trans-Volta region was removed. Senchi Ferry had become quite an institution to Gold Coast motorists. From its opening in 1920 till its closure in 1956 it was run on behalf of its owners, the United Africa Co. Ltd, by one family – first by Ebenezer Cato and subsequently by his son, James Cato. They were large, florid and wholly charming gentlemen (the family is from Cape Coast) with an endless fund of anecdotes about the past. Old Mr Cato had 'founded' the Gold Coast's first motor ferry; in 1917 he had lashed two canoes together and 'pulled' his model T Ford across the river from bank to bank and then proceeded on an excursion into the trans-Volta countryside along bush paths and across rough grassland. The part played by the UAC itself in manning the river ferries of the Gold Coast for almost forty years is, as is so much of the history of this British trading company, part of the history of the development of the length and breadth of the country — a far cry from the 'colonialism' of which British enterprise is so often accused.

It was hardly surprising that the Commission's report was not ready by the end of 1954. Plans for holding the Rubicon talks in 1955 were postponed till early 1956 by which time everything would be available, not in draft form, but printed and bound.

The consultants' engineering report, which comprises Volume 3 of the series and which concluded a total of five years' research, was duly delivered on the last day of October 1955 with the following covering words from Peter Scott: 'The policy of the Preparatory Commission has allowed us, and the searching nature of your queries has encouraged us, to carry our pre-contract investigations to a stage of detail seldom, if ever, achieved on a scheme of this nature and we feel, therefore, that we can say with some assurance that little in the design and estimates of this scheme has been left to chance.'

It was now three years since the white paper had launched the Preparatory Commission, and the new design and estimates differed in some respects from those on which the British Government had based its 1952 scheme.

The dam that had now been planned in detail for Ajena was to be a crescent-shaped rockfill dam with a sloping core of impervious clay built into the side retaining the lake. Its crest was to be 4,100 feet in length, and its height was designed to keep the level of the lake between the 252 feet and 276 feet contours. An imposing powerhouse had been designed on the east bank. Apart from its principal purpose, it was expected to be a centre for tourists and an object of national pride. Both the design of the powerhouse and the landscaping of the river valley adjacent to the dam site had received special care from an expert. who was lyrical about what he envisaged: 'The façade [of the powerhouse] is intended to contain the attributes of a monument. The office and reception block by dependence on human size is intended to give scale. The juxtaposition of these two structures is intended to suggest the power of mind over matter. It is paramount', he added, coming down to earth, 'that no odds and bods of buildings extend beyond the confines of the formal areas, for a single shanty or shed can spoil the grandeur of such a scene.'

Within the structure were to be housed up to nine separate turbines and generators – four for immediate use, four for later development and one again for future possible extensions to the national system. Each would generate 90,000kw, allowing an initial output of 360,000kw – ample for the early stages of the aluminium smelter plus a good margin (10 per cent more electricity than was proposed in the white paper) for public consumption. The new cost of the dam and power project was £60¼ million for the first stage rising to £67¼ million for the complete installation – almost exactly 25 per cent higher than the 1952 figures.

No major changes had been proposed for the smelter or the bauxite mines, other than more detailed planning of the townships and amenities, but the stark fact had to be faced that the estimated cost had risen from £64 million in 1952 to £91¼ million in 1956 – a startling rise of almost 50 per cent. The other major item, railways and communications, had also risen from £26 million (which included Tema harbour) to no less than £72½ million.

As against the estimate of £144 million in 1952 the Preparatory Commission's new total was £231¼ million. Even so they decided that it would not be realistic to tie the costs of a seven- to ten-year scheme to present-day estimates; a 45 per cent margin was therefore added, to achieve a grand total of £309 million for the Project as a whole. Compared with Duncan Rose's tentative proposals in 1939 for a £2½ to £3½ million scheme, this may well have caused enough red faces to make it worth renaming the forthcoming discussions the 'Rubicund' talks.

8

CROSSING THE RUBICON

In 1952, when Britain was thirsty for non-dollar aluminium and the producers themselves were eager to expand, the Volta River Project seemed assured, with Britain alone offering to throw in £50 million. But by 1956 the whole gamut of circumstances had changed. As Sir Robert Jackson[1] has since pointed out,[2] it was politically inconceivable that, so soon after the post-war debacle of the Tanganyika Groundnuts Scheme, the British Government should have risked entering upon a major financial overseas development commitment like the Volta River Project without the most painstaking prior analysis. Nor was it only the British Government which was obliged to tread the path of caution.

The British Government's white paper proposals had become a major political issue in the Gold Coast. The country was already inflamed with pre-independence passions, and apart from being used as a convenient stick with which the opposition could beat the Government, the white paper proposals were bound to be treated with some reserve by the new Gold Coast Government itself, who would not have been human if they had not suspected their old masters of some form of chicanery within its careful wording. So the delay afforded by the Preparatory Commission's investigations – publication of which had been timed to fit in with the programme for the country's independence – gave the Gold Coast Government time for thought and suited them well.

[1] Commander Jackson was knighted in 1956 for his services in connection with the Volta River Project and, as Sir Robert Jackson, KCVO, CMG, OBE, is now Senior Consultant to the United Nations Development Programme and also a Board member of the Volta River Authority.

[2] In an article in the Unilever quarterly, 'Progress'. N. 282: (1964)

The aluminium interests too had their reasons for wanting time to see which way the cat would jump. All along they had other potential non-dollar sources of aluminium which they were anxious to develop – those, for instance, in the neighbouring French Colony of Guinea into which Alcan was later to invest no less than £36 million of capital. Indeed, in view of Britain's declared policy of progressively granting independence to her colonies, there were in the early 1950s many who believed that a major investment in the French sphere of influence in tropical Africa, where no such policies had yet been declared, had some advantages over a comparable stake in British Africa. The Volta River Project had ceased to top the charts.

Whilst the motives for delay had been various the net results were similar. When the Preparatory Commission's comprehensive report appeared during the first week of 1956 both the British Government and Alcan were obliged to state clearly that the passage of time and its effect on the economics of the Project as it had been planned four years earlier had so radically altered the circumstances that a lot of rethinking would now be necessary.

On March 14th the British Government gave its verdict, and the following day Nathaniel Davis, writing on behalf of Alcan, added his findings.

'The Secretary of State for the Colonies', the Despatch from Whitehall began, was 'glad to note that the scheme had been found to be technically sound and could be carried out successfully.' He recognized 'that few if any projects of this kind have been subject to so detailed preliminary scrutiny' and he was 'happy to report that H.M. Government remain ready to participate in the Scheme'.

Most of us, having read that far, would skip the rest believing it to contain just so many more watertight reasons for the Government to cut in on the deal. But there we should be sadly deceived, for the second paragraph starts with the ominous words 'At the same time . . .' 'Substantial increases in costs' are emphasized, together with 'the reduced ability of the United Kingdom to contribute' and even the need for 'substantial financial support from outside the sterling area'.

After another paragraph starting 'In the circumstances . . . '

it becomes shockingly clear that without the aid of the World Bank it is the end of the Volta River Project as conceived to date. This was the gist of the message. It went on to propose that the Rubicon talks, instead of being devoted to technical matters and discussion of the date for the launching of the Project, should rather concentrate on the twin topics of rising costs and World Bank support.

Nathaniel Davis wrote more directly; it amounted to the same thing. The higher costs had tended to price the Volta River Project out of the competitive market and there were now other comparable projects which could not only be completed earlier (and thus avoid one cause of unforeseen inflation) but which also held fewer uncertainties. He supported the proposal for a new agenda for the Rubicon talks amounting, in effect, to a completely revised approach to the Project designed to offer the same sort of return from the investment as had been foreseen in 1952. As a business concern this was all that Aluminium Ltd could do. In his 1956 Annual Report Davis had made it clear that the demand for aluminium continued to grow and that Alcan intended to grow with it. But he also made it clear that the safest and most economic field of expansion was in Canada itself. As against the Volta's estimated seven years of construction for a 120,000-ton scheme costing £185 million, a similar project in Quebec was only going to take three years to produce 150,000 tons of aluminium per annum at a cost of £50 million.

It was over these issues that the long awaited Rubicon talks collapsed. From the outset it had been understood that without an aluminium smelter as a guaranteed customer for the lion's share of the Volta power output there could be no Project. And it was primarily Alcan (with British Aluminium as a very much smaller investor) who was to build the smelter and buy the current.

Everything then hung on the unit price of the electricity that had to be agreed between the Government of the Gold Coast and Alcan. Here again, the Preparatory Commission had left nothing to chance. Using the services of Cooper Brothers, the well-known firm of industrial accountants, a cost price for electricity had been calculated allowing for all possible variations. It concluded that the cost price would be a little more than ½d per unit (5 mills)[1] at the first stage of production falling to a little more than ¼d per unit (2.5 mills) at the final stage. Neither of these figures however proved to be acceptable to Alcan who were not prepared to go above ¼d per unit during Stage One and would clearly expect to pay considerably less in subsequent stages. In terms of cash this would have meant an initial annual electricity bill for Alcan totalling around £3 million. Since no basis for agreement could be reached, to use Sir Robert Jackson's own words, 'the original project failed to come to life'.

And lifeless, on purely economic grounds, it might well have remained had it not been, once again, for the determination of Nkrumah to see the Volta River Project through. To him power production was not just a desirable goal; it was a necessity without which the nation could not hope to emerge from subsistence on an agricultural economy into the age of scientific and technological development. And since the nation had already gone a long way with such plans for development, the Volta River Hydro-electric Power Project had to proceed. In this intention Nkrumah was supported by Jackson himself who demonstrated his faith in the Project by staying on in the Gold Coast rather than returning to the Treasury with the scheme unrealized. But as far as the British Government was concerned, the Project was 'on the shelf', though not put away. Answering a question in the House of Commons in July of 1956 the Colonial Secretary reported that HM Government was still interested but in no way committed.

Great as was the Gold Coast's disappointment that the Rubicon talks had failed, two factors helped to sustain public confidence in the scheme. The first was Kwame Nkrumah's own confidence in its ultimate success; and the second was the knowledge that 1957 was to be the year of Independence for the Gold Coast – to be known after March 6th as Ghana. Indeed there were many who believed that further negotiations on behalf of the Project would be wrong until Ghana was fully independent and thus able to negotiate terms for herself.

Nevertheless 1956 had one more contribution to make to the Project. In November a World Bank visiting mission to the Gold Coast carried out a routine examination of the country's economy

[1] 1,000 mills = 1 US dollar.

prior to considering independent Ghana's application for membership of the Bank. And since the possibility of assistance from the World Bank for the Volta Project was already on record, it was inevitable that this should have been one of the subjects for scrutiny.

After that, with general elections heralding Independence and a fever of excitement building up all over the country, the Volta River Project, though not forgotten, had a rest from inquisition.

After Ghana's Independence celebrations, which had attracted worldwide publicity, an interesting development occurred. A consortium of three American firms representing major aluminium and motor interests and led by Fraser Leith, entering into a field where Nathaniel Davis and Alcan had hitherto had grazing rights, paid a visit to Ghana to assess for themselves the prospects of its aluminium industry. To the surprise of the old hands, no doubt, they were given a limited option on the Project. Nothing in fact came of it, but it showed a renewal of interest that drew others' attention. Everyone now – including banks, governments and industrialists – was watching everyone else, waiting for the next move.

The Project, coupled with the forthcoming Prime Ministers' Conference and natural curiosity about the Commonwealth's first truly African Prime Minister and his country, prompted *The Times* to ventilate the subject. They quoted Dr Nkrumah as having said that his Government had decided to allow a maximum period of two years within which a decision about the scheme should be made, and during which time no other major long-term development would be initiated. They drew attention to the magnitude of the sum of £300 million which had been mentioned as the overall cost of the scheme and also to the falling world price of cocoa which was already beginning to strain Ghana's reserves. 'There is a justifiable anxiety in Ghana', they wrote, 'that if the Volta scheme is not carried out soon the tide may be missed.' Pointing out that Alcan's earlier interest in the scheme was now being followed up by US investigations, they urged that the scheme should only have Commonwealth support if the investment could be proved a sound one.

Then suddenly the scheme moved into gear again. The sequence of events which helped to bring this about possibly illustrates the philosophy that there is good in everything. In October Mr Gbedemah, who had been attending the meeting of Commonwealth Finance Ministers in Ottawa, followed it with a short visit to the United States. Dropping in for a glass of iced orange juice at one of the Howard Johnson roadside restaurants just outside Dover, Delaware, Gbedemah was told by the waitress, who was supported by her manager, that coloured people could not be served at the counter though he would be permitted to buy something to take away. The story leaked to the press who gave it a puff of unwelcome publicity. Seeking to make amends, President Eisenhower and Vice-President Nixon invited Mr Gbedemah to breakfast at the White House, and there the President, interested at what he heard of the Volta Project, asked for more background information about it. Dr Nkrumah, writing a few days later to President Eisenhower, said that he and his colleagues regarded the Volta River Project as being of supreme importance to the future of Ghana and that they were determined to do all in their power to implement it. He added that his Government was completely free to negotiate with any Governments and/or other prospective commercial partners. He sent them copies of the Preparatory Commission's report to study. A friendly and constructive correspondence followed between the President and the Prime Minister in the course of which Dr Nkrumah acknowledged that the interest shown by the US Government in the project had 'given us all fresh heart'.

Inevitably, however, progress was inhibited because the position of Aluminium Ltd was still unknown, and they had valid concessions for Ghana's principal bauxite deposits. In October however, when Mr Gbedemah had been in Canada for the Finance Minister's conference, Alcan had said that though they would naturally prefer to participate in the project themselves they did not feel inclined to adopt a 'dog in the manger' attitude to the bauxite deposits if the Ghana Government found that it could go ahead with the smelter project at a time when they themselves were unable to participate. Finally in February of 1958, when invited by the Ghana Government to make their position clear, Aluminium Ltd stated that in the present circumstances they were not in a position to proceed with the scheme immediately; and they made it clear that they would be willing if necessary to negotiate the surrender of their bauxite and other rights on reasonable terms with any seriously interested parties.

Now the door was open for Dr Nkrumah to accept the President's dual offer of help: an offer first to try to act as a catalyst in bringing together potentially interested companies who might finance the aluminium smelter and bauxite mines; and then, if this was successful, to consider making a substantial loan towards the power project itself. Small wonder that Prime Minister Nkrumah felt heartened.

Nkrumah's first step was to see that the US Government, through its International Co-operation Administration (ICA) agency in Ghana, was in full possession of all the facts concerning approaches already made to the Ghana Government. Some sixteen different organizations had at one time or another since Ghana's Independence expressed the wish to become involved in the Project. Some were still pressing very hard: Leith's consortium, for example, which was anxious to have a further two years' option on the whole project, confident that in that time it could finance the scheme completely without drawing upon a single penny of Ghana's. Though illustrative of the new interest and confidence being shown in the Project this was scarcely the sort of proposal that would commend itself to the Ghanaian public, and its sponsors were now told that they would have to put their proposals to the US Government, whose offer to coordinate the early stages of practical participation had already been accepted.

The man charged with this task, Carl Flesher, describes himself as 'one of a very small number of ICA executives who believed in using private enterprise in our foreign-aid program' and this was an occasion to put his theory into action. His was the idea that the US government should help to lend Ghana the necessary money to build the dam and power station whilst private enterprise, with or without government assistance, could build, own and operate the aluminium smelter. Then, with revenue from the sale of power to the smelter, Ghana could repay the US loans. There it was in a nutshell – the key, as it turned out, to the successful completion of the Project.

Happily for the smooth and swift progress of events President Eisenhower had, at the time of Ghana's Independence, invited Nkrumah to pay a state visit to the United States. Together with a visit to Canada, this had been arranged for July 1958. This proved to be the perfect opportunity to consolidate the progress that had already been made in their exchange of letters.

Their joint statement[1] had this to say: 'With regard to the Volta River Project, the United States expressed its appreciation of the contribution which this project could make to the economic development of Ghana. It agreed to explore with private American interests the aluminium manufacturing phase of the project and to consider how it might assist with loans if the required private financing were assured. The United States also expressed willingness to examine any proposals which the government of Ghana might advance for the use of power from the Volta River for purposes other than the manufacture of aluminium. The two governments agreed that it would be desirable to bring up to date the engineering reports which were prepared in 1955 and to share the cost of this undertaking.'

This decision to review the 1955 engineering reports represented the only possible solution to what had emerged as the main stumbling block to the otherwise exemplary Preparatory Commission proposals: the frightening overall cost of the Project. For at the time that Ghana was pushing her scheme for a new world source of aluminium the American aluminium companies had substantial surplus capacity. They had asked the President to assist them by means of a new stockpiling programme. Indeed it was this temporarily saturated market for aluminium that had obliged Alcan to step down when they did. This put President Eisenhower in a difficult position. But equally he was sensitive to the political necessity of responding to Ghana's appeal for help. He recognized that Ghana, as the first of the new African States, represented the shape of the newly emerging Africa in which the United States had an undoubted role to play. The UAR was still smarting from the withdrawal of Western funds from the Aswan Dam project and a second such rebuff could have had grave consequences.

[1] Signed on behalf of Prime Minister Nkrumah by James Moxon, at that time his Director of Information Services and on behalf of President Eisenhower by James Hagerty, his Press Secretary.

The obvious solution lay in a very thorough re-examination, amongst other things, of that seven-year timetable for building the dam. This was a major factor raising the overall costs. There was absolute agreement on this matter between the US and Ghana officials, and the US Government agreed to pay half the estimated £40,000 cost of the reappraisal.

It remained to decide who should undertake this all-important task. It seems to have been tacitly agreed from the outset that, in recognition of the helpful attitude of the US Government, coupled with the known expertise of US engineers in this field, it should be handled by an American firm. Lists were prepared and examined. Among the firms proposed was the Henry J. Kaiser Company of Oakland, California. Sir Robert Jackson had had experience of Kaiser's work for the Snowy Mountains Project in Australia, and impressed by his high opinion of the company Dr Nkrumah gladly accepted the recommendation. On July 28, 1958, Dr Nkrumah had his first meeting with Edgar Kaiser in New York, and from the outset an accord was struck.

9

THE MILLION KILOWATT RIVER

It is difficult to picture today what might have been the prospects for the Volta River Project had it not been for the warm relationship begun that July day between those two men. The meeting took place in the Presidential suite of the 35th floor of the Waldorf Towers. Edgar Kaiser had been a fraction nervous before the meeting, having little idea of what to expect, but no sooner had Nkrumah warmed to his subject and emphasized his absolute determination to go through with the Project than Chad Calhoun, the company's Vice-President, whispered to Kaiser, 'Do you know, he sounds exactly like your father!' Nkrumah overheard the aside and, in a burst of spontaneous laughter, the ice was broken.

Perhaps the most versatile figure in the history of American construction and industry, Henry J. Kaiser had been responsible for forming a vast family of enterprises. Having mastered modern road construction and all its components – including pioneer work in heavy earth-moving equipment – Henry Kaiser then helped to invent the Consortium technique for the construction of giant dams. At this point he was joined by son Edgar who graduated straight from college to mechanized shovel on the Hoover Dam. The Bonneville and Grand Coulee Dams followed, with the Kaisers using each new contract to develop fresh techniques of incentive, labour relations and medical care programmes that have since become standard practice in industry. With the Second World War Henry Kaiser turned to industry. Overnight he became the world's largest ship-builder when he applied his remarkable constructional methods to mass-producing the world famous Liberty ships at the rate of one a day. Simultaneously he ventured into the steel and cement industries and after the war expanded into aluminium and even the highly competitive motor industry. Having come near disaster in this field, father and son then turned the tables on fortune and proceeded to apply their magic touch to the future of the Jeep.

The Kaiser philosophy has been well explained both by father and son. 'There is an overriding secret to our success,' Henry Kaiser once said. 'That secret is to fill human needs. Every undertaking we've ever tackled was entered upon because we saw unfulfilled needs of people. There is an almost irresistible force in giving ourselves for the needs of others.' And Edgar Kaiser has added, 'The foundation of world peace is the real understanding of a country and their understanding of us. I don't know a better way for people to understand each other than to be in business together, to have joint investments and to be jointly dependent on income from a successful joint operation . . . But we must also make our investment of heart and soul, as surely as we make our investment of money. Our returns must be in terms of people – their aspirations, hopes and ideals, as surely as they are expressed in balance sheets.'

Kaiser began the reappraisal immediately. Four weeks to the day after the signing of the White House joint statement, the Kaiser 'crash action' party which had flown to Accra had initialled an agreement with the Ghana Government covering all the points decided in Washington. There was to be a complete review of proposals and estimates for the power plant, bauxite mine, aluminium smelter, railway connections and power transmission and, if possible, new power-consuming industries were to be suggested. Excluded from review, however, were such subjects as lake-side resettlement, new town sites, health measures and new ports, none of which were likely to have much bearing on the economies that were being sought. Within another month they had acquired additional jobs, and were to include a review of the Bui power project and irrigation measures, having as well *carte blanche* to introduce, if necessary, entirely new proposals for alternative sites for the dam, the smelter and even the bauxite mining, so long as the overall proposals combined practicability with economy.

One great ally, perhaps from an unexpected quarter, proved to be Halcrows. Their responsibility as engineering consultants to the Project, borne with great credit for almost ten years, had now been shifted to Kaiser. Though disappointed at the change, they transferred all their information to Kaiser and provided invaluable technical data without which completion of the Project would still be years away. And it was Halcrows who carried out on behalf of Kaiser the actual physical exploratory work on alternative dam sites. It must have been of some comfort to them to reflect that without their new harbour, which was nearing its first stage of completion at Tema, there could be no Volta River Project at all, and they still had other vital stakes in the Project – notably the implementation of their earlier proposals for trial agriculture irrigation projects on the Accra plains.

Within six months the Kaiser Reassessment Report was completed and delivered. Though relatively concise, it lacked nothing in surprises. First of all an entirely new dam site was proposed: none other than the spot at 'Akonsomo' earmarked by Sir Albert Kitson in 1915.[1] This is not to say that it had been subsequently overlooked. Indeed it was one of the seven sites investigated by Halcrows, but, in spite of its great advantage in river breadth – a mere 1,000 feet as against the 3,740 feet of the Ajena Island site – its consequent depth, calculated at 124 feet at its deepest point, had then ruled it out from the technological point of view. Great strides in underwater construction and coffer-damming had been made by dam-builders within the past few years and Kaiser was confident that Kosombo (as the survey maps then described it) was now a wholly practicable site in spite of its depth. George Gerdes, the Kaiser engineer who designed the Akosombo dam, tells the story of the cable he received in California from the surveyors at Akosombo who were plumbing the river's depth and reported that they had put down 700 feet of drill and still not touched the bottom. To his relief an amending cable arrived within hours to say that the drill had in fact curved out of its tube so that the greater part of the 700 feet had been penetrating the sand parallel to the river bed and the greatest depth was in fact more like 200 feet. This was considered to be workable. It had the additional advantage that

[1] See back end-paper (4).

it was to be a mere four-year job compared to the seven years Ajena would need, with the additional bonus that it had a greater power-producing capacity than Ajena. In fact, totalling the combined power potential of Akosombo, Kpong (an ancillary project some ten miles downstream) and Bui (on the Black Volta), Kaiser estimated an overall capacity of 1,116,000kw which is approximately double the capacity of London's Battersea Power Station and a net improvement of some 80 per cent on the 1956 estimate. It was not of course contemplated that the full capacity should be developed at once. As a start, it was proposed that Akosombo alone should be developed, at two-thirds of its potential, *i.e.* at 588,000kw. This would provide for the needs of the aluminium smelter and leave almost as much again for other industries and the domestic field.

The second Kaiser surprise was the proposal that the aluminium smelter should be sited at Tema and not at its own riverside township near to Kpong. This decision, since the proposal was duly accepted, has worried the supporters of calculated regional planning perhaps more than any other change within the Project, for the reason that it threatened to overload the embryo sea port of Tema. Against this Kaiser argued, unanswerably in the circumstances, that it would be an unnecessary additional expense to have to create all the civic services for a second new township, combined with costly railway facilities when these already existed or were provided for at Tema. Kpong was desirable but not essential and therefore had to go.

Kaiser's third unexpected proposal was dismaying, indeed alarming. For an initial period of ten years perhaps, the alumina powder from which the aluminium would be smelted would have to be imported instead of being refined from Ghana's own bauxite deposits. Kaiser pointed out that it was the capital cost of developing the national railway system plus the cost of developing the bauxite mines and building an alumina plant that was tipping the balance against the Project being financed. Postpone these items for a few years and some £60 million would be cut from the alarming present total.

So, reluctantly – for Ghana badly needed to make full use of her own resources – this proposal was accepted, though certain conditions were attached to make it very much in the interests of the owners of the smelter to use alumina of Ghanaian origin after an interim period of ten years. Since the appearance of the Preparatory Commission's report in 1956 there had been developments in this field. In that same year bauxite deposits near Kibi, which had been known to exist since Kitson's day, were found to be much more extensive than had been suspected; indeed it was estimated that there was sufficient bauxite at Kibi to keep even the largest smelter envisaged busy for at least fifty years. And the Kibi deposits were very much nearer to Tema than any of the alternative ones.

Towards the end of 1960 the newly formed smelter consortium was left free to acquire from British Aluminium, which had prospected them, the latter's concession rights to these deposits, thus bringing to a satisfactory conclusion a misunderstanding which, at one stage, had threatened to split the embryo consortium apart before it had ever seen the light of day. British Aluminium, on seeking in 1959 to validate in the Ghanaian courts their 1956 options on the deposits, were informed that the Government had in the meantime acquired from the 'traditional authority' owners all the rights to the bauxite deposits in the area and was now agreeable to re-negotiating the concessions on revised terms, bearing in mind the long-term interests of the Volta River Project. Inevitably the ugly word 'expropriation' crept into the discussions which followed.

It was at this time that Edgar Kaiser was engaged in the delicate task of sounding the major US and Canadian aluminium interests with a view to forming a consortium to operate the aluminium smelter. Amongst these groups was Reynolds Metals Ltd which had only recently acquired a 49 per cent interest in British Aluminium and was therefore deeply concerned at the situation that had developed. Indeed Reynolds went so far as to make it perfectly clear that unless they were assured by their British associates that no expropriation was intended they would be unable to consider participating in any further consortium discussions. And Reynolds were, after Kaiser, the backbone of the consortium.

The late Adlai Stevenson, who knew Ghana well and whose Chicago-based firm of attorneys represented Reynolds Metals, wrote a helpful personal letter to Sir Robert Jackson. He made

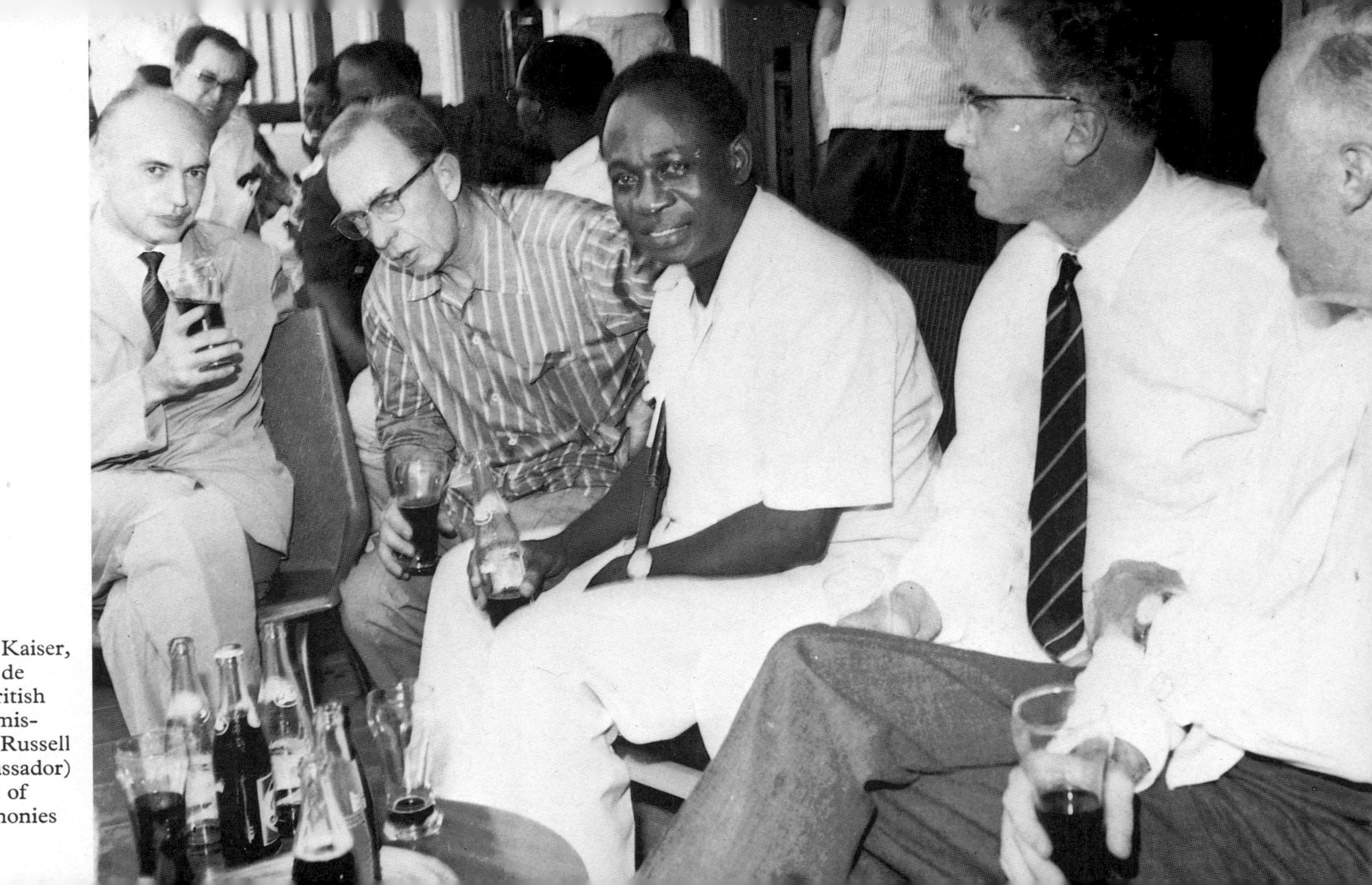

Lodigiani, Kaiser, Nkrumah, de Freitas (British High Commissioner) and Russell (US Ambassador) at the start of work ceremonies

Italians and Ghanaians worked harmoniously together at Akosombo throughout the five years of the dam contract

Welding the pre-fabricated steel plates into 50-ton sections for the six generator penstocks (tubes) was carried out at the dam site

it clear that it was his understanding of the Ghana Government that she had rightly earned a reputation for standing by her agreements. He conjectured therefore that there must be some unresolved misunderstanding that needed to be cleared up quickly, adding that 'we are so near to the long sought goal, Volta, that any delay or obstacle is almost as distasteful to me as to you'.

Certainly, the circumstances of the case had not been normal, for the system of land tenure in rural Ghana can be incredibly complicated and in this instance had been made the more so by a long drawn out chieftaincy dispute. In seeking to strengthen the title of the bauxite deposits by transferring it from a tottering chieftaincy to the state itself the Government had felt that it was effectively serving the interests not only of the people but also of the ultimate users of the bauxite – the proposed privately owned aluminium smelter.

As Reynolds Metals (of the consortium) were so closely associated with British Aluminium (of the bauxite deposits) it was a satisfactory ending to a prickly situation when later in the year British Aluminium nobly expressed themselves willing to pass up their claim in favour of the consortium. For the time being, however, there is little prospect of the £40 million alumina refinery for the processing of local bauxite being financed; for the foreseeable future the smelter at Tema will be dependent upon imported alumina.

The main achievement of the Kaiser Reassessment Report was its reduction of the original estimated cost of the project by 30 per cent, thus making it once again a viable enterprise for which potential customers and financiers could be found.

At £70 million for the power project combined with a national transmission system (on which the 1956 report had deliberately deferred a decision) it was still clear that the Ghanaian Government would need to look for outside assistance in the form of long-term loans; but the prospect was no longer bleak. And with £56.7 million as the estimated cost of the smelter there was still the formidable task, now being pursued in the US, of finding an operator or a group of operators who would be prepared to put up or otherwise secure the capital. But there was one very healthy incentive: the new cost price for electricity proposed in the Report for the initial stages of the smelter was calculated to be comfortably below the ¼d per unit (2.5 mills) that had been the subject of Alcan's last stand at the abortive Rubicon talks. In spite of the continued depression in the world aluminium market (which was expected to recover in due course) there was now a hope that a genuine basis for serious business had been found.

Already Nathaniel Davis had been to Accra with carefully worked out proposals in which Alcan was to take the initiative in forming a smelter consortium for Ghana. This itself suggested an improvement in the world prospects for aluminium since the day that Alcan had withdrawn from the scene almost a year earlier. The Ghanaian Government welcomed Alcan's new proposals, but could not commit itself to a price for electric power until study of the Kaiser Reassessment Report had enabled this factor to be verified. It was conceded however that the smelter, if built, should use imported alumina until such time as local bauxite resources could be processed.

But shortly after Davis's visit Edgar Kaiser came to Accra to present the completed Reassessment Report formally to Prime Minister Nkrumah. In the course of their discussion of some engineering problem, the Prime Minister suddenly asked, 'Now, how about taking off your Engineering coat, and putting on your Aluminium coat?' The request opened up new avenues for Kaiser who hitherto had been concerned solely with the technical and engineering side of the project. Now, at a still far from favourable time for the industry, he was being asked to follow up the State Department's lead at match-making and find within the aluminium industry a client for the smelter. He promptly accepted the challenge.

The situation was made easier for him when Alcan decided that, in all the circumstances, there was a better chance for combined US aluminium interests to play the major role in forming the consortium. In a helpful letter to Dr Nkrumah Nathaniel Davis said that his company supported the sponsorship role that Kaiser was now prepared to play. At the same time they remained interested and would certainly participate in ensuing discussions. The British Government, which had confirmed that they still stood by their 1956 statement – 'interested but not committed' – no doubt took note of the fact that sponsorship was now firmly entrenched in the non-sterling area.

Edgar Kaiser lost no time. He was able to summon a meeting in New York on November 4th, at which he formally reported to the Ghanaian Ambassador the formation of a company to be known as the Volta Aluminium Company (Valco for short). Its purpose was to work out with the Ghanaian Government the development of an aluminium smelter in Ghana. Represented at the meeting were five major aluminium interests (including Kaiser, Reynolds and Alcan), all in an exploratory and uncommitted capacity but all of them basically sympathetic to Ghana's aims and objects in spite of the temporary lull in the aluminium market.

Then in mid-December a full-scale meeting was held in Accra between Kaiser and the Ghanaian Government. Formal Principles of Agreement were signed between the two parties regarding the steps to be taken to establish the smelter. On the engineering side Kaiser undertook to complete all the design work for the dam and power installation with a view to having the tendering documents ready by September 1, 1960. Simultaneously there was to be an intensification of preparatory work at the dam site in Akosombo. Two suction dredges, each costing £160,000 and needing some nine months for manufacture, were to be ordered. It had been agreed during Edgar Kaiser's March visit that Kaiser would immediately start to prepare the Akosombo site on a preliminary basis and a tremendous amount of work had already been completed. Just as soon as it had been decided on which bank of the river the powerhouse would be (Kaiser's report originally sited it on the east bank adjacent to the spillways but moved it to its ultimate site after further geological research) it was possible to decide once and for all on which bank the township and access roads would be, and throughout 1959 work had proceeded apace. A first-class road from Tema to Akosombo was also commissioned.

These preparations were a considerable act of faith on the part of Kwame Nkrumah, supported by Edgar Kaiser, for it was not in fact until December 1961 that the necessary financing was assured.

10

FINAL AGREEMENT

So long as the Volta River Project had remained only a tentative, if special, part of Ghana's overall development plans it had been handled within the Development Commission. Now the formation of the Valco consortium set the seal on Nkrumah's determination to proceed and gave the project new life-blood. A new and separate body, the Volta River Project Secretariat, was then formed to co-ordinate all aspects of the complicated programming, continuing however to be the responsibility of Sir Robert Jackson as chairman of the Development Commission.

The new Secretariat came into being on January 1, 1960. Its first task was to ensure that a clear-cut programme of forthcoming events was followed. The first priority was the vital issue of power rates – the key to the profitability both of the power project and of the smelter. Top level discussions were proposed with Kaiser and with Cooper Brothers – the Government's cost accountants and financial advisers for the Project – to include consideration of such matters as taxation policy. The decisions taken would be incorporated in the draft Power Contract, the draft Master Agreement and covering draft legislation, all of which had to be prepared for ratification by the parties concerned before the Project could be started in earnest. Key consultant was power rate expert Weisfelt.

Meanwhile, however, a growing amount of work was being carried out on faith – again according to a careful programme designed to carry the Project as far forward as possible prior to the letting of the basic contracts. First of all came twelve miles of paved access and site roads; then varying styles of houses for engineers, foremen and skilled and unskilled workers; water supplies, electric power, markets and other amenities including a Swiss chalet-style hotel for 'visiting firemen' on a 500-foot hill top overlooking the whole panorama of the dam-site – all ready by the time the contractors bidding for the main contract came to Akosombo in early November 1960.

The invitations to tender had been issued in September. The response was extraordinary. Out of some forty-five responses fifteen contractors or groups were regarded as qualified to construct the Project and consequently qualified for the agreed assistance of £2,500 to view the site. Italy, France, Scandinavia, the United States, Britain and several joint international ventures were all represented amongst the qualified bidders.

Ghana was fortunate with the timing of its Volta contract, both in relation to similar contracts elsewhere, like the £120 million Mangla Dam project in Pakistan which was due to be advertised six months or so later, and also in relation to prevailing world contributions at the time. When the bids for the dam contract itself had been opened in Accra the following February and been duly digested and analysed by the consulting engineers, the contract was awarded to the Italian corporation Impregilo, which was still, as Impresit (Kariba), putting the finishing touches to the Kariba Dam. At £16 million, their bid, though not the lowest, was nevertheless almost £4 million lower than the engineer's estimates. Similarly the equipment contracts, for which ninety-eight firms from twelve countries had tendered, showed savings amounting to several millions of pounds.

Although a fortunate year for Ghana in terms of contract bidding, 1960 proved to be frustrating for the embryo Valco consortium, and for the raising of the necessary international loans. In many ways these were closely interlocked. The climate for attracting investors into Africa was not improved when in July 1960 – just after Ghana had become an autonomous republic within the Commonwealth – Belgium granted independence to the Congo and such confusion was let loose in the heart of Africa that the more timid investors-elect slipped back to base. But Kaiser and his vice-president Chad Calhoun were far-sighted enough to impress upon their consortium colleagues that it would be not only in their own interest to stay but also in the interests of US foreign policy, of which they could be a useful instrument.

Just before Christmas 1959 the Ghanaian Government decided that the time was ripe to invite the International Bank for Reconstruction and Development (IBRD or the World Bank) to send a mission to Ghana. It would survey the country's economy and assess its credit-worthiness as regards international loans for the Volta River Project and other development proposals. In some quarters it was thought that the World Bank, which is said to have a tendency towards paternalistic and even 'proprietary' interests in major development projects in developing nations, already felt that such a request was overdue. The mission arrived in Accra on January 25th, headed by Burke Knapp, the Bank's vice-president. Ghana for her part immediately rallied her own financial experts: Mr S. Ratnam, the Indian economist and financier, who for a number of years had been advising Ghana on all economic aspects of the Project, and Wilfred Molyneux of Cooper Brothers who had also been working for several years on the detailed financial breakdown of the Project.

In spite of the speed and thoroughness with which the World Bank worked, Calhoun and other Kaiser men were still uneasy. Trying to preserve the momentum of the smelter consortium they felt that unless favourable power ratios could soon be announced by Ghana, there would be some difficulty, possibly crucial, in keeping the consortium together. Valco of course, had already made its own calculations, based on Kaiser's estimates, indicating that a power rate of less than ¼d per unit would be an economic possibility. Cooper Brothers, too, had independently made their calculations on behalf of Ghana. Everything depended on the calculations of the World Bank.

In May 1960 Eugene Black, the World Bank's president, was in Accra and gave Nkrumah an outline of what the Bank's proposals would be, pending the full report in July. In brief their advice was that Ghana would be wise to put a ceiling of £190 million on her borrowings for general development – that is, for the Volta River Project plus all other proposals in the new Second Development Plan. This was calculated to be the limit of the country's effective borrowing power, bearing in mind repayment of the loans at a rate of about £7 million per annum. Mr Black felt obliged to conclude that, whilst the Volta proposal was 'good' from an engineering point of view, it was, in the words of the report, 'not exciting' as an investment proposition.

Nevertheless, the Bank was willing to make the largest loan in its history – up to £30 million, being half the estimated cost of the Project – subject to certain demanding conditions. One of these inevitably hinged on the negotiation of a satisfactory power rate; and this particular hurdle, eager as Valco was to jump it, was one which had already caught the Project across the shins four years earlier. The Bank's advice now was that Ghana should negotiate with the smelter for a guaranteed rate of almost ½d per unit (4.5 mills per kilowatt of current), with a flat rate of 1½d per unit (15 mills) for all other consumers. This was roughly equivalent to the actual cost of power generated by conventional thermal methods and therefore cheaper than existing commercial rates. As a bare minimum – and the Bank loan was conditional on this – they might drop as low as ⅓d per unit (3.5 mills) for the smelter rate. This would give Ghana an average return on her investment of 3 per cent over the first ten years and no more than 7 per cent during the life of the Project – not 'exciting' figures by any standard.

Valco, however, had made their calculations on a somewhat different basis. This had taken into account Ghana's potential revenue not only from the sale of power to the smelter and vicinity but also, since the Project was to be a multi-purpose one, from the proposed national transmission network; from the development of inland water transport; from additional food supplies, such as fish from the lake; from irrigation, and even from tourism. The ceiling power rate that Valco would consider was ¼d per unit (2.5 mills). Anything higher than this seemed certain to strike at the root of the smelter consortium.

Fresh talks with the World Bank in Washington were fixed for August 8th. If satisfactory agreement was to be reached with Valco and the power-rate gap bridged, some concessions had to be made on either side. The opportunity was also to be taken of discussing the US Government loan towards the Project that had already been agreed on in principle.

These Washington talks did finally seal the pattern for the whole financing of the Project. One of the drawbacks to the World Bank offer of a loan of £30 million had been the high rate of interest to be charged: a rate of 6 per cent. A new formula now emerged. It recognized that, of the estimated total of £60 million, Ghana would find half from her own resources in the form of an equity investment, but that the World Bank and the two countries which had taken most interest in the Project, the United States and the United Kingdom, would between them make loans amounting to the other £30 million. The World Bank was to lend £14¼ million at 5¾ per cent over a period of 25 years and the US Government £10¾ million. Part of this was to come from the Development Loan Fund (administered by the Agency for International Development), which allowed an attractively low interest rate of 3½ per cent for loans to governments, and which was to lend £7¼ million over a 30-year repayment period. Another £3½ million was to be loaned by the US Government's Export-Import Bank at a rate of 5¾ per cent for 25 years. These government loans had been intended to be largely, if not entirely, tied to the purchase of goods and services of US origin, but since the World Bank had advised that the contract be put out to international tender a partial relaxation had been negotiated.

Nonetheless, when it was time for Gbedemah, the leader of the Ghanaian delegation, to return home, the US contribution was still short of its proposed total by about 1½ million, leaving an uncomfortable gap in the financing. Gbedemah confided in an American friend that it was not so much the actual shortage of money that was troubling him as President Nkrumah's possible reaction. He feared that as soon as Nkrumah heard that the full amount had not been agreed to by the State Department he would lose patience, press a button, call for the Soviet Ambassador and turn the Project over to the Russians. This was how he was said to be behaving these days; and this was a course of action that Gbedemah, for one, was not prepared to consider.

Many who have followed closely the fortunes of the Nkrumah regime in Ghana feel indeed that July 1, 1960, when Nkrumah assumed absolute powers as President, was for him the point of no return. After this he seemed to move resolutely towards an ideological dreamland which ultimately seemed to separate him from reality.

Gbedemah's friend was sensitive enough to realize that this delicate situation was in many respects a test case for US-African relations, and that the crisis had to be taken seriously. But the Under-Secretary of State, Douglas Dillon, was away from Washington at that moment. The case was therefore put to Senator Fulbright as a man who, though himself in opposition, had a reputation for getting things done. Fulbright was interested but took the view that for political reasons he was not the right man to handle the matter. He suggested instead a fellow Senator from his own party who was rapidly making a name for himself: Jack Kennedy. Kennedy promised a quick reply, and came back after the weekend with the good news that the full amount of £10¾ million had now been agreed. Gbedemah had already had to leave for London and his friend was left with the problematical task of sending him an open cable that was both discreet and explanatory. It started: 'Recall the meeting with the young man in Washington that you had last Friday . . .'

Meanwhile in London the delegation was following up the British Government's continued interest in the Project after a letter from President Nkrumah to Prime Minister Macmillan, who had himself been to Ghana and visited the dam site at Akosombo only the previous January at the start of his famous 'wind of change' visit to Africa. The British Government promptly agreed to come in with £5 million over 25 years at 6 per cent (also tied to purchases in the United Kingdom), thus bringing the total loan to £30 million.

In spite of this progress, however, there was still one serious cause for concern. The August talks in Washington had again failed to see agreement between Ghana and Valco on power rates. Re-opened talks in New York in September and a visit by Kaiser to Accra in October, though friendly as always, had brought agreement no closer. Part of the difficulty was caused by the refusal of both the World Bank and the Ghanaian Government to show a copy of the World Bank Report to Valco, who wanted to study in detail the differences in the calculations – a situation that became ironic when Chad Calhoun was offered one by a friend and the analysis could then be made. On the basis of what he considered to be the over-cautious calculations contained in the report, Edgar Kaiser felt he could still convince the World Bank that his own figures were more realistic.

At the same time he wrote a long and explicit letter to President Nkrumah in which he set out his position. He recalled how in the first instance his firm had come into contact with the Volta River Project in order to re-evaluate the engineering proposals and had in fact succeeded in recommending great economies. At this stage they were definitely interested in constructing the dam but had had to withdraw as bidders because of their subsequent sponsorship of Valco, at Ghana's request, and the possibility of a conflict of interests. Now, however, as the Valco negotiations proceeded with Kaiser Aluminum acting as spokesmen for the consortium, Edgar Kaiser confessed to having personally observed a feeling among the Ghanaian Government's negotiators that his firm was trying to drive too hard a bargain for Valco.

He drew attention to the continuing depressions of the aluminium industry and actual idle capacity in existing US smelters, and pointed out that in these circumstances Valco shareholders could only agree to go ahead if the terms were attractive enough. Valco's total financial commitment was in the region of £125 million, if the cost of power as well as capital costs was included, and that was a lot of money to invest. But Nkrumah had personally asked for his, Edgar Kaiser's, help in pressing forward the Project and this had been given. Yet now, it seemed, the Ghanaian advisers were demanding more favourable conditions than those which had been outlined earlier in the discussions.

He emphasized that, as realistic businessmen, he and his associates genuinely wanted the Project to be 'good for Ghana' as that would in turn be good for them; and he went on to show that, although the Kaiser figures and the World Bank figures on the future load growth of Ghana's electricity did not altogether agree, Ghana could expect a net return of 81 per cent on her equity capital during the ten-year period following the opening of the smelter. Valco for her part, with the same equity participation, would have a return varying between 60 and 72 per cent over the same period depending on the mode of financing. His point was that they had been trying to negotiate terms which would be genuinely beneficial to both parties and had been disappointed that the healthy climate in which the discussions had started no longer appeared to exist. He was suggesting, then, that the first order of business at their forthcoming November meeting in Accra should be to restore that climate to their mutual advantage.

The letter had effect, together with his pressure on the World Bank. The Ghanaian Government announced on November 17th that, subject to the conclusion of satisfactory financing arrangements, full agreement had been reached between the Government of Ghana and Valco. A special Valco rate of 2.625 mills, about ¼d per unit, had been agreed. The same day, before leaving Accra, Edgar Kaiser wrote a brief note to Nkrumah thanking him for the personal attention he had given to the Volta Project matters, which were 'proceeding well'. He added a paragraph concerning the current visit to Accra of Stewart Alsop, the widely read US newspaper columnist who, it seems, had formed a poor impression of Ghana and was anxious to interview the President.

Kaiser was only concerned that Alsop should have a chance to get at the facts, for everything to do with the Volta still hung on those mutually agreed but not yet secured loans and he was much too canny a businessman to take them for granted yet – with the Nixon-Kennedy Presidential election not more than seven weeks away and nobody knowing what pattern policies would follow thereafter.

However, the informal initialling of the Master Agreement on November 17th by Edgar Kaiser and Ghana's Minister of Finance was a stimulating climax to the tough period of negotiation that had been continuing right through 1960 between Valco and the Ghanaian Government, and it was the cue for a vast amount of legislation and activity.

11

MONEY MATTERS

One of the provisions of the Master Agreement – which was the whole basis, reduced to legal terms, of the complex business relationship between Ghana and Valco – was that a series of transactions should follow, failing which the agreements could not come into effect. The first of these 'trigger' arrangements was for the Ghanaian Parliament to debate the Volta River Project, to signify its approval and to authorize the Government to conclude the outstanding financial negotiations.

A detailed white paper on the history of the Project having been laid before Parliament, President Nkrumah himself introduced the debate in January 1961. First he explained the events which had led up to the present position, and the action – particularly regarding financing – that was still required. He emphasized Ghana's vital need for an indigenous source of power to set in motion the industrialization that the economy demanded. He foretold (with accuracy) how the first power would start flowing down the transmission cables in September, 1965; and, taking Ghana's overall power programme one stage further, announced that the Government had recently reached agreement with the Soviet Union for the design and construction of a further hydro-electric project at Bui on the Black Volta tributary.

He paid a warm tribute to Edgar Kaiser, saying that from 1958 onwards he had shown enthusiasm and understanding, 'second only to our own', both of the Project and of the many problems involved in bringing it to life; it was an impressive acknowledgement of one who had been obliged to act in two vastly different capacities – as engineer, adviser and consultant on the Government's own power project – and both as prime mover and hard-headed business adversary in the Valco smelter negotiations.

Parliament then took over. For three and a half hours it satisfied itself, by debate and government bench reply, that this long-term investment project, the effects of which would closely affect the lives of generations as yet unborn, would be carried out in the best interests of the people of Ghana. The decision in favour was unanimous.

Very shortly afterwards Nkrumah paid a visit to the United Nations in New York, where he addressed the General Assembly on the current Congo crisis. Through Lady Jackson it was arranged that he should call informally on President Kennedy in Washington. He was the first head of state to do so. The *Washington Post* reported: 'President Nkrumah, visiting here for just a few hours, was given a reception almost equal to a State visit. Following a White House talk, which President Kennedy called "most fruitful", President Nkrumah was introduced to Mrs Kennedy and their 3-year old daughter, Caroline. He was invited to tea and a discussion of the Kennedy and Nkrumah children and taken on a tour of the White House living quarters . . . The two Presidents reacted well to each other, one source said, as each, without trying to lecture the other, set forth his own views about the Congo and the future of Africa and found considerable harmony of outlook.'

But what the paper did not say was that Nkrumah also got a 'balling' from Kennedy in the rose garden. What exactly was said between the two men in their ten-minute *tête-à-tête* is not on record but it seems that the new President pointed out that he was already under considerable pressure not to ratify the financial agreements entered into by his predecessor. In a sense this had been the whole purpose of this eleventh-hour invitation to President Nkrumah for Kennedy had been receiving more and more reports of Nkrumah's growing fascination with the Eastern bloc – and particularly with Red China – together with accusations that Ghana was only paying lip-service to her declared policy of political non-alignment.

Gbedemah was known to be extremely concerned at this threat to the current Volta negotiations. At this moment he was himself in Washington, leading an all-Ghanaian delegation in the essential task of re-opening with the new administration the negotiations that had been sympathetically begun on a personal basis by President Eisenhower. Their purpose was three fold. First, it was now a matter of urgency that the planned loans should be officially secured. Only the previous week the bids for the main dam contract had been publicly opened in Accra and it was important that the financing should be settled before the award was made in April or May. Secondly, there was still a gap of about £10 million to be filled and this required careful negotiation. Kaiser had for some time insisted that the World Bank report's exclusion of the national transmission network which was designed to distribute Volta power throughout southern Ghana was a false economy and that the network should be reinstated. Ghana supported this argument for political and social, as well as for economic, reasons. After further investigations the World Bank had relaxed its objections, but, whilst not opposed to the network, was anxious that the timing for it should be right. The estimated cost was about £10 million and this now raised the overall cost of the Project to £70 million. Thirdly – and this only concerned Ghana indirectly but it was important – the US Government had to be encouraged to meet Valco's needs for a substantial loan in order to bring their part of the project to life.

In a week of non-stop discussion the Ghanaians had two meetings with Secretary of State Dean Rusk and two more with Douglas Dillon – the only Republican still in the Government and now Secretary for the Treasury. They met George Ball of Economic Affairs, Eugene Black of the World Bank, and of course the directors of the Development Loan Fund and the Export-Import Bank as well. Rusk, who had grown up in the Tennessee Valley, was anxious that TVA mistakes should not be repeated in Ghana. Dillon too placed a premium on lessons learnt by others, quoting the case of the Taiwan Project that had taken shape so hurriedly that the dam had to be redesigned three times during construction. This time the thorough advance planning of the Volta scheme was acknowledged. The delegates left Washington satisfied that their visit had been fruitful.

Encouraged by the low bids for the dam contract and anticipating handsome savings, Ghana agreed to finance half the cost of the network herself; the other half was to come from the US. The Valco loans, it seems, were assured and the Ghanaian delegates returned home via London, where they had confirmation from the Chancellor of the Exchequer that the £5 million loan was to be made available to them.

It was now tentatively hoped that full agreement would be reached in all matters by July so that the official ceremony of starting work on the dam could take place and construction be under way before the peak of the flood season in September. But there were problems. One was the inarguable fact that this was, by general agreement, the most complicated project ever undertaken by the World Bank, involving three governments, several world lending agencies, the Bank itself and a consortium of, at that time, four aluminium companies. Two lawyers from Ghana, reinforced by Ghana's American lawyers, were working hard with the Valco lawyers in California to have the documents completed, and a further four-man delegation from Ghana was in Washington liaising with the lending agencies. But July came and went. Although full agreement on the loans was announced early in August it was evident that September would be the earliest month for the loan agreements to be initialled. October 5th was now the day appointed for the formal signing of the Master Agreement between Ghana and Valco.

Meanwhile the dam contractors, Impregilo, had of necessity started. Their contract had been signed (though with an additional clause enabling the Government to withdraw within six weeks if for any reason this became necessary). A whole year's delay in completing the dam would have resulted from failure to begin work then. Some risks had to be taken. If any last moment hitches arose, Ghana would have to meet her commitments, as far as they had gone, from her own resources. These were tense and nerve-racking months.

Then a hitch did occur. The trouble had started, in effect, more than a year previously whilst Nkrumah was in New York, together with nineteen other heads of state and government and fifty foreign ministers, attending what is remembered as the biggest meeting ever of the United Nations General Assembly. He had had a private meeting with Eisenhower in New York when, on the following evening at a Foreign Press Association dinner, America's Secretary of State, Christian Herter, was quoted as saying that Nkrumah had, by his United Nations address, 'marked himself as very definitely leaning towards the Soviet bloc'.

Not everyone supported Herter. C. L. Sulzberger writing in *The New York Times* and describing it as a careless public statement added that Herter's worst mistake was to have actually used the words 'very definitely in the Communist camp' and then to have tried later to change the record to the published version 'leaning towards the Soviet bloc'. Perhaps it was an unfortunate moment for anyone in Herter's position to make such an attack, since cold war tempers were high throughout that historic meeting and Ghana was being treated as little more than a whipping-boy in the general harangue. Nkrumah merely commented: 'Mr Herter was the last person from whom I should have expected such a remark. I thought that [he] understood the African point of view.'

But the harm was done and, with such a lead from such a quarter, a whispering campaign began. Then Nkrumah's two-month tour of Eastern countries from July to September 1961 brought the issue to the surface again. Meanwhile Herter's charge of a year earlier had been effectively developed by the principal opponents of US aid to Ghana, led by Senator Albert Gore, Chairman of the Senate Sub-Committee on African Affairs, who supported the theory that Ghana's policies were firmly oriented towards the Soviet Union and Communist China.

It was on September 25th – barely a fortnight before the Project was to be officially inaugurated – that Washington announced that a final decision on US participation would not be reached until after Mennen Williams, Kennedy's principal adviser on African affairs who was shortly to visit Accra, had reported back on 'the cold war orientation' of Ghana.

The day after this announcement an agreement was signed in Accra between the Ghanaian and Soviet Governments for detailed plans to be drawn up by Soviet experts for Ghana's second hydro-electric project at Bui on the Black Volta. With so many eggs already in the Western basket this was surely no more than a gesture of non-alignment; but not everyone saw it as such.

Meanwhile Edgar Kaiser too had been called in by President

Kennedy for advice. Edgar still had faith both in Nkrumah and Ghana and returned from a quick visit to Accra to tell the President so. At the same time he had to admit to Kennedy that things were made much more difficult for him personally because his father – Henry J. Kaiser – was constantly phoning him from Honolulu urging him to be cautious and to reconsider the wisdom of the whole project. 'Well, that makes two of us,' laughed Kennedy, whose own father had apparently been doing exactly the same thing.

Presidents Nkrumah and Kennedy, however, kept in close touch with each other. Recognizing the need for a speedy as well as a cautious decision, Kennedy appointed in October a three-man mission, led by Clarence Randall the retired steel-magnate who had been Chairman of the Council on Foreign Economic Policy in the Eisenhower Administration, to visit Ghana and 'review US participation in the Volta River Project'. Clarence Randall was no stranger either to Nkrumah or to the Volta scheme: the two men had met in the United States in 1958 and one of their principal topics had been Volta. His visit to Ghana was short but searching. He had been asked to take a 'final hard look'; and after three days of intensive study of conditions in Ghana and their relation to the Project the mission returned to Washington via London where final confidences were exchanged with officials at the Commonwealth Relations Office.

From London a few days later Queen Elizabeth and Prince Philip came on a much publicized state visit to Ghana. In spite of the gloomiest press forecasts, it was generally admitted to have been one of the most successful of her Commonwealth tours. Visiting Akosombo the Royal visitors saw for themselves that construction was well in hand. There may have been a temporary shortage of dollars, but there was no shortage of activity on the site. After an excellent lunch of pasta and the tenderest veal at the Volta Hotel the Queen asked if she could personally thank the chef, and when she enquired how long he had been at the Volta Hotel he replied in strongly Italian-accented English that in fact he had only been able to come that same morning as they had been working overtime on the concrete mixer where he was normally employed.

Kennedy knew that politically his final decision to back Volta would be unpopular in many circles. The decision made it clear that in the mature judgment of the people of the United States Africa had the right to better its lot in terms of twentieth-century development and that this was an honourable cause to support. What led up to this decision is not known in detail. However, it is known that Sir Robert Jackson was in close touch with Duncan Sandys, then Britain's Secretary of State for Commonwealth Relations, for they had both been involved in the Royal Tour of Ghana. Sandys in turn had been in touch with Harold Macmillan, his Prime Minister, and both of them supported the Volta River Project. Lady Jackson had been in touch with President Kennedy, of whom she was a personal friend. And Harold Macmillan and President Kennedy had subsequently met in Nassau.

Finally, on December 16, 1961 it was announced simultaneously in Washington and Accra, that US loans to the extent of £47 million (£13 million for the power project and £34 million for the smelter) had been approved. There was no doubt now that the World Bank's £17 million and the British Government's £5 million loans would be added, bringing the grand total – with Ghana's own equity capital of £35 million and Valco's £12 million – to £116 million.

After blessings from the Ghanaian Parliament a new, and this time final, date was fixed for the signing of documents in Accra: January 22, 1962. The ceremony was performed at the State House in a setting of great elegance, President Nkrumah signing for the Government of Ghana and Edgar Kaiser signing for Valco.

When the signing was over it was in an instinctive reflex of genuine joy and relief that the two principals in the drama rose and clasped each other. For Nkrumah, almost eleven years of patient and dogged determination since he emerged from gaol had now borne fruit. For Edgar Kaiser, who had undertaken to do his utmost to see the scheme launched, there was the satisfaction that he had not failed. The following day at Akosombo, before a vast crowd, President Nkrumah released a powerful blast which mushroomed above the dam site to signify the formal start of work on the dam.

12

ON WITH THE JOB

In February 1962 all 200 financial documents were signed in Washington, thus officially concluding what one participant described as 'the most complicated piece of international financing since Queen Marie was selling Roumanian bonds'. Now the responsibility shifted to the men on-the-spot. Who were they?

For nine years Nkrumah had personally conducted the whole Volta campaign. But he had relied for the execution of his decisions and for constant advice and international *savoir faire* on Sir Robert Jackson, his chief of staff for the Volta operation.

Since the Preparatory Commission had presented its report in 1956 Sir Robert had been Chairman of the Development Commission. In 1961 he had handed over those responsibilities to his Ghanaian successor, Emmanuel Ayeh-Kumi. Now, as Special Adviser on the Project, Sir Robert was asked by President Nkrumah to stay on to see the agreements actually signed and to attend the inauguration ceremony. Subsequently he has visited Ghana two or three times each year both as one of the VRA's consultants and on United Nations assignments.

Emmanuel Ayeh-Kumi, who led much of the 1961 negotiations, was one of Ghana's most accomplished businessmen. He ended the war, which took him to India and Burma, as a staff sergeant in days when it was almost impossible for an African (with one or two infantry exceptions) to aspire to a commission. After demobilization he founded his own business and by 1952 was, for a five-year period, President of the Ghanaian Chamber of Commerce. Rising to be an Ambassador Extraordinary and Minister Plenipotentiary, he was also a board member of the

Volta River Authority. His bubble burst however after the 1966 *coup d'état* when he was arrested[1] as one of Nkrumah's two principal economic advisers at a time when the nation's coffers – formerly well stocked with sterling and dollar reserves – were found to have been drained.

Jackson's two principal lieutenants, Eric Taylor and Robert Milton – both of them former members of the British Colonial Administrative Service who had opted for the Ghana Civil Service after Independence – were also now on the point of handing over to Ghanaian successors. Taylor, as Permanent Secretary of the Development Commission, had been very closely involved both in the Volta Project and in overall national planning and was now leaving to head a cement corporation in Australia. Milton had helped to take the Project several stages further forward and had made a good enough impression on Kaiser to be invited to join his staff at the London office of Kaiser Engineers.

Rising to the top administrative posts in their wake were four Ghanaian members of the pre-Independence British Administrative Service. Herbert Winful was a forty-five-year-old engineer who had headed the Housing Corporation before joining the Volta Secretariat. As Secretary to the Volta River Authority and head of administration he was supported by two former District Commissioner administrative officers, Kobla Kalitsi and Ahmed Futa, both of whom had been closely connected with the intricacies of the negotiation period. E. R. Hayford, another senior VRA man, was appointed to head the new Fuel and Power Secretariat which was, amongst other functions, to be responsible for the Soviet-planned Bui Project.

The post of Chief Executive of the Volta River Authority had naturally been regarded as one of the most vital factors in the whole Project. Finally, for this key post carrying £14,000 per annum, Frank J. Dobson, a Canadian engineer from Ontario Hydro was selected. He had an impressive list of major hydroelectric schemes behind him including the Chenaux and the Sir Adam Beck No. 2 (Niagara) Power Projects and Toronto's vast Lakeview thermal plant where he was in charge of construction at the time of his appointment. Dobson arrived in Accra

[1] and subsequently convicted on criminal charges.

in December 1961 in comfortable time to have the newly formed Volta River Authority running smoothly by the inaugural events of January 22nd and 23rd. Other major appointments within the Authority following his own were those of N. G. Abhyankar, an Indian United Nations economist, as Chief Finance Officer and J. H. Rogers and L. P. Larsen, seconded under the Canadian technical aid programme, as Chief Engineer and Chief Accountant respectively.

Kaiser also was adapting its ground organization from provisional to fully operative consulting engineers. In March 1961 Kaiser Engineers and Contractors Inc. had been awarded a £3¾ million contract under which they would prepare detailed designs, inspect the construction of the Project and procure major equipment for it. Together with their 1959 and 1960 site preparation contracts the total Kaiser contracts were now worth £9 million apart from the original reassessment report, the cost of which had been shared equally by Ghana and the United States. Resident in Accra during this critical period of long-distance negotiation and planning had been Roger Sheridan, an amiable and energetic man and a first rate ambassador-on-the-spot for Kaiser.

Now, however, two new fully operative Kaiser 'outposts' had become necessary. In London, where all the detailed drawings for the construction were to be prepared, Kaiser was working in conjunction with Balfour, Beatty and Co. Ltd. This was also a useful centre from which to keep in touch with the headquarters of all the Europe-based contractors – for the dam itself, for the transmission lines, for the penstocks, cranes, steel gates, etc. Whilst in Accra, with planning giving way to actual construction, Sheridan was handing over to Ray Ware who was to be Kaiser's Resident Director for the Project and, with him, Jim Conwell, Resident Manager at the site itself.

The Italian invasion began in May, when Impregilo was awarded the contract. Impregilo is a composite name combining the identities of the three parent firms: Imprese Italiane all' Estero (Impresit), Impresa Girola and Impresa Lodigiani, who operate together on major jobs in Europe, Africa and Asia. For the Akosombo Project the three partners were joined by a fourth, the Turin firm of E. Recchi – the first two letters of whose name conveniently fits the Impregilo letter puzzle. This remarkable partnership of Italian contractors, industrialists and financiers has to its credit more than sixty dams in Europe as well as the Trans-Iranian Railway, hundreds of miles of motor roads in Latin America, Africa, Asia and Europe and vast areas of land reclamation. Impresit itself, which gives the group its technical and financial backing, forms part of the Fiat complex and was founded in 1929, purposely to promote Italian undertakings abroad.

The other two, Girola and Lodigiani, are both Milan contractors (each since 1906) with an outstanding record of dam building both as individual companies and in partnership. Each can claim the construction of more than thirty dams as solo contractors, whilst jointly they have built the 462-foot Val di Lei concrete-arch dam in the Swiss Alps, the 480-foot Place Moulin concrete-arch gravity dam in the Italian Alps and, together with French contractors, the 394-foot Mont Cenis rockfill dam in the French Alps. It was early in 1960 that the three companies, which had by that time all but completed the 420-foot concrete-arch dam at Kariba on the Rhodesias' Zambesi River, decided to form Impregilo with the aim in view of tackling some of the world's largest civil engineering contracts.

Kariba had whetted their appetite for dam building in Africa, which has no dam builders of its own. Outside Africa they had already started to build the Middle East's highest dam – the 666-foot arch dam at Dez in Iran. This was quickly followed by a further contract for a £20 million dam at Roseires on the Blue Nile in the Sudan, and, later, for Nigeria's £35 million hydro-electric scheme on the Niger at Kainji.

In 1964 Impregilo joined forces with Swedish, German and French contractors to help to rescue the Abu Simbel temples from the waters of the rising Nile. Their particular task was to cut away the ancient temples from the solid rock of which they formed part, dismantle them and re-erect them above high-water level. Lodigiani did have a scheme for lifting bodily the entire hill, including the statues, with a total weight of some half a million tons, but although it was technically feasible the cost proved to be prohibitive and UNESCO, under whose auspices the work was carried out on behalf of the UAR government, was obliged to settle for the less expensive solution.

It was Giuseppe Lodigiani who gave the impulse to this post-war boom of Italian dam construction in Africa. Now in his late forties, Lodigiani was a student when war broke out; but he obtained degrees in electro-technical and aeronautical engineering before getting his commission in the Italian Air Force Corps of engineers. By 1943 he had completed his military service and was free to join his brothers in the family business – making the hydro-electric jobs his own speciality. They had made such headway with jobs in Europe that within ten years he was looking for broader horizons. The enormous prize for the proposed hydro-electric scheme for Kariba soon attracted his attention. Lodigiani's determination to secure this major international contract brought together his company with Impresit and Girola to make their daring bid. To the credit and subsequently to the satisfaction of everyone concerned, they won the prize.

The choice of an Impregilo man-on-the-spot at Akosombo was not difficult. After Kariba it could be no one but a giant amongst dam builders, Mario Baldassarrini, a man who more than once risked his life in the terrifying floods of the Zambesi whilst leading the team that was harnessing that river. It is not unlikely that men like Mario Baldassarrini and his partners, Corrado, Moresco, Cassano and Leto, will be remembered as the inheritors in our age of the great Italian tradition of skilled and devoted construction.

All things considered Impregilo could be pleased with what they found at Akosombo when they arrived to start work in June of 1961. There were 130 attractive houses, as well as bachelor quarters, in what was to become known as 'the Italian village'. These were for the higher income families – not only Italians but Americans, Ghanaians, British and others. There were 350 two- and three-room units at the adjacent Chiasi community for the middle-income group – mostly works foremen, tradesmen or those in clerical positions – and 600 one-room units at adjoining Asukwao for the daily paid unskilled employees. Each of these communities had been designed to form part of the proposed permanent township of Akosombo, which was to develop into a small industrial community after the structural phase was over. Consequently about a third of the houses in each group had been built as permanent structures, and other features such as the hotel, the school and the fire-station all helped to suggest something more permanent than the usual pioneer construction camp. The 38-bed hospital, however, was dogged by gremlin delays from the outset and was not completed for three years; a small clinic gave out-patient treatment to the dam-site workers and their families whilst hospital cases were sent to Tema or to Akuse, twelve miles to the south.

The contractors found ready for them enough 'unfurnished' mechanical and electrical workshops to make a good start. Quickly they set about expanding these and building office blocks and installing their own impressive batteries of cement and aggregate silos. These in turn were linked by conveyors to the highly complex and largely automated concrete batching and mixing plant.

Astride the river from bank to bank, several hundreds of feet above the river level, were stretched steel cables supported by two 'blondin' towers – named after the greatest tightrope walker of all times, the Frenchman Blondin, who 102 years earlier had startled the world by sauntering across the Niagara Falls, 160 feet below, on his 1,100-foot long 3-inch rope. But these prosaic cables were to support enormous iron skips designed to carry ten tons at a time of the carefully blended concrete to the scene of operations on the opposite bank.

Two specially designed dredges had already been delivered at the site and assembled ready for the contractor's use. At the speed at which Impregilo intended to work, however, to get the river bed clear of sand before placing the dam foundations on the solid rock itself, they now calculated that three dredges would be necessary and placed an order for a third, costing another £140,000.

This whole problem of Volta's sandy bottom and the way it was overcome is of particular interest since it illustrates the unprecedented conditions that had to be faced at Akosombo. At first the planning engineers had considered placing the dam on the sand itself which had accumulated in deposits of more than

100 feet in depth. So far as is known dredging for sand in such depths of water – 200 feet and more when the river was above average level – had never before been attempted, and the obvious choice lay between not attempting it now and having a go at cleaning it off the rock. There are plenty of precedents for the former process but whatever precautions are taken – and obviously they are many – there is always the chance that 'piping' will occur, when water bores its way through the sand and undermines the rock structure above.

Finally it was decided to go ahead and remove the sand, and pump specialists in California constructed revolutionary 'jet action' dredges which have since become a prototype of their kind. Capable of operation down to a depth of 208 feet they have a rated output of 200 cubic yards of sand an hour. By the time they had finished their job they had in fact removed 1,500,000 cubic yards of sand from the river bed, which would be more than enough to fill to the ceiling all 2,000 rooms in New York's Waldorf-Astoria Hotel.

This then was one of the first major operations to be tackled. Waiting until October for the 1961 flood season to subside and using both Italian and Ghanaian professional divers to guide the dredges' lengthy probosces right into the sandy bed, the floor of the river was progressively cleared to enable work to start on the two rockfill cofferdams that were required to span the river from bank to bank.

Many people have a mental picture of a cofferdam as a vast ring of reinforced concrete set in the river bed, within which work on the dam foundations proceeds, the whole structure being removed when the dam is above water level. This is the type that was used at Kariba and at other concrete dams. But this is not the method for a gravity rockfill dam, which, as its name implies, sits by the force of gravity and its own sheer weight in terms of rock, filter and clay core on the river bed. At Akosombo the two cofferdams, upstream and downstream, are themselves straight rock dams across the river from bank to bank and parallel to each other, which eventually form the toe and heel of the dam itself. But, as with concrete cofferdams, they do serve the purpose of providing a watertight caisson within which the foundations of the centre of the dam are laid 'in the dry'. The process of transforming these porous walls of rocky mass into watertight cofferdams is perhaps one of the most difficult tasks facing the designers and constructors of a rockfill dam.

The other prerequisite for having a dry river bed for constructional purposes was the 1,000-foot long diversion tunnel, and work had already been started on this, as it could be tackled without disturbance from the seasonal high river flow. Its diameter was to be 30 feet, larger than was originally planned, which might mean a gain of as much as a month each year in dry river bed construction. The Volta has an extraordinarily wide field of fluctuation in its annual flow – varying from a recorded minimum March flow of less than 500 cusecs (very much less than any other river of its size or catchment area) to a recorded maximum September-October torrent of more than 500,000 cusecs, which is the average volume of the world's largest waterfall, the Guayara on the Brazil-Paraguay border. But for six months of each year, from December to May, the river limits its flow to a maximum of 18,000 cusecs, which was reckoned to be the capacity of the 30-foot tunnel. From June to October the river level tends to rise so fast that no tunnel, however large, could cope with the flow. Meanwhile Northern Italians as well as Northern Ghanaians – many of whom are experienced mineworkers – found themselves at home underground so that progress was swift in the tunnel.

1961 at Akosombo ended therefore with plant erection completed, a large amount of sand removed and the tunnel well begun – before ever the Project itself was 'officially' under way.

13

REMOVING THE RIVER

Something of the true atmosphere of Akosombo in the early days of construction is conveyed by the *Volta Project Pictorial* whose author wields a more colourful pen than my own.

'The whir of machines, the shuffling, stamping feet of plastic-helmeted human beings and the constant thunderous dynamite explosions, all conspired to make one long earsplitting din that drove away crocodiles, monkeys, rodents and reptiles in an unprecedented stampede. Akosombo bristled and vibrated with intense engineering activity!'

And it is certainly true that the traditional wild life of the wooded river gorge was to a great extent exterminated by the noisy new arrivals. During site preparation there had been some nasty accidents from snake-bites and several unpleasant encounters with crocodiles; but by the time that Impregilo had arrived this particular hazard had all but disappeared.

In outline the construction job that faced Kaiser and Impregilo was this: a dam of the gravity rockfill type had been designed. The basic reason for using this type of dam was a practical one. It is for the same sort of reason that a Cotswold builder will choose to build in honey-coloured stone, a backwoodsman will make himself a log cabin and an Eskimo an igloo of ice blocks. The materials are there and, if they are sufficiently durable for your purpose, then it is wise to use them. The rock in the Akosombo gorge is, at its best, very hard quartzite which can be broken into workable boulders of anything up to ten or twelve tons. In addition there is plenty of lighter rocky material for compacting purposes and there is an almost unlimited quantity of river sand and adequate deposits of good clay for the impervious dam core.

The dam, 2,100 feet in length from bank to bank along its crest, is 1,400 feet wide where it sits on the river bed, and 370 feet from crest to bedrock. This makes it almost four times as wide as it is high. This solid mass of rock, enclosing an impervious clay core, makes a rockfill dam as permanent as the Pyramids, which in cross-section it closely resembles. This squatness is a vital factor in any area which is susceptible even to minor earthquakes, as Akosombo is; whereas a solid concrete structure of such a size might have a tendency to crack under severe earthquake conditions, a rockfill dam in similar circumstances would probably do no more than settle more solidly on to its base.

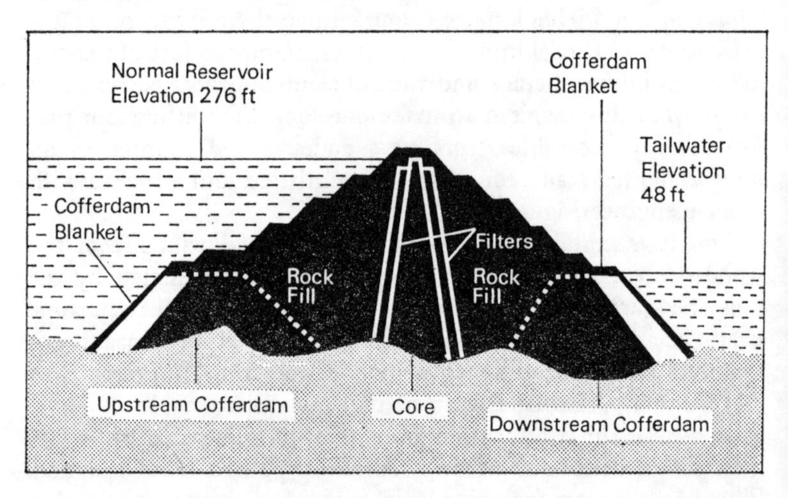

Akosombo however can boast not one but two such dams, since an inconvenient valley, just half a mile away from the main dam, would act as a permanent overflow from the lake if it too was not blocked. A second dam of similar design, known as the saddle dam, was therefore planned, to be built simultaneously 'in the dry'. This only needed to be 1,200 feet in length, 500 feet at its widest and 120 feet high, but this made it a 'large dam' in its own right in terms of the minimum qualifications laid down by the International Commission on Large Dams.

On the west bank, adjacent to the main dam, is sited the powerhouse with its provision for four 147 megawatt generators in the first instance and two more as a second stage, making a total proposed generating capacity of 882 megawatts.

High above the powerhouse and connected to it by 360-feet long, 24-feet wide penstocks, or steel pipes, is the concrete intake structure and the 400-yard long intake channel, carved in a deep trough out of the solid rock, through which the water flows from the lake to drive the turbine-powered generators.

Opposite, on the east bank of the river, and also adjacent to the dam itself, are the twin spillways, each comprising six 38 × 45 foot steel gates, designed to carry away any future floods surplus to generating needs. The dam's designers made allowance, in calculating the capacity of the twin spillways, for the worst flood that could be expected in a 10,000-year period, which is considered to be possibly twice the quantity of the 500,000 cusec flood of 1963. Such a volume of water could conceivably result from a disaster at some yet-to-be-built dam further upstream either within Ghana or even in an adjacent country. Dam designers are obliged to take into account such slender possibilities.

About the time of the formal start of work at Akosombo, Impregilo prepared a construction schedule in which they gave themselves targets month by month, the achievement of which would enable them to adhere to the crucial dates agreed on in their contracts for the completion of certain vital phases of construction. The ultimate target, the key to the whole programme, was that electricity from the first generator to be put into commission was to be produced by September 1, 1965. This was the date agreed with the World Bank to ensure that there would be sufficient revenue from the manufacture of electricity to start early repayment of the considerable loans involved. It was therefore, in every respect, a very important date – so much so that the contractor would have had to pay liquidated damages if it had not been met.

Worked back from this were other key dates, the non-observance of which would inevitably snowball into failure to produce current on time. Not only had all the equipment for initial power production to be in working order but, most important of all, the lake level had to be high enough to turn the first turbine. And for this to be certain the lake had to start to fill in July 1964.

To ensure this the contractor had to be certain that the overall height of the dam would at all times during 1964 be ahead of the rapidly rising lake level. The final portion of the dam foundations therefore had to be completed very early in 1964 – in fact, as quickly as possible after the 1963 floods had subsided at the end of the year. Meanwhile during the flood period, work had to proceed on the remaining portion of the dam, and to make this possible the water between the two cofferdams had to be removed by February 1963 and the foundations completed to above river level.

This, too, could only be done if the cofferdams themselves were completed as soon as possible after the 1962 floods and they could only be completed when all the sand had been dredged off their portion of the river bed and sufficient rock had been quarried to form them. It was also necessary for the diversion tunnel to be completed and functioning before its intake would be covered by the rising river in June of 1962.

It was essential to work to each of these dates in chronological order if the next one was to be achieved, and to their consternation Impregilo and Kaiser realized, before ever the month of the official start of work was over, that schedules were not being maintained on any of the four key fronts – dredging, quarrying, cofferdams or tunnel.

Impregilo had known from the outset that two dredges would not do the job in the time available, but the new one was not due for delivery until March and valuable time was being lost meanwhile. In the end its arrival could not have been more timely for, on the very day that it was being tested, the dredging ladder of No. 2 dredge was buried by a sudden cave-in of sand on the river bed and nothing that anyone on the dredge could do could extricate it. It was in fact No. 3 which came to the rescue and took over the work of No. 2 while the necessary repairs were being carried out.

But it was not only the dredges that were in short supply. Early experience of the quality of much of the rock had shown that additional trucks, mechanical shovels and drilling equipment were urgently needed if the 1962 floods were to be beaten and the two cofferdams completed and made watertight before the rising river inevitably overtopped them some time in June or July.

It is the ability to quarry, carry and dump vast quantities of rock, ballast and core material each and every day that is the crucial factor in the construction of a rockfill dam. Hitherto North America had pioneered the giant machinery that had made such building possible – which is why the rockfill type of dam has been in essence an American development of the twentieth century. Now Impregilo – one of the world's masters of concrete dam building – was venturing into this new medium of dam construction, and finding it testing. They had already calculated that if the cofferdam target was to be achieved before the floods they would have to maintain an average daily production rate of 15,000 cubic yards of suitable material. But by March their daily average was only a little over 4,000 cubic yards per day. Impregilo was master-minded however not only by first-class engineers but by astute businessmen who had to be sure that, in order to achieve their targets, they were not simply sinking capital into heavy earth-moving machinery in the right quantity but that they were also getting the most suitable machinery available for this particular job. And it was this that induced them to move cautiously during those first few months even though their own target of 11 per cent completion by the end of April fell short by as much as 4 per cent.

Valuable experience was nonetheless being gained on site both with machines and with men. Unlike the Kariba job where most of the heavy equipment had to be manned by Italians there was a reasonable reservoir of experienced Ghanaian bulldozer, scraper and shovel operators from Tema Harbour operations and elsewhere, and many others were quick to learn. Armed with on-the-spot experience, Impregilo called in all their consultants on quarrying, blasting, dredging and rockfill dams and worked out a practicable revised construction schedule that would meet the essential deadlines. By mid-May there were clear signs that work was going much faster than before. Before the end of May the last of the complicated hydraulic gate lifting equipment for the entrance of the diversion tunnel had been installed and tested and the tunnel was filled with water.

It was duly opened on June 9th and two days later the last gap in the upstream cofferdam was filled with rock so that one could now, for the first time ever, cross the river on terra firma. It was an exciting moment.

Even so, though the first essential deadline had been met, there were more problems in store. It had been decided that the top 10 feet of the upstream cofferdam should take the form of a temporary earth dike. This would prevent the cofferdam from being overtopped by the rising water before work had been completed on the essential task of waterproofing it below water level. At the same time, when breached, the dike would be quickly washed away by the river, which would then, it was thought, be less likely to erode the top of the cofferdam itself. This process of underwater waterproofing is perhaps one of the most delicate and difficult in the whole business of building a rockfill dam and nothing could be left to chance. Huge quantities first of transition material (of fine gauge) and then of blanket material (of impervious consistency) had to be dumped all along the upstream face of the cofferdam so that it would be forced by the flow of water into the gaps between the dumped rocks and would gradually seal the cofferdam and make it waterproof. In fact, before the job was finished double the anticipated quantity of material had been applied – part being tipped from the cofferdam itself and part being dumped from floating hoppers in the river.

Work on the downstream cofferdam had started early in May, a month ahead of the revised schedule. Here the principal anxiety was not so much as regards construction – for the ant-like technique of continuous quarrying, carrying and dumping was now beginning to work well – but as to clearing the bedrock of sand. It seemed as if because of the flood season work on this would have to be suspended from July till November. This would in turn mean that the downstream cofferdam could not possibly be completed until February 1963. Such a delay would constitute a major setback in the programme. Something had to be done quickly.

It was the river in fact that did it. No sooner had the tunnel been opened and the upstream cofferdam, surmounted by its 10-foot dike been closed, than the river started to rise at a

ecember 1962 – The Cofferdams virtually completed. Dredging the sandy ed continues

ay 1963 – The dry river bed – 150 feet deep – is filled with the dam's oundation, comprising clay core, sand filters and rock (see pages 131-135)

The Akosombo powerhouse from the air

startling pace. Within a fortnight the volume had multiplied more than six times and there was an immediate danger that even the earth dike would be overtopped. So a 200-foot breach was made in the dike to enable the flood to pass downstream and work could still continue on laying the necessary blanket material along the upstream face of the cofferdam. The river then barely fluctuated throughout July and most of August so that, contrary to all expectations, both dredging and construction at the downstream site continued apace. By the end of August not only had all sand been removed from the construction area but, following closely in the wake of the dredges, the rock dumpers had completed the whole of the downstream cofferdam to the original target of 57 feet – except for a 400-foot gap, purposely left to ease the flow of the flood. They reckoned that they could fill this gap in ten or twelve days, at the speed they now worked, when the flood had subsided. By the end of August the contract, now 14 per cent complete, was exactly on schedule; the Italians did not need long to learn.

Construction of the cofferdam, however, would never have proceeded so far if it had not dovetailed with several other operations progressing simultaneously.

Rock, in one form or another, was the prime commodity at Akosombo but comparatively little of it – about a third in all – had to be quarried without some other useful purpose being served. To the west of the dam site much excavation had been in progress in the proposed intake channel, which was to be the principal source of rock for construction, and a great proportion of the quarried rock had gone into the two cofferdams. Not all of it was of the standard required to be used on its own – in which case it was blended with larger rocks from the main quarry. Alternatively it was processed by a piece of equipment known as the 'grizzly' which graded the rock from the material required for transition materials.

The main quarry – known as W-3 – was being carved out of the rocky promontory south of the dam, which at that time was still crowned by the Overlook Point from which so many visitors to Akosombo gazed out over the river gorge trying to visualize the dam to be. A portion of this levelled area was later to become the Akosombo switchyard from which the generated power would circulate to Southern Ghana. Here again not all the rock had been up to expectations and there had been some anxiety about its usefulness. But all was well, for as the quarry deepened excellent quartzite was uncovered and this continued to be the principal source of rockfill and concrete aggregate throughout 1963. Across the river, on the east bank, the site for the twin spillways was also under excavation and this was producing a very good quality rock that had been used both for the east-bank ends of the two cofferdams and also for the saddle dam.

The saddle dam itself had been making steady progress until the urgent demands of the downstream cofferdam had temporarily diverted its supply of rock. Now it was moving ahead again. Impregilo's sub-contractor for the specialist task of 'grouting' beneath the various structures into the bedrock was another Italian firm with international connections called Rodio. The process of grouting is indispensable to dam construction: it prevents the pressure of water by-passing the dam. Rodio were now drilling along the axis of the dam a continuous line of 2¼ inch holes, 5 feet apart and as deep as 120 feet into the bedrock. Known technically as a 'grout curtain', the effect is to force the liquid cement under pressure into every crack and fissure in the adjacent rock so that a continuous cement curtain prevents water from undermining the dam. Simultaneously other forms of surface grouting across the whole rocky face that is to lie beneath the clay core prevent seepage upwards into the core itself, since experience elsewhere – at times disastrous – has shown that water, under the extreme pressures of a great lake, will, if not checked, force its way through the slightest of cracks. Not far distant a borrow-pit was being cleared to supply the impervious clay necessary for the dam's sloping core that was soon to be laid against its downstream rock embankment. The sloping core of the saddle dam as against the vertical core of the main dam is its principal variant in design and follows the very successful precedent of the Tennessee Valley Authority's Nantahala Dam. The Aluminum Company of America was so impressed by it that it subsequently built six of its own to a similar design.

The other major centres of activity at the dam site at this time were at the east and west abutments of the main dam. Here the giant rockfill structure would be 'welded' to the living rock so as to form, as it were, a continuation of the flanking slopes from bank to bank. Here the surface soil and rubble was being stripped off – a difficult task particularly on the east abutment where the slope was extremely steep – and the natural rock was then exposed, cleaned up and sluiced with water jets ready for its turn, in due course, for the Rodio grouting treatment.

In addition to these basic constructional tasks Impregilo was still establishing its base and was rapidly increasing the size of its plant and workshop facilities. Of these site facilities perhaps the most interesting was Impregilo's suspension bridge – similar to the ill-fated Kariba model and large enough to take light vehicles though not heavy machinery – which had been erected in order to permit easier access between west and east bank operations.

Throughout September the river rose steadily and achieved its climax for 1962 on October 2nd with a flow of a little over 300,000 cusecs – somewhat above the average peak for this time of the year. Nothing but a couple of dancing weirs stretching across the river indicated the location of the two submerged cofferdams – the earth dike having been removed before the floods rose, and the three dredges now being anchored to the west bank.

With the river left to its own devices, a great drive was made on the saddle dam and on stockpiling rock in W-3 quarry and the other excavation areas on either side of the river. The 'grizzlies' were working overtime. Indeed working round the clock had become the order of the day at Akosombo, where powerful arc-lights reminiscent of a sports arena turned night into day and a two-shift system of up to twelve hours each made the twenty-four hour day a perpetual affair.

The Volta is a wilful river, however, and within a fortnight of reaching its peak it had dropped fast enough to permit the dredges to go out again to clean up the base of the 400-foot gap. Within a few days repair work had started on the downstream cofferdam, the eastern portion of which had in fact been quite markedly eroded by the floods. But already it was feared that the 'ten or twelve days' required to complete the downstream cofferdam might well be a serious underestimate. The first discovery was a hole in the river bed[1] which was clearly more than 200 feet deep and was taking far longer to dredge than had been expected. So as to be prepared for the worst, adjustments were made so that dredging could, if necessary, be continued down to 230 feet. Then the river failed to conform to predictions and refused to shrink to the capacity of the diversion tunnel. Nevertheless at the upstream cofferdam the rock dumpers had been busy completing its height to the necessary 57-feet level, so that when at last, by mid-December, the river had dropped to tunnel capacity the upstream cofferdam was finally closed.

But the resulting delays were in danger of becoming critical if, as some feared, it would not be possible to dry out the river bed early in 1963. For this would make foundation-placing impossible before the 1963 floods, and the whole basic schedule would then fall through.

The main cause for anxiety now was that dredging delays at the downstream cofferdam had had the effect of also delaying the programme of waterproofing, and without this the next stage could not proceed. The finely graded transition material had successfully been applied along the length of the structure but the problem lay in adding the outer layer of impervious material, of which a great quantity would have to be used on account of the depth. The time available for this was limited.

So Impregilo, having put their heads together with their consultants, evolved an alternative procedure which so far as they could see would achieve the same objective – the sealing of the cofferdam – in a much shorter time and which could be carried out simultaneously with the operation of drying the river bed. Their plan was in essence a simple one. In a cavity in the river bed just downstream of the cofferdam they would dump a large quantity of clay. This would be pumped by dredge in the form of a somewhat adhesive sand-clay slurry along the downstream face of the cofferdam. Simultaneously they would lower the level of the water between the cofferdams by use of the battery of pumps assembled for that purpose. The effect would be that the fast falling water level would help to draw the slurry into the transition material so as to bind it into an impervious seal.

[1] Halcrows state that they knew of this in 1950.

It was good in theory, and it was good in practice. The downstream cofferdam having been finally completed early in January, the testing of the twenty-three 400 horse-power pumps followed at once and by the end of the month just as much advance sealing of both cofferdams had been completed as could possibly help the operation. Now everything hung on the actual exercise of pumping dry or 'dewatering' the river bed. The 'dewatering' operation that the engineers and contractors proposed was to remove every drop of water from the river bed between the two cofferdams, clean off all the remaining sand and debris, drill and inject a cement 'grout curtain' right across the river bed from bank to bank and then construct the dam together with its clay core from the bedrock upwards.

In February the pumps were set in motion, and slowly at first and then dramatically the water level fell. At the end of a week 6½ feet of water over the whole area had been removed. On the thirteenth day the bed of the east channel, 45 feet below the surface and almost exactly at mean sea level, lay bare. But inevitably there were seepages through both cofferdams and when, on February 28th, 116 feet of water had been dispersed (with 18 feet more to the lowest point) the stage had been reached when the incoming seepage equalized the capacity of the very reduced number of pumps that could still be accommodated in the river bottom. But not for long: the application of more impervious material to the cofferdams tipped the balance in favour of the pumps, which proceeded to dewater to the minus 85-foot contour at the bed of the west channel.

On the same day that dewatering was completed the river flow achieved its seasonal low of 1,500 cusecs. A week later it had already doubled. If a grim warning was needed that time and the elements were not on the side of the engineers and contractors this was it. There were four months at the most before the flow would exceed the tunnel capacity and by that time the whole dam – foundations, grouting, clay core, filters, and rockfills – all had to be completed to a height of 50 feet. Yet today there was a 150-foot chasm gaping up from the bed of the river. There was not a day to spare.

14

THE DAM

Deep into this new cavity came the access roadmakers, the excavators, the trimmers, the grouters and the rockfill dumpers who had already placed a quarter of a million cubic yards of material in the east channel before the west channel of the river bed was dry. This sort of speed was essential if full advantage was to be taken of the period remaining before the floods – and three months, or even less, was all that could be counted on.

The problem that had been facing Kaiser and Impregilo was to decide how precisely to deal with the 1963 floods, as they would inevitably overtop the foundations and they had to do so without materially damaging them. Basically the decision reached was to separate the area of the dam cavity into two parts. The eastern two thirds, where the foundations would be completed to approximately river level, would be sealed over to carry the flood. Meanwhile the western one third was to be enclosed with another earth dike and work could then proceed on the dam foundations and subsequent construction not only before the floods but right on through them.

But since it would take a month to seal the first stage of the eastern end, and since the flood might start any time near the end of May there remained in effect a bare two months for the eastern foundations to be completed. They were completed within six weeks. Fortunately the state of rock in the river bed had been found to be in excellent condition so that there had been no unexpected delays on that account. Into this bedrock, some 25 feet upstream from the dam axis, and parallel to it, were drilled the series of holes which, injected with liquid cement, formed the main dam 'grout curtain'. Simultaneously, the whole core area was treated with 'slush grout' in order to seal surface cracks, whilst particularly deep cavities were filled with 'dental concrete'.

Following hard on their heels were the placers of the fine and coarse filter materials which separate the clay core from the rocky mass that supports it on either side and protect it from 'piping'. This dangerous condition had, earlier in the century before filters were used, been a prime factor in the failure of a number of earth and rockfill dams, including one at Santa Barbara in California.

Next were the clay workers themselves, charged with the job of dumping, spreading, watering and compacting the solid core of red clay, which at this point was some 130 feet in width. Using 38 cubic yard scrapers for carrying and spreading the clay, sprinklers and disc harrowers for watering and mixing it and heavy sheepsfoot rollers for compacting it, they were a spectacular little army of workers now out in the open for the first time. Finally, to fill in between the dumped rockfill mass of the broadened cofferdams and the clay core and filters, was laid the dense compacted rockfill arriving in ant-like procession from the quarries.

Meanwhile a similar though longer operation was proceeding in the seemingly bottomless western channel. Here the channel was dominated in the centre by a 120-foot cliff of jagged, blackened rock that had once formed the base of a small island in the river centre.[1] The cliff itself had to be trimmed so that it could be effectively sealed. The contractor's aim was to raise the western third of the sandwich-like foundation the necessary 130-feet from bedrock to well above river level by the end of June, so that, whatever havoc the floods might wreak on the eastern side, at least work could proceed throughout the year on one portion of the dam.

[1] Here was found some thirty feet below lowest river level, a curious slab of rock into which in some prehistoric day had been drilled to a depth of an inch or two a smooth round hole encircled by a slightly less regular saucer-like surround, some twenty inches across. The archaeologists, genuinely baffled by it, assume that it was formed when the rock was above river level perhaps 3,000 years ago and that over the subsequent millennia it has steadily sunk to the level where it was found. This rock is now displayed outside the Volta Hotel at Akosombo while a more permanent home in a suitable museum is being considered for it.

The flood plan, as it was finally agreed, was that over the remaining two-thirds of the dam foundations, completed to water level, there should be constructed two channels – known as flumes – each 300 feet wide and specially designed to carry the flood water over the dam without damaging the foundation. Work on the first flume (near to the east bank) had started as soon as the foundations had been completed since, for caution's sake, it had to be ready by the end of May. The second flume, which was to run parallel to the first, separated from it by a wide earth dike on a rock embankment, was in effect the central one-third portion of the dam, and since the flood would develop in stages it was not considered necessary for this to be completed until some six weeks later – in mid-July.

A lot of planning and preparation had gone into these flumes, which had been tested in model form at the Sogreah Hydraulic Laboratories at Grenoble in France and approved with some modifications. The method of rendering the first flume water-tight was a novel one and had involved bringing in special materials, notably a large quantity of plastic-covered tarpaulin membrane, which was used to line the greater part of the area and was covered on bottom and sides with 14,000 rock-filled gabions – rectangular cages made from heavy steel wire. At the downstream end there was a concrete sill and, anchored to it, an extension to the membrane which was to protect the water-proofing materials from erosion. The second flume also featured rock-filled gabions to protect the vulnerable core and filter area, but for the rest depended on additional dumped rockfill reinforced by sunken ranges of gigantic 10-12 ton boulders known as 'rip-rap'.

A slight anti-climax developed however when the anticipated flood was a month late in coming, and it was not till the last day in June that the river level above the dam had risen to the point when the earth dike across the first flume needed to be breached.

Now, probably for the last time, the river was flowing again through the Akosombo gorge. It asserted itself almost immediately. The force of pent-up water that charged down the flume took the downstream protective membrane by surprise and set up such a vortex of turbulence in the river below the dam that it had the immediate effect of washing away a portion of the waterproofing materials. At once water started to penetrate the downstream cofferdam in such quantity that a considerable area of the west portion of the dam was flooded and there was nothing that the available pumps could do. The day was saved however by the foresight of the contractor who had ensured that the clay core in the west channel had by this time reached a point well above water level and could therefore be continued.

But worse was to come – the total destruction of the materials of the first flume, tarpaulin, gabions, everything. For almost three weeks the flume appeared to be carrying the flood well even though the volume had increased four times over. And then early on the morning of July 20th the floor of the channel near to the downstream sill, which must have been undermined, was seen to cave in. As the flood volume increased hourly so the force of the water, having once undermined the gabions, progressively spread the havoc backwards up the floor and sides of the flume not unlike a piece of knitting where the crucial strand has been pulled. Within days the damage was complete right as far as the upstream edge of the flume, and, with the loss of the stepped gabions on either side, the whole channel had widened by 70 feet until heavy rockfill prevented it from spreading further.

Meanwhile finishing touches were being put to the second flume which was brought into operation before the end of the month. For the present the river was quiet (already the engineers suspected that the erosion to the now exposed east channel core was as deep as it could be) so that the second flume flowed powerfully but properly. Official attention was diverted to other more urgent matters.

Then on September 23rd when it was cold and wet with more than seven inches of rainfall during the previous four days, the river sprang and thundered down the gorge with a full 510,000 cubic feet of water per second – certainly its mightiest flood for forty-six years and indeed within living memory, and possibly (since the 1917 figures were simply estimated from reputed water levels) for very much longer – no one knows.

Although at the time it made no great impression on Akosombo the effect on the riparian communities was more startling. Upstream the people had been repeatedly told to expect floods, permanent floods, from 1964 onwards but no one had said anything about 1963. Yet whole riverside villages were flooded and had to be evacuated during the critical period. Downstream from the dam it was worse: here they had been told not only that flooding would not affect them but that, for the duration of the lake-filling period, the river flow would be at the minimum all the year round, and that, because of the controlled flow at the dam, there would never be floods again in the lower reaches. But none of this applied to 1963; and, if they were never to see floods again, at least they saw them now. At the Accra-Tema Waterworks at Kpong the river pumping stations were submerged for several days and water supplies were severely curtailed.

But though the main excitement had been down by the river, great progress had been made all over the site. The days of quarry W-3, which had given up so much rock since it was first opened, were now numbered and what remained was needed for concrete. A new quarry, W-5, had been earmarked upstream from the dam. At the same time the intake channel, that vast canal bed that was being steadily carved out of the solid rock between the future lake and the top of the penstock area, continued to give its planned share of the rock for construction, though its major contribution was being conserved until the time for intensive work on the dam in 1964.

In March a serious set-back had threatened the site of the intake structure when a major rock slide occurred, making necessary a further ¼ million cubic yards of excavation. However, excavation had now been virtually completed both here and in the powerhouse and penstock area where forests of steel reinforcement were being steadily engulfed in bastions of concrete. The powerhouse structure itself was rising from an outsize crater that would eventually form part of the tailrace and now, standing erect in the centre of this crater, was a 360-foot high steel trellis mast that together with its 215-foot boom constituted one of the world's largest derricks. It was there to put in place, section by section, the six penstocks that were already waiting in welded 50-ton portions on an adjacent site.

Across the river comparable progress was being made on the overflow spillways where concrete, delivered by blondin from the west bank, was now being poured into the excavated areas.

Only the saddle dam, now almost complete, was being neglected. Originally planned for completion in March 1963, it had constantly had to defer to the more urgent priorities of the main dam itself. In December, however, it was finally crowned with its last 20 feet of crest and given a rip-rap coat of outsize boulders; it was now directly keyed in with the main dam itself by means of the mile-long grout curtain extending from the west bank beneath the dam and spillway and right along the spillway ridge (which had needed some internal waterproofing) to the far end of the saddle dam itself.

As the 1963 flood subsided there was a deep consciousness that the last lap of the race against the river was about to be run, for was it not now, in mid-November, little more than six months to go before Lake Volta had to start to fill?

Once again the contractors and their consultants had conspired to produce a river-proof solution to the new dewatering operation that now faced them as a result of the flood damage. They knew that this year they could not rely on the success of the normal sealing methods, though they intended to use them as fully as possible. When the first flume was destroyed by the 1963 flood an enormous carpet of loose rock had been scattered downstream over the river bed and it would now be virtually impossible to seal so large an area. As a second line of defence, they decided to construct, just within the downstream toe of the clay core, hollow cells of steel plate extending down to bedrock which, when filled with concrete, should give the core the necessary protection. And if the conventional methods failed to waterproof the upstream cofferdam too, then more steel plate would have to be used upstream of the core as well.

As they had anticipated, the damage beneath the first flume was bad; almost all the clay core and much of the rock had been washed out. But the second flume, apart from losing its upstream sill gabions, had weathered the storm well so that, after tidying up and rebuilding the upstream cofferdam, the contractors made an immediate start on raising the rockfill shell and, later on, the core itself.

The visitor to Akosombo at the beginning of December 1963 could for the first time feel the impact of the growing dam itself. During the flood season, good progress had been made on the western third of the dam; and by now no less than 140 feet of completed dam could be seen rising above river level. With the middle third now rising as well it was not difficult to imagine what the dam would look like when it stretched across the river and joined bank to bank. To the west, beyond the workshops and assembly yards, the first sections of two of the giant penstocks were in position, curving down from the concrete intake structure. To the right was the first third of the dam, partly completed. To the right again was the river, now tame, cascading through the narrow gap in the upstream cofferdam that was about to be closed for ever. Then came the great scars in the east abutment where the spillways had been scooped out of the rock; and away in the distance to the right of Spillway Ridge, the saddle dam.

The next three months were full of anxiety, frustration and disappointment. It was true that, in terms of percentages, the construction contract was now half completed and the goal, if it could be achieved, was in sight. But first the washed-out foundations had to be replaced; and no one connected with the construction was prepared to consider any short cut to the target. The aim was to have electricity on September 1, 1965; but nothing, not even failure to meet the delivery date, was going to jeopardize maintenance of the planned integrity of the dam. As if to underline this, preparations were even considered to safeguard foundations during yet another dam overtopping in 1964 – but no one really believed that this would be necessary.

The downstream cofferdam had been completely restored by Christmas and work started at once on the process of sealing it. First of all the transition material and then the sand-clay slurry sluiced against it from the dredges. Simultaneously they had started to erect the 50-foot high steel plate cells along the downstream edge of the core area but inevitably this was a slow and painstaking business. Meanwhile the pumps were being assembled and mounted on pontoons in the channel itself, ready for dewatering to start. But this time, as the wary contractors had anticipated, the water level refused to fall. Through January and the greater part of February, whilst the steel sheetpiling took form, the slurry was hurled against the foot and toe of the dam and the pumps drew out endless streams of water; at best, the water level dropped by 18 feet and was held there, but so great was the seepage beneath that beyond this they could not go. At the end of February further attempts at dewatering by this method were abandoned and all energy now directed towards completing the huge sheetpile cofferdam as early as possible.

First the cells themselves had to be dewatered and filled with concrete, and then, for stability's sake, they had to be anchored with tensioned steel cables to a concrete wall specially built for that purpose. This was positively the last stand against the river's subtle infiltration and there was no margin for failure.

By mid-March everyone was ready to go, with the fourteen pumps mounted on two pontoons – one in the upstream pool which covered the clay core area itself and one in the downstream pool which was to be partially dewatered simultaneously, though independently. And then at 5 a.m. on March 19th, just as dewatering was under way and the necessary differential had been established between the level of the two pools, disaster struck.

No one knows why the downstream pontoon, with its battery of ten pumps, suddenly sank – possibly with metal fatigue. But it did so in 20 feet of water and nearly succeeded in wrecking the whole programme for the year – and the year after that.

These pumps were vital to the dewatering operation, and at first it seemed impossible to salvage them quickly from a depth now of 40 feet of water. But Sir Robert Jackson was in Accra at the time, on a visit as one of the Authority's consultants, and he was able to apply his flair for logistics to the joint determination of contractor, engineer and Authority to have a new set of pumps operating within hours. One solution was to fly in a completely new pump assembly from the Illinois manufacturers in a specially chartered plane. With the minimum of delay, this was done. Meanwhile an SOS had been sent out in Ghana to contractors, mining companies, government departments and anyone else who could lend temporary pumping capacity. The response was instant and generous: President Nkrumah himself sent an engine. Within a few days, the sunken pumps too had been recovered. This great effort of co-operation meant that the dewatering could be resumed within five days after the disaster – and on that day the Volta retreated with the lowest river flow of the year, a mere 1,400 cusecs. Five days later, on March 29th, dewatering was complete. By April 16th all the ingredients of the dam had been replaced to the level of 42 feet, which was exactly where they had been a year earlier.

There was now no other way in which the river could do harm, short of overtopping the dam during the forthcoming flood season. However high the lake rose behind the dam, the contractors had to be certain of being higher. Everything had been calculated well in advance on the most conservative basis possible, for Kaiser's Board of Consultants had had experience in a number of recent projects of unusual floods during construction, and the 1963 Volta flood was fresh in everyone's memory. So they had calculated the worst possible flood they could think of, and called it the Project Design Flood. It had been decided that the diversion tunnel, now that its basic purpose had come to an end, would be closed on May 18th except for a small quantity of water to keep the river flowing downstream until such time as the first turbine was turning. At once the lake would start to form. In order to beat this possible flood of floods, the dam, which was to be completed to about 100 feet when the lake started to form would have to be 200 feet by the end of July and 260 feet (only 30 feet from its crest) by early October when the peak flow could be expected. In fact the exercise, though necessary, was academic, since 1964 was a singularly mild year for the river. When the year ended, the lake level was still a little short of 200 feet.

But that was later. This present phase ended on a note of triumph. For on May 19, 1964 at a small ceremony on the east bank of the river President Nkrumah lowered the solid steel and concrete gates that finally blocked the tunnel. At once there started to form – it rose 3 feet the first day – a new feature for the atlases of the world: the 250-mile long Lake Volta, soon to become the largest man-made lake in the world.

Part Two

15

AKOSOMBO

The Volta River Authority had been long in the making, dating back to the 1951 Halcrow Report. In those days its pattern was a reflection of the system that reserved all policy-making posts for expatriates, with space allowed for 'two Africans nominated by the Governor'. Both the British Government's 1952 white paper and the Preparatory Commission's recommendations modified and expanded this sytem. The final pattern emerged in May 1961 when Parliament passed the Volta River Development Act. Apart from making provision for the resettlement of the people in the areas to be inundated, it finally established the Volta River Authority as a Statutory Corporation. Its importance to the country was emphasized when it was announced that the President himself would be Chairman of the Board. With him were to be seven members representing the major consumers, the people of the Volta Basin, the Government and the Authority itself. The last was of course the Chief Executive, Frank Dobson.

Both the contractors and the designers were responsible to the Government's statutory agents – the Volta River Authority. But while being ultimately responsible for the success of the enterprise the Authority has – at least as far as the dam construction is concerned – perhaps the least glamorous role of all: that of paying the bills. However, whilst the day-to-day, hour-to-hour headaches of design, supervision and construction were being handled at the site, the Authority was able to put the benefits of its wide experience to use in the fields of overall planning, financing, accounting, hydro-electric operation, lake conservancy and transport, health promotion, social and agricultural resettlement, irrigation and many other related subjects. For it was essentially the Authority's responsibility to co-ordinate the multiplicity of projects that interlock in Regional Planning ventures of this nature and, in the words of the Volta River Development Act, 1961, 'to plan, execute and manage the Volta river development'. And a prime responsibility was to ensure that Volta power would be available as cheaply as possible – that the whole Project would be carried out at maximum economy and with the greatest saving possible.

In this the Authority has undoubtedly acted with skill and judgement. To its credit the overall capital cost of the Project was reduced by 20 per cent from an estimate of over £70 million to just above £56 million. The Chairman's bold decision to proceed with the main contracts before the financing had been concluded led to the saving of some £8 million, and the Authority's own participation in the development of Akosombo town itself brought further important economies. Throughout the construction period such potentially expensive items as interest on the considerable loans involved were kept to the minimum by using to best advantage Ghana's own equity investment funds and drawing on the overseas loan funds only as and when absolutely necessary.

Among the Authority's responsibilities from the outset, was the new town of Akosombo. It was to become a carefully planned township of the future which, when the construction phase was over, could serve as a small inland industrial centre. For this purpose the services of Doxiadis Associates had been obtained. They had already completed a master-plan for Tema, the new seaport, and were now supervising its implementation. At the same time the Authority appointed as Akosombo's Resident Manager one of its most experienced Ghanaian administrators, Ahmed B. Futa a former District Commissioner.

As a township Akosombo can basically be divided into two distinct parts. The upper part, nearest to the dam site, includes the Hotel on its hill top overlooking the dam itself. In a fold in the wooded hills below the hotel is a pretty little residential area of about 700 houses for the professional, administrative and overseas staff connected with the Project; for lack of any other name, it was called 'the Italian village', which at peak occupation was almost wholly correct.

The other part of Akosombo lies in the valley about half a mile away as the crow flies, but because the connecting road is obliged to go round the steeply wooded slopes in between, it is almost two miles away by road. It is this distance that divides Akosombo into its two parts. In the lower town there is the market and shopping area; Main Street, Akosombo, which has an atmosphere of improvisation like a gold-rush town, with the same amazing conglomeration of business interests – bookshop, football pools office, First Ghana Building Society premises, Frank Sinatra Barbering Shop, tailor, photo studio and Akosombo's own drinking saloon, Djaba's Bar, where they sign off at closing time, appropriately enough I have always felt, with the touching ballad 'Goodbye, Jimmy, Goodbye'. There are several residential areas for differing wage groups, ranging from pleasant two- and three-bedroom houses for foremen, junior executive and supervisory staff to the simpler single room quarters of unskilled labour. Unlike earlier days they are now comfortably shaded by groves of plantain and banana trees, many with their own gardens and allotments, and today blend pleasantly into the valley landscape.

Not far away are the hospital – on its own elevated site – the police station and quarters, the fire station, the community centre-cum-cinema, the Mobil petrol station and the new Post Office. There are several churches, including one of real architectural interest. This is the Roman Catholic chapel of Santa Barbara set on an attractive hill-top site on the wooded ridge that separates upper from lower Akosombo. Shaded from the sun and the rain by a capacious tent-like roof it is open to the fresh air on three of its four sides. Its architect, Igor Leto, Impregilo's last Project Manager at Akosombo, also designed his company's gift of a chapel to Kariba. Hearing in advance that Cardinal Montini (now Pope Paul VI) would be visiting Akosombo in August 1962, they worked day and night at building the chapel, and completed it within six weeks. Lined with Ghana mahogany it also has a beautiful stained glass window; and not far away stands a tubular steel tower with a carillon of three bells, cast in Milan – the gift of the three leading partners in the firm.

Students of the Kariba scene will have read with glee of such colourful figures as Maria Whiskey and Kariba Kate, who thought nothing of chartering a plane for a day's shopping in Salisbury. In Akosombo it is doubtful if girls prospered to this extent or indeed if the more successful ones ever really settled in Akosombo itself. For with the comparatively populous seaport of Tema only fifty miles away, and Accra itself a mere sixty-five – and excellent roads in between – the habit was rather to slip down to the coast for a night's entertainment.

The Authority and Impregilo itself made every effort to provide alternative entertainment and diversion for the residents. Two cinemas were opened with a constant turnover of Italian and American films – the latter mainly of the highspeed Wild West variety most favoured by Ghanaians, many of whom rely on action rather than words for their entertainment. The Italians introduced bowls and basket-ball and it did not take long for the Ghanaians to start a regular league for their beloved football – with additional matches against the Italians, visiting naval teams from Tema and any other teams who considered that a trip to Akosombo would combine sight-seeing with sport. Akosombo too became a centre for some of the country's most exciting boxing tournaments and Impregilo presented the community a full size professional ring and lighting equipment.

Clubs were opened in both communities and at the Impregilo Club in the lower town a kind of open-air discothèque was named after the Company's popular Chairman, 'Lodigiani's Dancing Pavilion'. The Akosombo Community Centre combined a wide-screen cinema with a theatre for visiting companies, as well as a bar, games room and a general gossiping centre. An Olympic-size swimming pool, opened in 1963, added that extra touch which makes life in a somewhat humid tropical climate that much more comfortable. And as the lake began to fill a Boating and Yachting Club flourished, drawing weekend members not only from Akosombo but from Tema and Accra.

Commanding a view of it all is the popular Volta Hotel, featuring, not least of all, its remarkable host, Peter Economides, whose photo graced the walls of the foyer in the company of every VIP of note who had ever visited Akosombo, from Queen

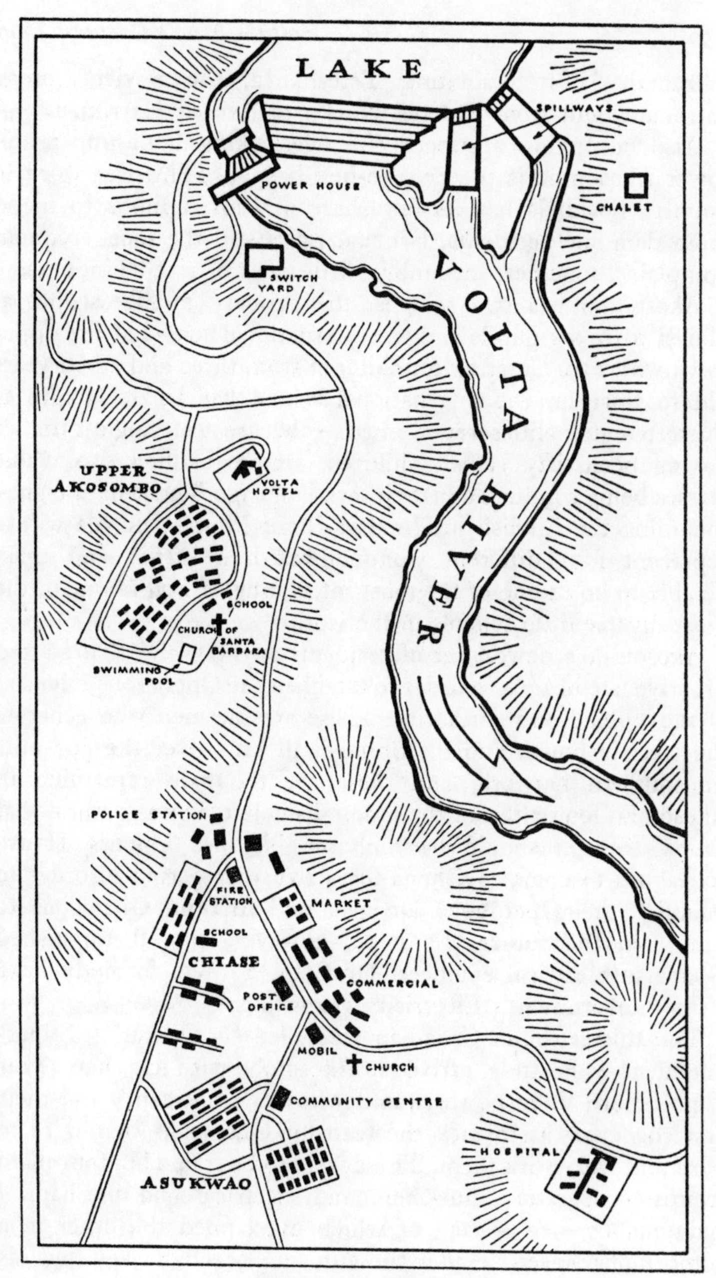

Plan of Akosombo

Elizabeth II to Valentina Tereshkova, the Soviet woman astronaut, and from Colonel Nasser to Averell Harriman.

Also occupying a superb site overlooking both upper and lower Akosombo is the new 50-bed hospital. This last word in country hospitals has its fair share of broken limbs to mend from dam site accidents, but malaria is still the most frequent complaint, together, inevitably, with cases of river blindness.

Akosombo has two schools, the primary middle school at Chiasi with 500 pupils and the international school at the upper town with 120. Catering for children from three and a half years old to thirteen, the international school has had as many as thirteen nationalities represented – the greatest single number having been fifty Italian children, which justified two whole classes being conducted in their own language. The staff of eight – including the English headmaster Brian Morris and his wife – represent four different Commonwealth countries and must be able to boast one of the most interesting as well as one of the most diverse little schools in the world.

Akosombo's newest set of residents is the group that started to arrive late in 1964 in order to establish the Operations Division of the Volta River Authority. These are the men who generate the electric power and distribute it in bulk over the 500-mile transmission network, and these are the men remaining in Akosombo long after all the others have left. It was natural that Frank Dobson should have chosen his own Ontario Hydro colleagues to come to Ghana for a two-year period in order to establish this Operations Division and to train Ghanaians to run it in the future. Its head, however, is a distinguished Ghanaian electrical engineer, Dr E. A. Sackey, formerly head of the Government's Electricity Department.

The thirteen-man Canadian team, led by Operating Superintendent Al Perttula, arrived at Akosombo with less than a year to go before Volta power was due to be 'on stream', and their first concern was to pick the team of Ghanaians that were to learn and work with them. These were to be trained in four main groups – operators, line-men, and electrical and mechanical maintenance men – each of which overlapped the other in a number of respects. Under the guidance of Dr Sackey and his Generating Engineer, E. A. Mensah, the Canadians were quick to adapt their own training material to local conditions and draw up advertisements for the 100 well qualified men they needed. Many of them naturally came from the Government's own Electricity Department, which was now destined to become more of a power-retailing organization as the greater part of its combined installed capacity of 80,000kw from its diesel-operated power stations was soon to be replaced by Volta power.

As dam constructors moved out so, early in 1965, did the students and their instructors move in – taking over some of the fast-emptying bachelor quarters and adapting empty houses to class-rooms and a mess-hall. Generator operators formed the largest group with a total of almost fifty, and these were received in two more or less equal groups for three months' classroom work followed by three months of practical work divided between the Akosombo power house and the Volta transmission sub-station at Tema. Similar courses were run for the linemen, in whose care are the 2,000 miles of silver cable that encircle the greater part of Southern Ghana, and for the electrical and mechanical maintenance technicians with their respective responsibilities for generators and turbines. A fifth group of specially qualified engineers, responsible for protection and control, also had to be selected, absorbed and co-ordinated into the overall operations, and all the while September 1965 was drawing closer when, training apart, the Operations Division had to be ready to take over from the installation engineers four of the world's largest generators, just as soon as the final tests had been completed.

16

MAN'S GREATEST LAKE

The world's largest man-made lake unquestionably demanded a very specialized system of lake transport. Keenly aware of this, the Volta River Authority very early in its existence commissioned Kaiser to study the problem in general and submit a report. Presented late in 1964 the report first points out that the natural trade area for the lake transport system includes not only large portions of northern and eastern Ghana but extends into the five neighbouring countries of Upper Volta, Niger, Mali, Dahomey and Togo. The area embraced is in fact four times the size of Ghana itself and has a population of some 9 million people. The report's most encouraging aspect was the revelation that really low-cost lake and connecting transport coupled with smooth trade relations would provide the whole of this area of West Africa with much cheaper import and export rates than it now enjoys through existing road and rail channels. Furthermore existing livestock imports from north to south would be appreciably cheapened and it follows naturally that Tema, as the seaport and industrial centre serving the lake and beyond, would benefit considerably.

The other important flow of lake transport, the report pointed out, would be between the southern terminal and the busy intermediate lake ports such as Kete Krachi and Kpandu, and those serving the rich cocoa growing areas fringing the otherwise inaccessible Afram plains. The importance of the local cargo and passenger services to the lakeside dwellers, and more particularly to those who would not at first be well served by motor roads, could not have been overemphasized: it was, and remains, the lifeline of their economic and social well-being.

In contrast to a hypothetical lake traffic figure of 340,000 tons of cargo in 1962 (based on a percentage of actual ferry and bridge traffic) the Kaiser report estimated that by 1970 870,000 tons of freight and 240,000 passengers would pass through the lake's southern port – the greater part being through traffic from south to north and vice versa, and the rest being intermediate traffic. Carefully integrated road and lake transport facilities would enable economy to be combined with a flexible system. The recommendations included a lake fleet of three 1,000-horsepower tugs and nine barges, three 360-ton cargo boats, and three 275-passenger boats. Together with a road fleet of 100 tractors and 1,000 trailers and sundry facilities including nine lake ports this would make a total capital investment of £9.3 million – a total that would have amused Commander Paget Jones, whose proposal for a modest capital outlay of £50,000 was brushed aside at the turn of the century and whose estimate of an annual freight load of 840-tons could now be multiplied a thousand times over.

An embryo Marine Division of the Volta River Authority, an efficient but economical fleet of modest-sized lake craft, came into being soon after the lake had started to rise in 1964. An early start was made with flat-bottomed fishing canoes powered with outboard motors which were at first a somewhat frightening improvement on the mere canoes themselves. Taking a look at a submerged village, a full load of visitors were swept, like Mary Gaunt, bottoms-up into the wet sump of the canoe when the cox tried to steer under the lake-swept branches of a tree that, only a day or two before, had no doubt been well clear of the water. But the fleet quickly expanded to over twenty vessels, ranging from the fast 420-horsepower patrol vessel, the *Obosum River*, to the powerful but slow tugboats that are used for hauling heavy freight. Paget Jones would have been particularly impressed by the four 60-ton flat pontoons used for transporting tractors, heavy earth-moving equipment and other freight across and up and down the lake, for these are what he had in mind for towing by his stern-wheel steamers. During a 250-mile lake trip that I made late in 1965 on one of these pontoons I couldn't help thinking of the naval Commander's bold vision of 65 years before. We too had to tie up to a tree for a few hours sleep when the night was at its darkest and heard only the sound of the water slapping against the underside of the pontoon and the mysterious noises of the forest all around. And we too, when the moon was high, heard the midnight drumming and dancing of the lakeside fishermen just as Kitson and Paget Jones, Mother Gaunt and Sir Henry Stanley and countless thousands besides had done so many years before.

On our return trip we must have borne some superficial resemblance to Noah's Ark as we carried, apart from our main cargo of yams, a varied selection of cattle, sheep, goats and poultry. Indeed there were Ararats all around us, for Lake Volta is very beautifully fringed particularly on its eastern shore, with handsome mountain ranges, the continuation of the Akosombo gorge range, that ultimately form the border between Ghana and Togo.

There are some who affect to despise artificial lakes as being potentially scruffy and unkempt. I cannot deny that the lovely natural sands that fringe the shore, for example, of Lake Malawi are something that Lake Volta can never know within centuries; but every lake has its own characteristics and, in its formative years, Lake Volta had great beauty, great charm and a great peace on its surface.

Submerged trees are in fact the one shortcoming on the surface of Lake Volta's beauty. They protrude from it for the 4,500 miles of its shore-line, though many of them have been drowned now that the Lake is reaching its normal maximum level of 276 feet. Inevitably they are also a handicap to the fishermen who have adopted Lake Volta more quickly than it has risen. Using seine nets which they float across the deepest part of the lake suspended from bamboo floats they are already making heavy catches of tilapia, catfish and a variety of carp. This has surprised some of the sceptics who were quick to surmise that the combined effects of rotting vegetation, oxygen deficiency and lack of plankton would make the increase of fish in the lake unlikely. Now, on the contrary, observation has shown that the lake water is thick with plankton and the fish themselves are not only increasing rapidly but appear to be altogether better nourished and richer in oils than they were before. One old man in a town close to the lake recently pointed with pride to a group of children outside his house and said, 'Look how fresh all our children have become now.' It is true that the lakeside people have never had such regular supplies of fresh and smoked fish, which being so plentiful is much cheaper than it used to be. This is the first swift dividend from the Volta investment.

The Ministry of Fisheries in conjunction with the Volta River Authority is now encouraging the independent and self-sufficient Tongu fishermen to form themselves into fishing co-operatives. The Tongus are born fishermen. Their homes are on either bank of the river below the dam, but they have always had migrant tendencies from the time that they first discovered that fishing was more profitable further north at certain seasons of the year. Some migrated annually and returned home for the Tongu fishing season, others built fishing villages on the river banks and qualified as permanent communities. Consequently, of all the people directly affected by the lake formation, no less than 10 per cent were Tongus. Theoretically rehoused along with the others in the new resettlement townships some miles away from the lake, most of them spend the greater part of the year in their lakeside fishing camps which, as the lake rises, they move steadily backwards. And as the word has flashed downstream of the sensational opportunities for fishing in the lake, so have many more flocked north leaving behind them the semi-stagnant stretches of river water below the dam. This state of affairs has been particularly acute for them during the period of lake-filling but will progressively improve as the water flows in increasing quantities through the turbines.

Now Lake Volta is already fringed with Tongu fishing re-settlements up and down its length; in a very real sense, the Tongus are the people of the lake. At first, however, many aspects of it took them by surprise. As they found to their cost, a squall of quite alarming proportions can quickly blow up, with waves comparable to a rough sea, and in such conditions their flat-bottomed river canoes are little safer than a cockle shell. More than a few fishermen have already perished in such storms. The answer appears to be to adapt the heavier and more buoyant dug-out canoes that are used all along the coast by the seaside fishermen. They evolved over the centuries as vessels of good shape and safety for use by a stalwart crew battling through the heavy coastal surf and may well be too solid to be used conveniently on the lake by two or three fishermen. But some modified dug-out canoe or storm-proof dinghy will need to be developed if disasters are to be averted.

Amongst the growing number of substantial vessels now afloat on Lake Volta is the 56-ton RMV *Tilapia*, a specially designed Fisheries Research vessel, having laboratories and living accommodation. Built in the Isle of Man in 1964, it has since been used by the University's Volta Basin Research Project, which has been undertaking, along with other subjects, fundamental research into most aspects of the lake's development, including the question of aquatic weed growth, the preservation of items of archaeological interest, and a variety of other medical and biological problems. At the same time Ghana's Academy of Sciences has found the new lake to be in many ways an aquatic biologist's paradise, and the Institute of Aquatic Biology, under its Director, Dr Letitia Obeng, is very active in the field.

One problem which Lake Volta has so far been spared, however, is invasion by that beautiful but wholly disastrous weed, the blue flowered water hyacinth, which today costs the government of the Sudan something in the region of half a million pounds a year to keep in check on the Nile. But it daily becomes apparent that the lake's own weed, the water lettuce (*Pistia*), which was formerly considered to be at worst a small nuisance, is now breaking out all over the lake as a major factor of its biology. So far it is only really thick and solid in the western reaches of the lake, where it tends to be driven and blown by the effects of wind and wave. Here, however, it has become so dense that VRA vessels were at one time unable to penetrate it, and an attempt to start a pontoon ferry service across the Afram arm of the lake had to be abandoned temporarily. Scientists fear too that a tendency for mosquitoes, flies and snails to breed in and around the weeds could be an additional threat to health, not to mention the fact that snakes and crocodiles appear to find comfort in its solid greenery.

The scientists' most pressing concern, however, is with the health of the people who live near to the lakeside. The Volta has always been associated with a terrible affliction known as river-blindness (*Onchocerciasis*), transmitted by the simulium fly which frequents in particular fast running water such as is found above and below the Akosombo gorge. Thus in the village of Atimpoku, near to the Adomi Bridge, 68 per cent of the population was found to be infected including 92 per cent of the adult males. The effect of the lake of course has been to eradicate entirely breeding grounds in that area, but recent research has shown that these flies are also capable of resettling themselves and are already congregating in a number of streams and water courses all round the lake. And the problem still exists below the dam, where it is tackled by very thorough spraying.

Whilst the lake will probably help to mitigate the river-blindness problem over a wide area it will have exactly the opposite effect on other serious waterborne diseases such as bilharzia and hookworm. The former is carried by water snails and the lake will inevitably become a breeding place for them. Fortunately, early in 1966 Ciba, the famous Swiss drug chemists and manufacturers, announced that they were ready to market a new drug called Ambilhar which they say will cure 90 per cent of bilharzia cases within a week and without any of the unpleasant side-effects of earlier drugs. But it does not solve the problem, as a cured patient can become reinfected within minutes if he continues to expose himself to snail-infected water. So there remains no substitute for rigid control measures all around the lake's perimeter, although there are reports now of a new Shell chemical which can actually destroy the bilharzia germ in the water. Hookworm too is another horrible affliction, communicated by infected water supplies: the inundation of a village latrine pit, for example, could easily infect the lake over a wide area. It is partly for these reasons that the new townships have been sited well away from the lake with their own pure bore-hole water supplies and septic-tank latrine blocks, but old habits sometimes die hard. Malaria too must increase to some extent as the 4,500-mile lake perimeter inevitably provides new breeding grounds for mosquito larvae.

But the lake contains prettier things than these: it has its mermaids. In Ghana a mermaid is appropriately known as a 'mammy water' and these delightful, slippery creatures figure in a lot of the fisherman's folk lore. Scientists, who are well known for their habit of debunking fairy tales, claim that Ghana's own 'mammy water' is none other than a manatee or sea-cow. The manatee which grows to a length of six feet or more is said to be thick-skinned, greyish in colour, wrinkled and with sparsely distributed hairs (a formidable mermaid!). It is not unlike a seal, having paddle-like flippers and tail. The female has a pair of breasts at which she suckles her young, apparently in a rather human fashion by raising the upper part of her body out of the water, so that a short-sighted fisherman might be forgiven for mistaking her for a watery trollop. They are herb-eating vegetarians, and in Guyana the South American species is used on sugar cane plantations for keeping the irrigation canals free of grass. But they are good to eat, something like pork, so that it usually becomes a race to see whether the manatee eats the grass before the men eat the manatee. During the dam construction at Akosombo fully grown manatees were frequently seen in the pool below the dam, often swimming in pairs like dolphins and rising for air – sometimes accompanied by their young. Two, in fact, apparently bent upon moving house to Lake Volta got themselves trapped in the diversion tunnel, where their skeletons were found when the tunnel was emptied for plugging. Certainly an attempt should be made to resettle one or two couples in the lake itself – if only to set in motion a Lake Volta Monster myth with all its potential as a tourist attraction.

17

NEW TOWNS FOR OLD

The House under the Water, *The Village that was Drowned* and *The Flooded Valley*, all are book titles that conjure up the awful fascination of whole communities of people – or at least of their immovable possessions – being condemned to lie forever on the bed of one or another of the world's new lakes. But in the case of Lake Volta there was at least decent burial. Starting with the early Halcrow investigations and accelerating fast after that, a great deal of detailed investigation went into examining the needs of the people who would be displaced.

From the outset it had been realized that it would not cost less than £3½ million to cover the minimum necessities for resettling the 60,000 people originally thought to be affected, and this figure came to be written into the estimates from 1951 onwards. Indeed its retention right through the Preparatory Commission's investigations and estimates – and then on through the Kaiser, Cooper Brothers and World Bank calculations, thus to be entrenched in the Master Agreement – points to everybody's determination to keep the goal of cheap electricity to the fore and not to saddle the Project itself with an unlimited bill for resettlement.

Inevitably the Ghanaian Government itself, from its own exchequer, had to find the difference between the £3½ million set against the cost of the Project and the amount – ultimately £12 million or more – that was in fact spent on resettlement either directly or indirectly. This is the sort of dilemma that all too frequently faces a developing nation. On the one hand it is trying to produce a marketable product such as electricity at a price that will attract large-scale industry, and on the other it is pursuing a social obligation, not simply to resettle its displaced persons but to do so in such a way that their new lives will be richer in every sense than before. Its choice is in fact a simple one: either to inflate the price of electricity and lose its customers or to grin and bear the extra cost, as Ghana has done.

Commander Jackson's Preparatory Commission set the pattern for the resettlement operation with its detailed survey of the affected area and its peoples. Convinced that human factors would determine the real success of the Project, the Commission spent more time on this specific problem than on any other. Broadly speaking, Jackson's idea was that self-help should be the governing principle and that the settlers should build their new homes themselves, with such technical and material assistance as might be needed. Apart from keeping costs down, this would help to keep the men occupied at a time when the steady drift of their lives had been shattered and when time might weigh heavily on their hands. Moreover, it would prevent them from developing the dangerous, apathetic attitude that the Government would do everything for them – an attitude which if it once became widespread would lead to a loss of initiative and enterprise at the very time when they were most needed.

When the scheme was put aside in 1956 ground work on resettlement was not resumed until the Kaiser proposals had been accepted and financed early in 1962. Jackson had done his best from 1957 onwards to persuade the Government to follow through the Preparatory Commission's proposals for resettlement in carefully planned stages, but agreement was never possible. A crucial factor that had meanwhile emerged was Kaiser's intention to build the dam in four years instead of seven. A mere two and a half years was now left between the start of work and the moment when the lake would begin to form and the first resettlement houses would have to be ready.

It is difficult to guess what would have happened if two remarkable young Ghanaians had not now entered the field: Kobla Kalitsi, who was put in overall command of resettlement, and Godfrey Amarteifio, his principal welfare officer. Kalitsi had been a district commissioner in pre-independence days and had absorbed the meticulous passion for detail and step-by-step planning that had typified the best of his British contemporaries.

Experience is showing that the graceful but solid dug-out canoes used by sea-going fishermen (behind) are safer on the lake than the flat-bottomed river canoes

Smoked fish ready for market represents an early dividend from the rising lake

The Akosombo Dam and Lake Volta

Amarteifio, an Olympic boxing referee and an ex-soldier and policeman, had at thirty-nine already acquired the legendary reputation of the man who had resettled the turbulent Tema fishermen into a new township two miles away from their ancient preserves when the new harbour had been built.

With two years to go before lake formation was due to start, Kalitsi, who is a modest but strong-minded man, initiated his Working Party system, comprising social workers, architects and town planners, soil scientists and agricultural officers, surveyors, valuers, lawyers, engineers and public health and education officers. In something of the style of Jackson before him, Kobla Kalitsi led this team of qualified professional men and women by a system of regular meetings which he both chaired and secretaried. He encouraged them to work from their own parent organizations but with a system of blank cheques with which to pay their way, drawn on and honoured by the VRA.

This was a very personalized control which had little if any statutory power to back it. It depended more than anything else on human relationships, tact, and knowing the right people. That it worked – at a time when virtually all other government operations in Ghana were firmly guided by the day-by-day political and ideological pressures of Nkrumah's Government – is a great tribute both to Kalitsi and his team, and to the Government's own realization that it was only without political pressure that the job could be completed at all.

Almost the first decision taken by the Working Party was that, in the short time available, it would be quite impossible for the settlers themselves to build their own houses. But the fact that they should be encouraged to participate remained a valid point. A valuable compromise was evolved in the shape of a 'core' house which could be mass-produced at about £350 apiece: having an aluminium sheeting roof supported on pre-cast concrete pillars, large enough to cover the cemented floor space of two rooms, a cooking porch and a verandah porch. However, only one room (the core) with walls of landcrete blocks – moulded under pressure by a handpress from earth and cement – would be completed in the first instance, so that scope for self-help would still remain. By a process of careful architectural planning the houses were sited in such a way that they could be progressively extended, so that ultimately they could take the traditional form of a single-story house, built round and opening on to a central courtyard.

Though for many reasons this broad solution was not wholly satisfactory it was the best that could be achieved in the time and was successfully carried through. There were slight variations in design and conception, reflecting the ideas of different architects and planners, but basically the rule was 'one family: one room', irrespective of the type of house that the family had lost. These had varied from thatched shelters worth a few pounds to substantial premises of £1,000 or more. But whilst, at the bottom of the scale, the poorest family would be fortunate enough in exchanging a worthless pile of grass and sticks for a £350 house, families at a higher level had to be compensated in cash for the difference in value between their old property and the new core house. Thus, no one would be worse off, and many, of course, would be considerably better off.

The Working Party's second basic decision, advised by the Ministry of Agriculture, was that the new communities should not revert to traditional subsistence-farming practices. Instead they should grasp this opportunity to move with the times and balance their own staple food crops with crops that they could sell for cash and with scientifically fed livestock. This would mean at least partial mechanization of the land and the clearing and stumping of vast acreages.

Taking the lake area as a whole the Kalitsi team set to work on a broad regional scheme and evolved a master plan of new towns, villages, communications and industries. Though it has not yet fully materialized, this plan served as a useful guide to the development of the 52 resettlement towns which did emerge to replace the 740 assorted settlements that were condemned to disappear.

The detailed house-to-house social surveys which had been initiated all over the area to be flooded had now shown that there would be some 80,000 evacuees, of whom no less than 70,000 had chosen resettlement rather than cash compensation. Intelligently planned, with a good balance between theoretical considerations and practical knowledge of the areas concerned, this major survey was a model of its kind. Ultimately it was processed for follow-up action on the University computer at Kumasi. Not only did it help to show which villages chose to resettle together and vice versa, conditioned by a variety of social and other prejudices springing from tribal disputes, religious beliefs, past scandals and feuds and ordinary jealousies, but it also made it very clear which particular family you did *not* want as your next-door neighbour.

It is significant that by the end of 1962, with all this intensive study and consultation, coupled with soil analysis and water drilling, no less than 35 out of 38 new sites which had been chosen by the people themselves had been approved. And such is the determination of the Ghanaian villager that the remaining three sites, which had been vetoed largely because of the expense of communications, were ultimately approved as well – no matter what the cost of the new access roads. A year later all 52 new resettlement sites had been agreed and more than 1,000 families had already moved in.

It had not of course been as easy as that. Godfrey Amarteifio who, more than any other one person, became between 1962 and 1966 personally identified by the 80,000 Volta settlers as the prime mover in taking them away from their ancestral homes, derived much of his success from his realistic understanding of the fundamental religions and beliefs of these isolated communities. In this respect he was to a great extent following through principles laid down by the Preparatory Commission. It was he who, as its Principal Welfare Officer, appealed to the Volta River Authority for a special grant of £10,000 to be made available for the purpose of propitiating ancestral gods, fetishes, shrines, graves and departed souls through the medium of libation – both before and after the evacuation had taken place. Libation, in the form of the offering of liquor and blood sacrifices together with prayers to the ancestral spirits, merely recognizes the Ghanaian belief that the physical and the supernatural worlds exist closely side by side and that, if a geographical move becomes necessary, then it follows that the ancestral spirits must be called upon to make their move at the same time.

Ghanaian beliefs and customs, however, though wholly ingrained and deeply sincere, are also capable of being applied in a sensibly elastic fashion – so long as the underlying significance is not compromised. Amarteifio came up against one such problem in a village a little way from the east bank of the river, which for a number of good reasons preferred to resettle on the west bank. But there was a genuine snag, and as Amarteifio listened to the tale he realized that here were the makings of a stalemate. Although the people themselves would have liked to move, it was taboo for their fetish, without which no one could even consider leaving, to go near the water. Whatever route was taken, this seemed to be unavoidable. It seemed as if, against all inclination and better judgement, the village would have to join one of the east bank townships. But as he sat there amongst the chiefs and elders Amarteifio began to think about other resettlement problems and about aerial surveys – which led him to suggest, with his tongue in his cheek, that the fetish might not be averse to the idea of an air-lift by helicopter from one bank of the river to the other. He could guarantee that it would not at any time be nearer the water than it was now. Miraculously, after consultation the offer was accepted as being in no way in conflict with the fetish's known taboos. Another problem had been solved.

Still bigger problems, however, had to be contended with. On a basis of half an acre of land for each house, 6–7,000 acres, mainly of forest, had to be cleared for the 52 townships, spread over an area 250-miles long by 50-miles wide. Then twice that amount of land again had to be cleared for the first phase of farm development. Experience had shown that in thick forest about 2 acres per day could be cleared by one large Caterpillar tractor. On this basis there were more than 10,000 tractor days' work to be done. As this was quite impracticable, new ideas were considered and two gigantic £40,000 tree crushers were ordered. With their three 10-foot high steel-bladed rollers they were formidable monsters and were capable of pushing down and crushing into pulp 2½ acres of forest an hour.

Theoretically at least, it should now have been possible for the back of the work to have been broken, except that, in addition to the clearing of town sites and farms, all-weather roads had to be cut through the virgin forests both to move the equipment and to give access to the construction teams and later to the settlers. In all, 500 miles of road costing about £1 million had to be constructed around the lake. But, just as the 1963 floods had almost confounded the dam builders, so the same year's devastating rainfall slowed down almost to a standstill the forest-clearing and road-building. For weeks the giant tree crushers, which were far too heavy for the season's soft and muddy subsoil, were unable to work, and township clearing had to proceed in most cases at the expense of the farmlands.

As if nature's own contrary forces were not enough to harass the contractors, there were human difficulties as well. To the casual observer it might appear as if the greater part of Ghana's forests belonged to no one and were there to be cleared at will. In fact this is far from being the case. No one prizes his ancestrally inherited land more than the Ghanaian, and he knows his boundaries well. In consequence, either because of some misunderstanding over survey pillars, or of some local dispute as to ownership, there were not infrequent instances of tractor drivers being chased away at gunpoint. On one particular occasion, indeed, a crone who had forbidden the bulldozer driver to touch her farmlands had lain down in the direct path of the machine screaming ancestral oaths in open defiance. It is sad to think that such a gesture is unlikely to have gained more than a few hours' reprieve for her land, which no doubt she had helped to till since childhood.

But there are many stories of less hardship than this. One began with the removal of a small village from far up the west bank of the lake which had elected to move further south on to higher ground. Their problem however was that there was no kind of road by which they could make the 30-mile direct journey together with all their possessions. So Godfrey Amarteifio had to organize a major lift by which the villagers were to cross the lake by boat and then proceed by road down the east bank, across the river bridge south of the dam site and then up the west side of the lake by means of new roads and a ferry, to their new home – a journey of 280 miles or so, in order to return to within 30 miles of their point of departure. This, however, was just the sort of challenge that Amarteifio and his remarkable team of friendly welfare boys and girls had grown accustomed to. Then a couple of days before the great trek Amarteifio received a somewhat garbled radio message at his headquarters to say that the party included eighty-nine old ladies, so that in addition to the heavy lorries already ordered the necessary taxis should be sent. At such short notice it was not altogether easy to rally the thirty or so yellow-winged taxi-cabs that would be necessary to meet this request, but in fact the procession formed up and left overnight for the take-off point a hundred miles or so up the lake. It was some twenty-four hours later that the confirmatory copy of the message arrived reading 'Party includes 89-year-old lady so please send necessary taxi', and by this time the more enterprising of the villagers had commandeered the twenty-nine spare ones and were doing the journey in style.

18

AN ORACLE GOES HOUSEHUNTING

It is not in every generation that a famous oracle is obliged to close down and experience all the humiliation of having to find a new home and a new shrine or temple from which to continue its business. This however was the fate of the Dente fetish[1] of Kete Krachi from the moment that the decision was taken to construct the dam at Akosombo and to flood a considerable area of the Volta Basin.

Krachi Dente – as the fetish is usually known – has for two hundred years or more enjoyed a reputation throughout West Africa as a major oracle. It ranks with one or two others, such as Kankan Nyame in Guinea (supposedly Kwame Nkrumah's favourite ju-ju shrine) and Broukou in Togo, as the most powerful and most sought after on the West Coast of Africa.

Kete Krachi in fact, before it finally disappeared in 1966 beneath the waters of Lake Volta, was a twin town – Krachi itself, the ancient river port and traditional capital of the Krachi people, and Kete, a mile inland, which was founded by the stranger communities who came here during the eighteenth and nineteenth centuries to help establish the prosperous trading link between north and south. *Kete* is an Ashanti folk dance and

[1] The word 'fetish' was first used in West Africa by the Portuguese meaning 'sorcery'. It has been used down the ages in many different ways – sometimes to describe an inanimate object e.g. an amulet or a figure, which is in itself an object of worship; sometimes to describe an oath which may only be sworn in exceptional circumstances and, of course, in its colloquial sense as anything capable of unduly influencing public or private actions.

Missionaries used the word to summarize all anti-Christian activities.

The Dente fetish of Kete Krachi differs from many in that it is regularly and widely consulted as an oracle.

it is usually believed that this popular pastime is what gave the new town its name.

But above all it was trade that had made Kete Krachi into a busy, solidly built market town of 6,000 or more people. At first it had been the Saharan caravans that had linked these inland parts of Africa northwards with Mediterranean trade. Then it was the river trade southwards to the Gulf of Guinea with its up-river terminal at the Krachi rapids. The twentieth century had brought with it the motor road. The sign-post in the centre of Kete Krachi which pointed as the water rose both north and south into the lake, was one of the poignant reminders that Kete Krachi was no longer on the way to anywhere. Even so there was the air-strip which, when all other links had been severed, still acted as a vital means of communication; then that, too, disappeared beneath the lake and had to be resited on higher ground. Krachi was no village at the time: it was a large and thriving commercial centre, with general stores, petrol filling stations and lorry parks, beer bars and dance halls, post office and hospital, churches and mosques, schools and playing fields. And all this was now to lie under the lake.

The Krachi people themselves, like so many of the small Akan groups on the east bank of the Volta, had migrated here from further south early in the eighteenth century. A powerful warrior king had formerly ruled the greater part of this inland area west of the river until he was ultimately defeated by his neighbours and apparently chased as far as the Volta. Tradition has it that, like Jomo Kenyatta, he splashed the waters with his fly-whisk and a crocodile appeared and ferried most of his surviving subjects to the eastern bank, where they have settled to this day. Defeated however, he himself followed the only honourable course. He brought his proud empire to an end by dumping his stool and other regalia into a deep abyss in the river and then vanishing himself – possibly in its wake.

It was some of his descendants who are said to have been hunting one day in the forest when they came across a group of strangers who said that they were refugees from further south and were looking for a place to settle. Apart from the leader, there were seven brothers, and they were carrying with them the Dente god. At first they stayed a while on the west bank of the river but later crossed to the east bank and founded the town of Krachi where, in some rocky caves not far from the river bank, Dente was destined to stay, more or less undisturbed for the next two hundred and fifty years. I qualify his security of tenure only because, shortly after Queen Victoria had given this parcel of Africa to the Kaiser as a birthday present, [1] the Germans in an over-zealous drive to christianize the area had bombarded Dente's cave but, so far as one can tell, achieved nothing and did not do it again.

There is no doubt that by the start of the nineteenth century Dente had become a great power in the land. Successive kings of Ashanti appear to have gone to extreme measures including war to have control of the fetish. When King Kofi Karikari found himself confronted with the British expedition of 1873 he at once sent to Dente for advice. The oracle was at least realistic on this occasion: it advised that the Ashantis could not hope to succeed, since the very gunpowder that they were going to use against the English had been bought from them.[2] Dente indeed, through his priests, treated the King's enquiry less than seriously and advised him to 'purchase for himself and for each man in his army a pair of stout sandals, with which they may escape with facility and not have their toes sprained or their feet bruised when routed and pursued by the English'.

The oracle had subsequently let it be known that the destruction of Kumasi, 'which these people ascribe to a superhuman power, had taken place as a result of the supernatural influence of Dente on the Queen of England'. It had been said that Queen Victoria had allied herself secretly with Dente so that 'the Grandfather [Dente] is so closely bound up with the Queen of England that a division of persons is impossible and only they themselves can say whether the Queen is the Grandfather, or the Grandfather the Queen'.

Possibly the old queen held other views for, not long afterwards, she 'dashed' the whole territory, oracle and all, to her German cousins. During their thirty years rule in Togo the Germans gained the reputation for 'autocracy, cruelty and

[1] By deed of gift in 1884.

[2] Prior to the final departure of the Dutch from Africa the previous year the Ashantis had had an alternative source of supply, and their new predicament must have amused their opponents.

arbitrariness with destruction of fetish cults'. This is probably not a fair verdict on their period of rule in Togo for they did much in the fields of education, technical training and agriculture but, sadly, they are still remembered for their cruelty and intolerance.

Krachi Dente, however, survived and continued to dispense useful advice on diverse subjects to pilgrims coming from far and wide. A barren queen would happily be blessed with a son following a visit to Dente's cave; a merchant from as far away as Lagos would come to seek advice concerning a business deal. He is consulted by farmers about their crops and sometimes by policemen about some difficult court case or prosecution. There is virtually no limit to the problems that are put before the oracle and it is doubtful if his influence is less strong today than it was a hundred years ago.

The last of Dente's seances in his time-honoured cave was late in 1964 when he was asked to say, at a time when the rapidly rising lake was already approaching the shrine, whether or not he was willing to move, along with the townsfolk, to the new site on higher ground some two miles away. Though the decision had been left rather late, in fact almost till the last possible moment, Dente agreed, adding that he was ready to move as soon as they were. However, there were things to be done first. In a letter to the Government the chiefs and priests of Krachi had said that 'there are certain performances involved when these Black Stools (the thrones of the ancestors) and Fetishes are removed and settled but these cannot be repeated in this civilized Ghana'.

Nevertheless a cheque for £1,120 was hastily issued by the VRA to cover the cost of 32 cows, 90 sheep, 100 fowls (including 48 white and 2 red), 96 bottles of rum and 2 pots of a local beer called *pito*, which in all was considered to be an adequate substitute for those unmentionable performances.

Amongst Dente's strict taboos is human blood and others, possibly by implication, are circumcized men, and women during their periods. Paul Hutter, the Swiss trader who during the 1930s lived the life of a hermit across the river from Krachi, once told a friend that he had often heard the groans of Dente's human sacrifices who were buried up to their necks. And the *Krachi-wura* (paramount chief) confided to me that there had at one time been other methods of human sacrifice than by bloodshed but that he had put a stop to these and now it was only 'sheep and goats'.

The removal, at least of the physical paraphernalia such as the Black Stools and other sacred emblems, took place at dead of night with not a light showing. Lights of any kind are yet another taboo to Dente. Each of the thirteen stools was wrapped in a sheepskin. In this manner the procession set out with chiefs, priests, stool carriers and followers, all in mourning dress, walking in single file through the night to the place selected for the stools to be concealed.

As it happens the procession was obliged to pass the District Commissioner's bungalow on the higher outskirts of Krachi, the residence of one of Ghana's more colourful DCs, Wilhelm Henkel, whose father before him had been German Commandant at Krachi and had married into the country. Wilhelm had inherited some of his father's authoritarian ways and, whilst entertaining a party of British Tory MPs to a gargantuan lunch in 1960, had been asked how he rubbed along in his district with the local members of the opposition. 'Opposition!' exploded Henkel from his end of the table. 'I'd have anyone horse-whipped who even suggested such a thing in this district,' and he dissolved into infectious laughter.

On this night Henkel was again entertaining friends and the bungalow was ablaze with lights as the procession approached. A messenger, sent ahead to ask the DC to conform with the custom and extinguish his lights, was given a flat 'no' for an answer and returned to report. This time a more resolute member of the group marched up to the bungalow and, angry at the turn of events, made it clear that, if the lights were not extinguished, the procession would return to Krachi and, after that, anything might happen. Mischievously, Henkel told them to take the stools back to Krachi and he would promise to come tomorrow and carry them himself in broad daylight. Some of the elders who had arrived meanwhile could hardly believe their ears or suppress their feelings. But the amusement over and before he was taken too seriously, the DC told his servant to turn all the lights off, and he stood there in the darkness with his friends as the procession silently passed by.

Almost a year later, on a visit to Krachi, I called on Nana Kofi Badumgya II, the young paramount chief of Krachi, and was talking to him and to Dente's high priest about the resettlement and how it was affecting them all. Generally speaking they were not pleased with it. Trade, on which they had always depended, was reduced to almost nothing, and the royal court itself was now hopelessly split, as most of his sub-chiefs and elders, rather than try to live in the single-room houses provided for them, had moved to their farming villages and were scattered. At least for the present, things were not normal. But concerning Dente he had good news. Dente, after a year or so of 'resting', during which time pilgrims had been obliged to return home with a view to making new appointments, was now in business again. Would I therefore be very kind and, when I was back in Accra, let it be known publicly that the oracle could again be consulted? And this I did in the course of a series of articles in a local newspaper, only too glad to help restore dignity to a historic African oracle.

When he was not presiding over the Krachi Cabinet and trying hard to keep his court together the young ruler was, like so many of his subjects, fighting to reconstruct the vanished township on its new site and to enter into the spirit of the new style of farming. As I left him on the step of his modest settler's home Nana was resplendent in a superb robe embossed with royal symbols; minutes later, I heard a tractor start and there was Nana in blue jeans and a T-shirt waving as he drove off to his farm.

For generations, yams have been the staple of the Krachi farmer – and they grow yams to be proud of, weighing as much as 100 lbs a tuber and as big as a motor wheel. Somewhat coarser than a potato, they are not dissimilar to them in the hands of a good cook and can be enjoyed in a variety of ways. The farmer plants a small slice of the tuber in the ground and then builds a dome-shaped mound over it, so that a yam farm, with its neat rows of mounds, has a very attractive and professional appearance. A stick is then inserted for the vine-like foliage to climb up. Without the use of fertilizers, however, a single season's crop only can be grown on one plot, which has then to lie fallow for six or more years, so that it is only possible to maintain this system where large surplus areas of land are available, such as round a small village. Krachi will, no doubt, continue to be Ghana's principal source of yam production. But, with the greater concentration of farmers in one area, there has to be a new approach entirely for many of them and it is here that Nana and his tractor are giving a good lead. Working closely with the Ministry of Agriculture, the new arable farmers are rotating yams with maize, groundnuts, tobacco, cowpeas and legume in farms ranging from 10 to 30 acres. Other families have opted for vegetable farming and have their own rotations on 2 acre farms. The third category is intensive livestock production, for which 3 acres per head has been granted. Voluntary co-operatives help with supplies of seeds, fertilizers and other common services including marketing the produce itself, but experience has shown that the emphasis must always be on voluntary co-operatives.

Kete Krachi's handicap however, since the lake started to rise, is that she is virtually cut off by water from her time-honoured yam markets to the south, whilst the lake, which was to have been (and may yet be) her life-line to these markets, has yet to generate a transport system – which for economic reasons will probably take some time to develop and need assistance from the Authority or private enterprise now that the lake is fully formed. Meanwhile a community which, as the half-way house to the north along the old eastern motor road, only knows how to exist on the regular flow of business through its trading houses, now knows what it is to be a dead-end town. Under the lake has gone the old motor road, and the new one, with its unreliable ferry service across one arm of the lake, completely by-passes Kete Krachi by thirty miles or more, leaving it isolated at the tip of its peninsula pointing southwards down the lake towards the trade route that never seems to develop. It is barely surprising that many of Kete Krachi's traders have taken their business elsewhere – to Tamale further north or to Kumasi further south – at least until times change for the better.

What is surprising, and speaks volumes for the spirit of Kete Krachi, is that so many of those well-to-do traders whose old business houses have, as they say, been 'taken by the crocodiles', have set about converting their little one- and two-room settler's houses into comfortable homes. Already they give a clue to the appearance of the Kete Krachi of the future. The roofs come off, the ceilings are raised or another storey goes up, the window and door frames are replaced with superior ones and a wing is thrown out here and there and already the settlement with its flat chess-board pattern is assuming a new character. On a hill a Roman Catholic church is rising, the schools are already buzzing with children, the bars have their 'regulars', the barbers are busy with their 'Presley' or 'Cliff' stylings under a convenient tree, the new mosque is taking shape, the market is a riot of colour and of people and the rough tract of bush land of three years before is already a thriving community.

Several rather more solid features help to give the impression of greater permanence and continuity, and are the fruits of forward planning from several years back. There is the three-storey mansion on the edge of the lake. And there is Dr Horst Schumann's hospital. It is the 40-bed government hospital built several years ago, which serves as the only strand of hope between disaster and recovery for many thousands of peninsula dwellers. Dr Schumann, a former Nazi SS doctor, has since been extradited from Ghana to West Germany charged with war crimes at Auschwitz concentration camp. But as chance travelling companions for two days on a slow ferry trip up Lake Volta in 1965 we had had ample opportunity to talk, and later he showed me round his well-kept hospital at Kete Krachi. A depressingly high proportion of its cases tend to be without hope; the patients have often been brought to it, sometimes over long distances, as a last resort. But the patients I saw were obviously well cared for, so that one was tempted to feel that here was a relatively thankless task being handled efficiently and painstakingly, and that it could be argued that, in the interest of everyone concerned, a measure of rough justice was being done, so far as Dr Schumann was concerned, without the need for the full process of the law.

There was however one health problem that was causing particular concern in the new township and that, like the classic case at Clochemerle, centred round that proudest of new edifices in any rural community – the new public lavatory. The Volta River Authority had been at some pains to design the last word in lavatories for all its townships. The result was that an entirely new style of building emerged with its pipes and other vitals in quite different places from those shown in the standard manual issued to all qualified sanitary inspectors. Thus, as so often happens, an impasse was reached in which the city fathers, on advice from their local experts, declined to bless the house on the grounds that it did not conform. In the town the situation was quickly getting out of hand, as available records show: having waited for several months, 'the settlers can wait no longer', and 'as all the temporary ones are filled up they need to use the new ones very badly'. But still nothing was done, and several months later the people of the town are said to have celebrated the *coup d'état* of February 1966 (which automatically threw the city fathers into gaol) with a victory march destined to end with an appropriate ceremony of dedication at the vacant shrine itself.

19

MODEL COMMUNITIES

It had not been possible in the available time to survey in the detail necessary for really accurate maps all the 4,500 miles of future lake shoreline that follow the 280-foot contour. Consequently there were cases in which small towns and villages were inundated by the rising lake some time before this could have been foreseen, and the evacuation programme, taken unawares, assumed the proportions of a national emergency. This was particularly the case up the western arm of the lake – the Afram River – where in the autumn of 1964 I myself saw from the air the startled evacuation of the little town of Worobong, which had believed that it still had several months more to exist.

The river itself, which with its rocky pools had been a pretty place for holiday makers and had not been an obstacle for those wishing to cross it, had quickly become a frightening barrier. Principally on account of the forest trees, it was neither possible to see nor even to be able to guess the position of the fast widening shoreline. This was no longer a river – it had become a nightmare forest with no tracks, no landmarks and no means other than guesswork for finding one's way. Yet it had to be crossed, if only by canoes with or without outboard motors, for life on the Afram Plains beyond had to continue.

It was the beginning of a new school year and, amongst others, there were new teachers arriving from home to take up their first teaching posts in some small and faraway village school. One had arrived by 'mammy lorry' from the city, had unloaded his suitcase and a few personal belongings by the roadside where the road now dipped into the lake and, anxious first to reconnoitre and find his bearings, had joined a motor-driven passenger canoe on the sinister crossing among the withering trees to the opposite bank. Skilfully navigated, they quickly made the crossing, and the young teacher made his way to an adjacent village which was now serving as a lorry terminal for that side of the river. As luck would have it there was a passenger lorry leaving in an hour's time for his destination forty miles beyond – the only one for a day or two and he was due to report that evening. There was no time to lose. He had to get back and fetch his luggage – or miss the bus.

But the ferry had already gone and no one could say when it would be back. What to do? It had not been a long crossing. Only five minutes or so through the trees. What about this canoe here? There was a paddle in it and he had frequently used one at home. He would borrow it and be back in next to no time with his things. What a stroke of luck.

Instead it was a tragedy. The boy was never seen again alive. No doubt he had lost himself in the thick, watery forest and perhaps panicked, thinking of the waiting lorry and his new job tomorrow morning; or tried to climb a tree to see the way and fallen into the water. Anyhow the canoe was found, empty, and his body was found floating in the water and handed over to the police. There was no cemetery there. It, too, had been flooded and the new site not yet selected. So the police dug a grave where the body lay by the waterside and buried him there.

The police had found his name and home address in his unclaimed luggage and wrote to his father and mother to give them the news. The letter took a few days to arrive and the family hurriedly hired a lorry to drive them down to the lakeside to bear the body home. On arrival they were given the suitcase and the other odds and ends but the boy had been claimed by the rising lake. The policeman could only point several yards away into the water and say that he thought the grave was somewhere there.

A lesson had been learnt, however. Soon after this tragedy, a group of five young ex-servicemen living in the neighbourhood had the sensible idea of stringing together some large gourds which they painted bright red and slung through the branches of the trees from bank to bank so as to indicate the shortest route, and they even ran a free ferry service for one month until a more reliable system could be organized.

Probably the worst hardships occurred during the unforeseen floods of 1963 before the lake had started to rise and before there was much housing completed. 'The true picture of untold hardships suffered by these people', a Ghanaian welfare officer's report reads, 'cannot be vividly described here but imagining how some of them are sleeping on tree tops can throw some light on the seriousness of their present situation.' He goes on to describe how '400 people find comfort in a school of only two rooms' and adds with a touch of self-satisfaction that 'it needs a high degree of technique to control and keep the settlers quiet during this time'.

However, very gradually and as the result of hard won experience the programme got into its stride.[1] The carefully rehearsed and, where possible, computerized exercise of moving whole communities into new wards of much larger townships than most of them had been used to, settled down to a not altogether steady routine.

It is unlikely that anything approaching the ambitious nature of this mass evacuation scheme has ever been essayed before. In effect the whole exercise took the form of an unprecedented experiment in the disposition of human beings. It speaks volumes for the good nature, adaptability, lifemanship and sense of humour of those 80,000 human beings that they moved in accordance with the carefully planned but wholly makeshift machinery and did not break their hearts in doing so. They grumbled, of course, and complained and petitioned and stuck out for their rights, like all good citizens, but in the event they co-operated and applied themselves to the historic task of founding their new communities.

Even so there were still to be setbacks – some serious. In February 1965 one of the resettlement towns on the east bank of the lake was hit by a violent wind storm which severely damaged 229 houses – in many cases completely removing the aluminium sheeting roofs. Within two weeks three other town-

[1] Anyone wishing to benefit from the lessons learnt by the VRA's resettlement pioneers should not fail to read 'Volta Resettlement Symposium Papers' (VRA and Kumasi University, March 1965), which states the problems very clearly.

ships had been similarly, though less seriously, damaged. The engineers were quick to detect a basic flaw in the method used for securing the roofing sheets – which are light-weight though normally very durable – and on top of all their construction work were obliged to fix additional ties to the roof of each of the 15,000 resettlement houses.

The shift would seem to have worked, for a year later another resettlement town also suffered something similar to a tornado, accompanied by hail stones as large as inkpots. Where the hail stones had struck they had cut straight through the roofs and the tremendous power of the tornado had also torn a number of roofs right off, as it had done to neighbouring houses built to conventional design. But for the most part, though the storm had torn at them and even crumpled the edges of the sheets, the aluminium roofs had held.

It was not the houses for those 70,000 settlers who had elected to stay in the valley that were any longer the worry. By 1965 the families had either grown used to them with all their limitations, or they had set about improving and enlarging them, and that, after all, was what had been intended. Far more serious was the fundamental problem of the farming lands. Could the resettled farmers flourish or even survive on the land set aside for them? Speaking to an international audience of specialists in March 1965 Kobla Kalitsi, the resettlement chief, in a remarkably down-to-earth address, laid bare some of his anxieties. 'Soon after evacuation into the first township had been substantially completed,' he said, 'a survey showed that the people were already leaving that town for other villages or drifting back to the water to set up fishing camps. One hopes that this drift will be seasonal and that the people will farm the lake for fish and also farm the land being supplied to them and make the settlement towns their permanent homes. It is possible that they may not, and if they don't we cannot plant it on them. . . . If that ever happens we would have wasted over £8 million of Ghana's valuable investible funds and we would also have ruined the lives of 80,000 people and shattered the country's finest opportunity to introduce into society cells of change to activate the whole rural population of Ghana. The spectre of a ghost town hangs over every settlement we have built!'

Kalitsi's 1962 Working Party had ultimately agreed on a modified target of 12 acres of field crops per family – half of which was to be developed in the first instance so as to progress in stages. Even so this amounted to a grand total of 54,000 acres to be cleared, taking into account the respective needs of farmers engaged in arable, tree crop and livestock production.

From the outset, however, the clearing of farmlands had always taken second place to that of town sites and access roads, mainly on account of the undisputed urgency for houses. When therefore a visiting World Bank mission was in Ghana towards the end of 1965 to examine thoroughly all aspects of the country's exhausted economy it did not fail to note that only 16 of the 52 resettlement townships had had their farmlands cleared and estimated that, at current rates of progress, it might take a further 20 years for the target of 12 acres per head to be achieved.

Meanwhile £1 million worth of tractors and agricultural machinery, which had been ordered in bulk in anticipation of full clearance, had arrived and was either earning its keep on the 16 completed farmlands or otherwise augmenting the limited equipment available elsewhere.

In these circumstances a completely new approach to the pattern of agricultural development in the resettlement areas had become necessary and did in fact evolve during 1966, in part from the World Bank recommendations and in part from the immense experience already gained by the Volta River Agricultural Resettlement Unit.

Whereas the original pattern had perhaps been excessively paternalistic and given the farmer too little freedom of decision and of action, the new emphasis was first on complete legal security of land tenure, then on ensuring that the farmer, with guidance, could control to a far wider degree his own enterprise. Membership of co-operative bodies, both for the provision of agricultural services and for marketing, was to be wholly voluntary. Recognizing however that not all farmers would enter into the spirit of the new order it was agreed that the Agricultural Resettlement Unit should as a matter of policy favour those farmers who showed practical signs of wishing to progress from the old method to the new. In this way it should be perfectly possible for the goal of an annual cash income of from £300–500 according to acreage, to be achieved, as against a maximum of £120 by the old methods.

The new order, however, depends entirely on the presence of cleared land and in itself still leaves unanswered the problem of clearing economically the remaining 36 farmlands. In a sense the solution to this has been one of *force majeure* – that is, if it is no longer possible to clear by machinery, then you must, if you are to clear at all, clear by hand. There is in fact a practical justification for this, since the further north you progress up the lake, the thinner the forest becomes until ultimately it is little more than open savannah. So the heaviest of the clearing had already been completed in the south and what remained for the most part was not too heavy to clear by hand.

The actual formula for this exercise is an attractive one of mutual co-operation. The farmers themselves, who were beginning to drift away because of the shortage of cleared land, were halted in their tracks by the Authority's new offer to pay them to clear their own farmlands. Payment however was not to be simply in cash. Ever since evacuation had started, the United Nations' World Food Programme had been distributing to the settlers through the VRA regular supplies of large quantities of foodstuffs – flour, rice, maize, tinned meats and fish, cooking oil, butter and milk powder – in order to tide them over the period when their new farms were not producing. Now it was proposed that for a further period of two years, starting from December 1966, the WFP rations would be issued to all the settlers in the 36 resettlement towns and that in addition all settlers working on the forest clearing would draw a cash bonus of 3s 3d for every day worked (this is half the basic day's wage for a labourer). It was reckoned that during the two-year period all clearing could be completed by 10,000 settlers, assisted by a further 5,000 neighbouring farmers, who would be offered the same bonus as the settlers themselves, together with a personal daily food ration. And, as a superb gesture of international goodwill, the French Government offered to carry the cost of supplying all the necessary hand tools – cutlasses, hoes, axes, matchets, shovels and rakes – for the full two years of the exercise.

But if a solution has been found for some of the basic agricultural problems in the lake area, what of the broader problem of these displaced people's own contentment with their new way of life? From the outset the Government promised them that 'no one would be worse off' as a result of the evacuation, which was itself a bold but perfectly proper challenge with which to bind its future actions. In material terms, few of the settlers could be said now to be worse off than they were before the lake started to rise. Certainly the Kete Krachi traders – those who have not moved to the cities – must be feeling the pinch, isolated on their lake-bound peninsula, but this is a condition that will swiftly disappear when the VRA or private enterprise opens up the vast potential of lake transport. On the other hand the Tongu fishermen – now ringing the lake in their fishing camps – are thriving as never before on their rich harvests of plankton-fed fish.

What worries Kobla Kalitsi – the man who has spent more thought and concern on the future of the lakeside people than anyone else – is not only the material well-being of his 80,000 charges, for Ghana has a generous combination of soil and climate and the necessities of life tend to grow profusely, but also the deeper social problems of community relationships and good government. He worries that, in the translation of more than 700 villages to 52 rural townships, the old regime of traditional law and order may bend and crack when 10 or more village chiefs have to share their authority not only amongst themselves but also with a democratically elected Town Development Committee. He is concerned that people who have been used to the simplest form of house construction and village planning are now expected to extend their tiny core houses to architects' specifications, using comparatively strange building materials – remembering always that an open space is the equivalent of a sacred grove in terms of modern town planning. And in what he terms 'permissiveness versus limited capacity' he wonders for how long it will be possible to indulge the whims of some of the settlers who were permitted to settle in outlandish centres of their own choice, barely concerned with the heavy cost of constructing all-weather roads linking them with the outside world. And who will now bear the cost of maintaining these roads? All these problems as well as those of the 10,000 displaced persons who opted for cash compensation rather than a core house, and then changed their minds and expected to get (and got) a house, and of those others who asked for a house but instead left it standing empty and moved to another part of the country – all these problems, though handled gently at first, have sooner or later to be rationalized. 'Where then', Kalitsi asks, 'do we draw the line between the permissiveness which marked our approach all along and the limited capacity of any resettlement organization to cater for the commitments imposed by the permissiveness?'

Now as Director of Finance at the Volta River Authority Kalitsi will be able to play an important part in finding answers to these questions. In Israel, experience in founding and running the *kibbutz* system showed that a period of ten years was necessary before a new community could adequately stand on its own feet, and there is little doubt that in Ghana the experience, although not the conditions, will be similar. It would certainly be regrettable if these 52 model communities, with all their obvious advantages in terms of planned and healthy living, new ways of farming and earning higher incomes, and of breaking down traditional isolation and backwardness, could not rub off something on their neighbouring communities, so that this expensive experiment, which has been and will continue to be a major burden on the country's economy, may after all blaze a trail of rural development and self-help across the greater part of the country.

20

DOWNSTREAM FROM THE DAM

Below the dam at Akosombo the Volta flows some seventy miles to the sea at Ada. For the first five of these miles it is in effect a very narrow natural lake – no wider than a river but vastly deeper – blocked at the lower end by the rocky channels of the Senchi rapids that made such an impression on Mary Gaunt and Paget Jones. On a map the Senchi rapids look like enormous gall-stones blocking the ureter – and such an obstruction in effect they are.

To the north, as the river pinches to leave its wooded gorge, the elegant steel arch of the Adomi Bridge spans the river. A further five miles southwest and yet another major stricture, in the form of the Kpong rapids, deflects the whole course of the river by ninety degrees so that it now turns south-eastwards at the start of its majestic sixty-mile sweep to the sea. This is the point at which Kaiser has proposed that an 11,000-foot barrage should be constructed, as the next phase of hydro-electric generation when all six generators at Akosombo are working to capacity – theoretically from 1976 onwards. Thus a small but secondary reservoir would be formed extending for the ten miles between Akosombo and Kpong, more or less engulfing the existing rapids at Senchi. The steady 38,000 cusecs of water entering this reservoir from the Akosombo turbines coupled with a head of some 40 feet at the Kpong barrage would be sufficient to generate a further 140 megawatts of power. Embankments would protect the town of Kpong and the Accra-Tema water pumping station from the risk of floods.

From this point, the spectacular excitements of the river are over: from Kpong to the sea the broad expanse of river, flowing between its high, crumbling, treeless banks has only a few inches to fall before it enters the sea. Indeed, when the river is low, as it has been consistently during the lake filling period, it is tidal for up to thirty miles inland and the tendency for salt water to penetrate further up river than usual has been one of the problems that has had to be dealt with, for this is something that affects not only the drinking water of the riverside communities but fishing and farming conditions as well.

And yet, as the river cuts through the sunbaked expanses of the flat plains that border the sea, it may well be that in the future this parched and little inhabited area may become the granary, plantations and lush vegetable gardens of the coastal cities a few miles to the south. The key, of course, is irrigation. Following Halcrows' recommendations in 1951 for intensive experiments in the area, which had been supported by the Preparatory Commission, the University of Ghana's experimental irrigation project was started at Kpong. Though started on a modest scale – 60 acres in the first instance, rising to 200 acres – it was designed to enable neighbouring farmers to take part in the experiments and gain a working knowledge of the mysteries of irrigation.

Halcrows had also made broad recommendations for a scheme for irrigating the greater part of the Accra Plains by means of a gravitation canal from the lake. But nothing more than experimental progress could be made until Kaiser was commissioned in 1963 to make a detailed survey of overall possibilities.

Kaiser's scheme was estimated to cost £128 million and to take 53 years to complete – though there was provision for an initial programme covering a 21-year period. This sounds ambitious, but during the next 25 years Ghana's population will have more than doubled from about 8 million to some 18 million, whilst that of the Accra Plains itself may well have increased five-fold to half a million. Although, within the terms of the country's development plan, considerable progress should be made towards meeting the growing demand for foodstuffs, the Accra Plains Scheme remains a vital factor in the national programme. It is certainly logical to plan the country's principal bread-basket as near to the capital as possible, when in

25-years' time the combined population of Tema and Accra is likely to be well over a million.

Kaiser had calculated that out of the 828,000 acres of the Accra Plains a little over half was suitable for irrigation purposes. Over this area the soils varied considerably; indeed it was calculated that a selection of twenty-five crop rotations was perfectly practicable. In this way the total anticipated demand for vegetables could be met and, within 25 years, virtually the full demand for citrus and other fruits. Sugar cane and rice would be prolific crops. There would be grazing pastures for livestock production, though not on a scale that would in any way parallel the country's major meat producing areas in the north. Sorghum, maize and cotton could also be grown, but again in second place to the principal producing areas elsewhere in the country.

Here, then, were all the constituents of a future Accra Plains Development Authority. It would buy its 2,000 million gallons of lake water a day from the Volta River Authority at an estimated cost of 25s per million gallons. This would flow through 429 miles of canal and 9 miles of pipeline from the lake at Akosombo to its far-flung irrigation channels and would be assisted by 11 pumping plants.

This is a far cry from the modest little experimental farm at Kpong. It might have remained so if the Government's industrialization plan, with its emphasis on industries that go hand in hand with agriculture, had not included a 24,000-ton a year sugar factory on the banks of the Volta at Assuchuari, about 10 miles downstream from Kpong – a project which meant planting 6,000 acres of sugar cane. The factory has been planned and built under the terms of an agreement with CEKOP, the Polish Government export group, Poland also supplying the agricultural experts who have given the project an impressive start.

Halcrows came in as the Government's consultants for this pilot irrigation project. And the well known Anglo-Italian contractors, Stirling-Astaldi, carried out the construction of irrigation channels, drains, roads and pumping stations. Thus Assuchuari, with its modern Doxiadis-planned township of neat houses, flats, shops and riverside hotel, during its growing stages appeared like a miniature Akosombo with its population of 22

Italians, 120 Poles, a handful of British and more than 2,000 Ghanaians.

Looking down now from the hill slopes on to the broad expanse of former marshland one sees for almost as far as the eye can follow the gently waving plantations of tall, green sugar cane. Immediately before you and beyond the now completed factory are the 250 acres of seed cane with which the plantation began. Away to the right are block after block of cane in every stage of growth from full maturity to mere seedlings. Further away still are tractors ploughing and levelling to complete the 1,500 acres of phase 1 plantation. Phase 2, with its balance of 6,250 acres for sugar cane and another 4,000 acres for rice (2,000 acres in rotation will always lie fallow) will extend over a further 3-year period.

The Poles have been experimenting with a great many varieties of cane – from Florida, from Barbados, from Cuba, from Guyana and from Australia. They have been very pleased with the yields which suggest that the reasonable target figure of 40 tons per acre may well be exceeded.

The first campaign of harvesting and processing into sugar 1,000 acres of cane took place by coincidence on February 24, 1966, the very day when, fifty miles away in Accra, the armed forces' coup was overthrowing the Nkrumah regime. How much sweeter the sugar must have tasted. It is a happy augury for the future that amongst the useful by-products of the sugar factory will be not only pulp for making paper, fuel for the steam turbines and rich black molasses, but also rum. Originally imported in exchange for slaves, it will now by an irony of fate mature on the banks of the very river from which so many thousands were sent into slavery for it.

The Assuchuari irrigation project, though the first, is not the only one to have been started. The Assuchuari scheme represents the centre 8 miles out of 24 being developed for irrigation on the south-west bank. Downstream a team of Japanese irrigation experts have been carrying out a pre-investment survey, and field trial experiments in rice, sugar cane, vegetable and fodder growing cover a further 25,000 acres. Upstream and extending several miles inland, the United Nations Development Programme, in association with FAO, were due to have moved in during 1966[1] to follow up an earlier survey with a full-scale irrigation project covering an area of 13,000 acres.

A physical start on the main scheme to irrigate the whole Accra Plains area was also to have been made early in 1966[2] when Kaiser Engineers were authorized to make the necessary preparations for irrigating the first 14,500 acres, on the plains immediately surrounding the Krobo Mountain. Here again sugar cane was to be the major crop with rice as a subsidiary. Appropriately, the scheme was to start on some of the farming lands of perhaps Ghana's most successful food crop farmers – the Krobos.

A very thorough study by computer had shown that in fact the most economic approach to the whole scheme – which includes a new major water supply channel to Greater Accra – was to go the whole way and construct the main 60-mile canal from Volta to Accra, rather than bow to the obvious temptation of starting near the river and extending southwards in stages. Clearly the advantages of growing food as near as possible to the principal markets must be the overriding economic factor. For all that, when the decision was taken a shortage of capital had led to the lesser of the two schemes being accepted.

It has been less easy even to plan similar projects on the opposite bank of the river due to the lack of good feeder roads. But a start was made by the Chinese (until their hurried departure after the coup) with a textile factory and mill at Juapong where locally grown cotton is being processed and woven into grey baft as raw material for the textile finishing and printing mills at Tema.

Further downstream, with the lake filled and the river flow at its steady 38,000 cusecs or more of water, the tendency towards excessive salinity above the estuary has been repulsed, and the process of extending the irrigation projects even further can be continued until it is ultimately possible to link them up with the long-term canal system.

This permanent irrigation of areas which have in the past yielded little more than subsistence crops on a basis of annual

[1] and [2] See Chapter 26. Following the 1966 coup these projects were deferred for two years for economic reasons.

post-flood plantings will be of particular benefit to the Tongus. There are five or six Tongu waterfront towns with populations varying between one and two thousand, and until comparatively recently none of them was served by a road (though now they all are) and depended entirely on the daily motor launch – one day southbound and the next day northbound – for communication with the outside world.

The villages are neat and tidily kept like most rural communities in Ghana. The houses, facing on to lanes or streets shaded with nim trees, are mostly of wattle and daub construction and follow the pattern a stage further with a thatched roof except where modern salesmanship has brought in corrugated zinc, asbestos or aluminium roofing sheets. Some of the larger houses form a hollow square enclosing an open courtyard or patio where the family attend to their daily chores – or relax with a bottle of home-made gin, as the case may be.

In the town centre, near the chief's house, there will be a particularly shady plaza furnished perhaps with fallen tree trunks, polished with age, which serve as benches for occasional gatherings. At the fringe of the town there will be one or more four- or five-classroom schools – perhaps of Methodist, Presbyterian or local authority origin – in a setting of well kept lawns, hedges and gardens where the boys in their khaki shirts and shorts and the girls in their yellow, blue or green tunics complete their primary schooling before going further afield for secondary or technical education. If the school does not also double as a place of worship there may be one or more churches, not large but well attended. And nowadays there may also be a local council office and associated workshops of more modern construction. On one or two days a week there will be a market and this is always a colourful affair, not only with the reds and greens and yellows of the tomatoes, vegetables and fruits but also with the dashing colours of the market mammies' clothes – only matched by those of the men when they dress up on Sunday or the day of a festival. Most of the menfolk will now be in their working dress – shorts and a shirt or possibly a hunter's smock of blue or beige homespun. Down by the river they will be mending their nets or perhaps making fish-traps or repairing their canoes.

The Tongus are, before anything else, fishermen, and on home ground, as against their immigrant settlements around the lake, they divide their fishing habits into three sorts: clam fishing, which is easily the most valuable, and mid-river and creek fishing.

The banks of the lower stretches of the Volta are cleft at irregular intervals by some four or five hundred creeks or channels which connect the river to lagoons or ponds lying a mile or two back from the river bank. In pre-Akosombo days the creeks and lagoons were dry or shallow for half the year during the dry season but were brim-full during the flood season at which time they teemed with fish of many varieties. All you had to do to catch the fish was to fix a net across the creek where it led into the river and when the river level dropped in October and November your nets were full. It may well be imagined that ownership of the creeks was jealously prized.

But while the lake was filling the creeks have obviously remained empty and this particular source of fish has, quite literally, dried up. Their future too is uncertain. With a steady river flow of 38,000 cusecs in the future some of the creeks and lagoons will certainly be inundated again, though not as fully as in bygone flood seasons. Others, with a little deepening perhaps, may also continue to be good fishing grounds. But undoubtedly creek fishing has had its hey-day.

A lot depends of course on the effect that the dam proves to have on the migratory habits of the fish themselves. If it transpires that some specimens have been in the habit of breeding upstream and then swimming south to the limit of the fresh water it may well be that they will now be limited to the lake and will gradually die out downstream of the dam. Others may well survive and even multiply in the steadier conditions of the new river.

This of course will also affect the second type of fishing – the mid-river fishing, where conventional seine and cast nets are used. But, of the three, it is the clam fishing industry which possibly has the least chance of survival in the new conditions. Locally known as 'oysters', they are in fact clams of the variety *Egeria radiata* about the size of a large chestnut. They breed in sandbanks along the thirty-five mile stretch of relatively shallow fresh water between the Kpong rapids and Tefle.

Curiously, the harvesting of the clams is exclusively a female occupation and is pursued for six or seven months a year whilst the river flow is relatively slight. Mostly the women dive from canoes into one or two fathoms of water and pick the clams out of the sand. But when the river is very low they stand in the water and pick the clams out of the sand with their toes. It is a fascinating sight to observe these groups of glistening black and shapely torsoes wriggling in the water as they lever the clams from their sandy beds. It was the practice that when the seasonal creek fishing was over and the river level had dropped, the Tongu menfolk would migrate north for several months on end to fish in the deeper river above the rapids, and this must in part explain the exclusive femininity of the clam industry. Some of the women actually laid out clam farms in the shallower water, where they planted small clams early in the season and left them to fatten by as much as 60 per cent before they were ready to re-harvest. Economists who have studied this industry in great detail, and particularly Rowena Lawson of the University of Ghana who in a sense 'discovered' it as a significant factor in the Tongu domestic economy, have estimated that it provides an annual income of more than £100,000 to some 2,000 full-time clam fishers. This is a considerable sum in the otherwise subsistence-level economy of most of the riverside people.

It is difficult yet to forecast what the future of the industry holds. In theory the regular flow of the Volta below the dam will in future be too great and too swift to permit the women to dive for clams as they have done in the past. But there will be plenty of submerged sandbanks, no doubt, where the clams can be harvested by the 'wriggling' method, and there may be room for expanding the clam farm technique in some of the creeks and lagoons, though large quantities of sand would first have to be moved. Here, as with the possible deepening of some of the creeks themselves, heavy earth-moving machinery would have to be used and any such artificial developments to the clam industry would cost money. Foreseeing this, the Preparatory Commission, which went to great pains to explore the possible effects of the dam on the downstream communities, made a strong recommendation for a sum of half a million pounds to be earmarked for such purposes, but at the reassessment stage this did not appear to have been followed up. While it is clear that the Government's policy of developing the Tongu and Accra Plains area by means of large-scale irrigation will generally raise the standards of the people living in that area, it would be regrettable if this valuable source both of personal income and of much needed protein was lost from the river.

Yet another industry which may be threatened is the Ada salt industry which has been one of the traditional mainstays of the river trade. The salt is obtained from the 20-square mile Songaw Lagoon, which in the past has been flooded annually when the river is high so that a large amount of salt water from the river estuary is left to evaporate during the dry season. Production can reach 10,000 tons of salt in a good year. In the absence of regular floods in the future other methods of introducing sea water into the lagoon will need to be considered.

But if the lower reaches of the river are looking for a permanent monument with which to symbolize their share of the Volta River Basin Development Scheme they need look no further than the magnificent new seventeen-span road bridge that was completed in 1966. Amongst other advantages, the bridge for the first time gives uninterrupted coastal road communication along the 360 miles that separate Accra and Lagos, through the intermediate countries of Togo and Dahomey. Long waits at the Tefle ferry have for years been a source of frustration and irritation on this main coastal highway. Planned to be both flood- and earthquake-proof the bridge has been designed and constructed by a West German joint industrial venture. Even if no one else on the Lower Volta had blessed the lake-filling period, when the river flow below the dam was negligible, at least fifty West German engineers and their Ghanaian colleagues were thankful. To have attempted to construct such a bridge facing flood conditions, or even facing the flow at its new mean average, would have been to have accepted a challenge very much in the true Impregilo spirit.

An aerial view of the 1983 Kpong Hydro-electric power plant on the Volta River

Nkrumah – Kaiser Rapport: ground breaking ceremony Tema's Valco plant

21

INSTALLATIONS

The principle of package deals, either from sterling or from dollar sources, with which to supply the equipment needed for the Volta Hydro-Electric Project had been rejected from the outset. It was only by means of cut-price competition on a worldwide scale that the scheme could be sure to be economic. The bidding had, by all standards, been brisk.

So from Asia was ordered nearly £1 million worth of turbines and governors, to be supplied by Hitachi Ltd of Japan; from two different parts of Europe were to come some of the principal steel products, £½ million worth of penstocks from Chicago Bridge Ltd of Britain and £¾ million worth of cranes, hoists and gates from Waagner-Biro of Austria; and the General Electric Company of Canada (CGE) manufactured more than £1¾ million worth of generators, transformers and other major electrical equipment. The destination of all these items, shipped from Yokohama, from Middlesbrough, from Hamburg and from the St Lawrence Seaway, was the seaport of Tema in Africa.

In addition a £5 million contract was awarded to Italy's Sadelmi to supply and install the eighteen 161 kilowatt electrical sub-stations throughout southern Ghana, and the £2½ million contract to link up the sub-stations to the Akosombo powerhouse with a 500-mile transmission system was won by Powerlines Ltd, another Italian company.

One of Kaiser's jobs, as designer and consultant, had been to co-ordinate the design and manufacture of these complicated components of the Akosombo jig-saw puzzle so that they would arrive in sequence and fit together to manufacture electricity.

The first necessity had been to find a headquarters more accessible and more central than were Kaiser's own headquarters at Oakland, California, and somewhere in Europe seemed to be the answer. London proved to have the greatest advantages, partly due to the ready pool of available engineering talent, partly owing to its advantages as a centre of communications (including regular non-stop flights to and from Accra), and partly because economical operating costs would provide real savings to the Project.

Kaiser had come to an arrangement with the London firm of Balfour, Beatty and Co. Ltd to use their premises, engineers, designers and draftsmen, working in conjunction with a team of Kaiser engineers from Oakland, as a Project design centre. Work started as soon as the first members of the US team arrived in mid-1961, and the first job was to issue all the supply and construction contract documents (other than the main dam contract, which was already awarded) and subsequently to receive and analyse the bids. Christmas 1961 saw the remaining contracts awarded and, with the formal start of work on the dam early in 1962, detailed design work then began in earnest.

Led by Al Chan, the Chief Design Engineer, the London office covered a vast amount of ground. Some 500 project drawings emerged from their drawing boards whilst 5,000 more, submitted by contractors and suppliers, had to be examined. Half a million pages of contract specifications and reports were printed, £6½ million worth of invoices reviewed, and if all the working papers, drawings and records could have been stacked in a single pile, they would have risen higher than the dam itself. The ultimate success of the Volta design office in London was recognized in 1965 when Kaiser Engineers, having completed their contract with Balfour Beatty, opened their own London branch office for Europe, Africa and the Middle East. Here they completed the final details of Akosombo engineering and, largely due to the challenge afforded by the Volta Project, established a base from which to continue their engineering services in the African and European continents.

The award of the contract for turbines and governors to the Tokyo firm of Hitachi Ltd was very significant for it included the world's four largest cast steel turbine runners – larger, at

90-tons each, than any other made either in or outside Japan. These are the wheels which are actually spun by the water falling through the penstocks, and they have to be so large – capable of delivering 176,000 horsepower each – because of the quantity and pressure of available water and the amount of electricity due to be generated. In Japan, and progressively abroad, Hitachi is a household word synonymous with refrigerators, transistor radios, television sets, computers. They are also one of the pioneers of the Japanese monorail system and their streamlined expresses now cover the 300 miles between Tokyo and Osaka in a matter of three hours and at speeds of up to 120 miles per hour. With more than fifty years of hydro-electric manufacturing experience behind them and with half of Japan's export market in this particular field in their hands, Hitachi were in no way dismayed by this new call on their skills.

Logically, the first items to go into production were those which the contractor on the site would need first, and a careful timetable of completion and shipping dates had been agreed. January 1, 1963 – a year after the contracts had been awarded – was the date for the first deliveries at Tema and these were the items that had to be embedded deep in the solid concrete monolith of the powerhouse foundations. Some surprises were inevitable. The first runner casting made in June 1963 (just, as it happens, as the great Volta flood was about to burst) was found to be faulty. Calmly and efficiently the second casting, which was up to standard, replaced the first and the time schedule was quickly restored.

By now the dockhands at Yokohama had grown accustomed to the large crates, cradles and bales stencilled 'Volta River Authority Akosombo via Tema' that were being regularly slung aboard the *Yamataka Maru* and other Africa-bound vessels. But one strange exception no doubt escaped their notice, for in April 1964 Hitachi consigned not to Tema, but to the Canadian inland port of Toronto, *en route* for General Electric's works at Peterborough, the first of four turbine shafts. For accuracy's sake, these had to be aligned in the Canadian workshop with their brother generator shafts prior to shipment on to Tema – a circuitous journey that lasted six months.

The contract for generators, transformers and other major

electrical equipment had in fact been awarded to the International General Electric Company of New York City who passed it on to their Canadian subsidiary in Peterborough, Ontario. Established in 1892 CGE was in the first instance a merger of the Canadian interests in the Edison Electric Light Company and of the Toronto Construction and Electrical Supply Company. Manufacturing everything electric from lighting bulbs to street cars, generators and electric railways – mostly under one roof – the company immediately prospered and expanded to its present-day total of 15 separate factories, the Peterborough works alone covering an area of 1½ million square feet on a 50-acre site.

At CGE the task of detailed design of the enormous generators was placed in the hands of Scandinavian-born Vaino Aare, Chief Design Engineer for hydro-electric generators. He and his team produced a final design in which the stator frame, manufactured in four sections for transportation and subsequent maintenance purposes, was to be 42 feet in diameter and wound with coils containing some 2·75 miles of copper wire. The rotor had been designed with a diameter of 34½ feet and the total weight of the rotating parts, including the shaft, was to be 360 tons.

Soon after manufacture had started the first two of the four steel shafts, each of 44-inch diameter, arrived by sea from England where the forgings had been made in Sheffield. Manufacture now proceeded apace, with generator foundation equipment being completed and shipped first, and all the complex phases of generator construction continuing simultaneously. One by one the generators were test-assembled and the components packed and shipped, including of course the Sheffield-made generator shafts with their Tokyo-made running partners.

A hundred and fifty miles away, on the other side of Toronto, another CGE factory at Guelph was manufacturing the 110-ton transformers that would step up the current from generating to transmission level. As these had to be shipped virtually complete they presented a special problem of transportation. This had been anticipated, however, even at the Preparatory Commission stage almost ten years earlier, and Ghana's Black Star Line had equipped itself with a vessel with a 120-ton derrick, which with suitable prior planning was able to fetch the transformers and other cargo from the St Lawrence Seaway at three-month intervals during 1964 and 1965.

Penstocks may not be spectacular compared with generators and turbines, but even so, at 24 feet in diameter by 360 feet in length, all six Akosombo penstocks could swallow a fleet of about ninety double-decker buses. This £½ million contract was awarded direct to Chicago Bridge Ltd of Wembley, Middlesex, thus making the company the only British supplier having a prime contract within the Project. In fact, as its name implies, it is a wholly owned subsidiary of the US firm of Chicago Bridge and Iron Company – one of the main penstock contractors in the world though today it no longer builds bridges.

This contract was really in two parts: the fabrication of the individual penstock sections at the Darlington workshops of Whessoe Ltd in the north of England and subsequently the welding of them into 15–20 foot long sections (weighing up to 50 tons each) on the site at Akosombo. They were much too large to be transported, even in sections. Chicago Bridge accordingly sent an experienced construction man to Akosombo to establish their base there and he, with his assistant, established a welding school on the spot to teach Ghanaians the techniques of welding the heavy steel plate. The results were excellent and when the quality of the welding was checked by 100 per cent X-ray of all seams the result showed that the standard was exceptionally high.

The first 400 tons of steel sections were shipped from Middlesbrough docks in July 1962 and were at Tema a month later, ready for the 50-mile haul to Akosombo. The entire operation had then been rounded off within a year and the welded sections handed over ready for installation – the first of the major supply contracts to be completed.

The last of the major supply contracts were those for cranes, and for gates and the rolling hatches that cover the generators, and both of these had gone to the Austrian firm of Waagner-Biro of Graz and Vienna. Landlocked as it is in its mountainous Carinthian setting Graz is in fact less than 150 miles from the sea at Trieste, but when the time came to ship the completed equipment to Ghana it was over the 1,000-mile rail-haul to

Hamburg, Bremen or Rotterdam that it had to go – such are the logistics of long-distance communications.

Waagner-Biro was founded a century ago, and like the other firms we have seen has an immense international programme covering almost every conceivable field of engineering and steel-work, from supplying complete theatres and television studios to bridges, chemical and nuclear plants and whole power stations. They have supplied equipment to twenty-six countries in all five continents for major projects such as Australia's Snowy Mountains scheme, India's 740-foot high Bhakra Dam, Egypt's Aswan power station and Thailand's Yanhee project.

Knowing that the Volta could bring down a phenomenal flood it was Waagner-Biro's responsibility to manufacture spillway gates that would not only contain the top 40 feet of the lake level but also spill the largest conceivable flood whenever this might occur. Waagner-Biro found that the very size and scale of the Volta operation made their work easier rather than more difficult. In Austria they are accustomed to the minute-by-minute variations of the Danube's rise and fall so that all gate-control equipment has to be capable of instant operation if dangerous waves and stranded vessels are to be avoided. The Volta however, though unpredictable, moves ponderously, and the lake, even during the most exceptional flood, is unlikely to rise by more than a foot a day even when all twelve gates are closed. Consequently there is no overnight danger and ample time to operate the spillway gates one at a time. For this reason there are only two mobile hoists, one each to operate six of the gates – and each of which, in the form of a railway coach running on railway lines, halts on the concrete decking above each gate in turn and raises it, like a medieval portcullis, with massive chains.

But without doubt the *pièce de résistance* of the Waagner-Biro contracts was the 450-ton gantry crane for servicing the power-house. The firm owns that it has built larger cranes and others with more complicated equipment but never before one with such an enormous load capacity, and at one stage it was to have been greater still until the generator designers found that they could modify the original size of the rotors. Nevertheless it remains one of the greatest capacity cranes in the world and is most impressive.

The power at Akosombo is generated at a strength of 14.4 kilovolts and is then, for purposes of national transmission, stepped up by the transformers to 161 kilovolts at which high-tension level it sings through its lilac-coloured aluminium conductor cable all round southern Ghana. At selected points, 18 in number, the high-tension electricity has to be reduced to manageable proportions and this accounts for the series of sub-stations that had to be designed, supplied, built and installed at key distribution points round the loop.

The supply and the installation contracts, together worth £5 million, had gone to the overseas division of a seven-member Italian consortium of electric generator manufacturers, GIE, who had the contracts jointly with Sadelmi. Generally speaking, the power carrying and steel tower equipment was being manufactured in northern Italy ready for shipment from Genoa, whilst the complicated communications and supervisory systems were taking shape in the Westinghouse factories in the USA and would be shipped via New York. The sub-stations themselves had been designed to be virtually unattended so that the role of the Westinghouse equipment was not only to relay back to the transmission system's nerve centre at the Volta sub-station at Tema a constant record of the fluctuating load at each sub-station by day and night and of the amount of incoming current, but also, by remote telecontrol, to close and trip circuits when necessary and perform other operational functions. All these vital impulses would be carried by high frequency signal over the main power lines themselves, together with a normal interconnecting telephone system for use as and when required. The whole installation together made a closely integrated transmission and control system automatically demanding and receiving from the power station the exact amount of current required at any hour of the day and night. At the same time a constant record of its circuit-wide activities is available to the duty-engineers and operators at the system's headquarters. Never before, it seems, has such a comprehensive plant been required to perform simultaneously so many varied functions over so wide an area.

Linking the Akosombo powerhouse to its eighteen distribution sub-stations, like some giant silver necklace set against the green forest of southern Ghana, is the 500-mile transmission line. This £2½ million contract had been awarded to Powerlines Ltd, which had already proved itself in many parts of Africa, including Kariba and, as SAE of Milan, the parent company, in many other parts of the world. This new Ghana contract was a useful addition to extensive jobs of a similar nature in Nigeria. Possibly this was why Powerlines were able to tender well below the other bidders and claim that, to all intents and purposes, they completed the job 'free of charge' – by which they mean, no doubt, with little if any margin for profit.

There seems to be little doubt that, of all the contracting jobs connected with the Project, that of the transmission lines was probably the most frustrating and exacting in terms of physical conditions. Their lines of communications often led far from existing motor roads into the heart of dense rain forest and across 2,000-foot mountain ranges into areas probably only penetrated previously by hunters. Here camps had to be established and, at least for the overseas staff, spaghetti and chianti rations constantly supplied to make life tolerable in otherwise trying conditions. Nor were the conditions trying for the Italians alone, for the Ghanaian workers suffered their share of malaria and other upsets from poor water supplies, and made it quite clear that there were certain places – sacred hilltops and other spirit-bound localities – where it was out of the question for them to remain after dark. Transport then became a further problem.

To show that they were not merely playing at being afraid of the dark one steel erector arrived at his construction site early one morning to find the headless body of a woman on the cleared fairway. Having as much presence of mind as physical strength he tucked the body under one arm and, grasping the dismembered head firmly in the other hand, he marched off to the nearest police-station to report his find. Possibly well aware of the ritual significance of the discovery, the arm of the law it seems 'went for bush' temporarily until the performance of necessary purification rites had made it safe for them to return to make the routine entries in the station log-book.

Somewhat surprisingly these pioneers, working in the heart of the forest, had few if any serious encounters with snakes, scorpions, bush pigs, leopards or any other dangerous animal.

Certainly during the forest-felling operations the noise of the fleet of D-8 Caterpillar tractors would have kept most of them at bay but it is remarkable that there was not more trouble from this quarter during the extensive surveying stages. At one camp however, where a pit latrine had been dug at the edge of the clearing, one early morning patron returned rapidly to base with the alarming news that the pit was seething with a family of snakes. The remedy was swift: a drum of petrol was poured into the pit and a lighted firebrand tossed in after it.

Progressively, then, the 500-mile long and 100-foot wide swath of cleared forest or grassland was prepared and excavators followed, digging the four 8-foot deep pits for the concrete foundations of each of the 2,150 steel towers. These had been designed and supplied to Powerlines by the parent company, SAE, who had carried out comprehensive tests on them by the entertaining process of erecting them at their test plant on the shores of lake Como and then deliberately destroying them, under the sharp eye of the Kaiser inspectors who declared themselves satisfied that all the required safety margins had been covered.

With the towers complete and the 104,000 Staffordshire porcelain insulators in position it only remained for the 2,000 miles of best Kaiser Aluminium cable to be strung, together with 1,000 miles of continuous lightening conductor. The whole system was then to be examined and tested prior to the great day in August 1965 when, starting with the test runs on the first generator, the cables could progressively be energized. During September the current was directed through Tema and Accra to the coastal towns and the mining areas round Tarkwa. At the same time it was directed north-west to Kumasi and the Ashanti Goldfields at Obuasi. Before Christmas the whole loop had been connected, so that there was now a continuous flow right round the system and the added safety margin of an alternative supply to each sub-station. Finally on January 19, 1966, four years to the day after the Powerlines contract had been signed, the final branch line over the 2,000-foot hills between Tafo and the diamond-mining town of Akwatia was completed and formally handed over.

The contract too was complete – and there were still three days to go before the formal inauguration celebrations at Akosombo.

22

VALCO

The Volta Aluminium Company[1] had started its life in November 1959 as a consortium of aluminium interests, brought together by Edgar Kaiser to explore the possibility of establishing a smelter in Ghana. In addition to the Kaiser Aluminum and Chemical Corporation there were also Alcan (who had a little earlier ceded to Kaiser the role of convener), Alcoa (the Aluminum Company of America), Olin Mathieson (the Rockefeller associated group) and Reynolds Metals (who had had Volta connections as far back as 1949 through Duncan Rose and Wafal).

Not all had stayed the course. Alcan first withdrew in 1960, having commitments enough as one of the world's two largest producers of aluminium. Alcoa too dropped out early in 1961, and later the same year Olin Mathieson, who had other interests further up the West African coast in Guinea, also withdrew. This left Kaiser and Reynolds as sole participants in Valco with respective interests of 90 per cent and 10 per cent. When the US loans for the Akosombo Dam Project were announced in December 1961, it was also made known that the US Government, through the Export-Import Bank, would loan £34½ million to Valco and, through the Agency for International Development (AID), would offer a guarantee of the Kaiser and Reynolds investment of £9½ million. This guarantee was protection against possible expropriation of the smelter and of certain other events which were strictly of a non-business risk

[1] Valco, though American owned, is registered as a company in Ghana which makes it the Volta Aluminium Company and not the Volta Aluminum Company as it would otherwise be.

nature. The Ghanaian Government had in fact given a written assurance that no expropriation of the £46 million smelter would take place but loans on this scale naturally have to be safeguarded against possible changes of government and changes of heart.

Against these hard-headed top-level safeguards which tend to present the partnership in its coldest light should be set the warm gesture of Edgar Kaiser who suggested the formation of an independent Special Fund into which an agreed part of Valco's profits will be paid each year to be used for educational and social projects in Ghana. The fund itself is administered by a board of directors appointed by the Volta River Authority.

Valco's agreements with the Ghanaian Government had embodied the standard concessions granted to new industries such as the tax holiday (which might extend for as long as ten years) and a declared limit to other forms of rates, duties and charges. For its part Valco guaranteed to buy, for a 30-year period, a round-the-clock supply of 300,000kw of Volta power (about half the four-generator output) at an annual cost of about £2½ million. This made it possible over this period for the whole estimated capital cost of the Project – £70 million – to be defrayed, less interest, from this source alone. There was to be an initial period of six years leading up to the full 300,000kw, April 1967 being the date scheduled for the smelter to start operation with an initial supply of some 100–200,000kw.

Valco's agreement with the Government also spelt out the arrangements made by the smelter both to import alumina powder and to export the processed aluminium ingot. This was to be the responsibility of the two parent companies, Kaiser and Reynolds, in proportion to their investment. Thus Kaiser would be responsible for supplying nine-tenths of the raw alumina and for disposing of that portion of the end-product with Reynolds handling the other one-tenth. Over the 30-year period this amounts to almost half a million tons of aluminium for Reynolds alone, worth at current rates some £100 million. Kaiser's turnover would be almost a billion.

These were the economics of the scheme. Though it did not at this stage permit the export of aluminium processed from local minerals it ensured that vast quantities of local power were, in a sense, being exported, for every ton of aluminium represents a little over £17 of electric power, equivalent to the export of more than £5,000 worth of current a day during the first phase of operation, and twice this amount when the smelter is in full production. It is now Ghana's aim, during the first ten years of operation, to invest or attract investment for the necessary £40 million required to process alumina from locally mined bauxite.

Valco's first task, as a newcomer to the newly established seaport of Tema, was to carve out for itself a carefully integrated complex stretching from its own private quay within Tema harbour to its adjacent storage area for alumina and materials and thence to its 450-acre site two miles north-east of the harbour area. Detailed planning for the smelter had started in fact almost as soon as the Valco Principles of Agreement had been signed in Accra in December 1959, and within a year by dint of a vast amount of detailed negotiation all the main decisions arising from the Agreement had been taken and a complicated measure of legal draftsmanship had placed everything on record.

One of Valco's obligations within the Master Agreement was to have the smelter ready for initial operation not later than the Permanent Delivery Date. This had been fixed for April 25, 1967, by which time a steady uninterrupted supply of current could be guaranteed. At the same time, if circumstances were ideal – and both politics and the current state of the aluminium market were clearly the main factors here – Valco was prepared to start building the smelter at a time referred to as 'power minus three', which meant 3 years before the first power was expected to be available, that is in September 1962. There was therefore a 4½-year period during which the smelter could be built, and as the construction period from ground levelling to actual production was estimated to be almost three years there was a comfortable latitude within which Valco could operate.

But a host of minor complications appeared to have been designed to keep the Valco executives, and many others, agitated. First it was discovered that the new transmission line, which would eventually serve the smelter, crossed the site for the new petroleum refinery from corner to corner. Then Valco noticed that the refinery's pipe lines both to and from the harbour were obstructing the site for their harbour quay. Next, the exact location of the smelter site and its access roads was found to conflict with the re-vamped master plan for Tema, so adjustments had to be made. And another road within the harbour area was about to cut right across the site leased to Valco for their enormous 100-foot high aluminium dome which was to be used to store the imported alumina powder. The exceptionally deep draught of the alumina-carrying vessels was going to necessitate deeper dredging of certain parts of the harbour. However with patience and goodwill the problems were gradually resolved; cables were realigned, pipe lines lowered, boundaries varied and roads re-sited and everything fitted into place.

It should not be thought that all the problems were Valco's. There was one that gave me a few anxious moments. Whilst doing some delving into the general sequence of events I came across a letter on one of the VRA's files which carried the words, 'I should be grateful if you would let me have the additional £150 now so as to enable the smelter to be erected'. As the letter was dated a little time before the smelter was due to be built I could not help asking myself why – in the face of their £46 million commitment – Valco should have been at a loss for the last £150. And then I realized. The letter, which was from the government contractors, apparently concerned something called an anemograph which is used for studying wind velocity, duration and direction, details of which were needed in respect of the smelter site. The structure needed to house the instrument was estimated to cost £550, only £400 of which had been made available. There was therefore some urgency for the balance of £150 – to enable the *shelter* to be erected.

Then, as has so often happened during the fluctuating history of the Project, a delicate situation arose which seemed to test the determination even of Edgar Kaiser. In November 1963 President Kennedy had been assassinated. Six weeks later an attempt was made on President Nkrumah's life. Five shots were fired at him outside his office, killing his aide-de-camp, but none of them harming him. A period of intense security shake-up followed when the top twelve police officials were dismissed and the whole security structure reviewed. Even before Kennedy's death an uneasy feeling had been created in Ghana that, quite distinct from the USA which most Ghanaians instinctively liked and respected, there was another less tangible USA whose aim, if it could be clearly seen at all, seemed to be to use its power secretly and underground in order to steer the politics of smaller nations in the 'right' direction. Ironically perhaps, credence had been given to this line of thought by a 50-cent paperback book written by a young American journalist, Andrew Tully, simply titled *C.I.A. – The Inside Story* – a bulk distribution of which had been made by Nkrumah's own office.

As the feeling intensified a series of ugly rumours started, linking Nkrumah's name with the death by pistol shot of one of the military guards at Christiansborg Castle where Nkrumah was then living. The swift assumption was that they had been deliberately spread by Americans in order to discredit the President, the state and the nation. On February 4th a noisy but non-violent organized demonstration of about 1,000 people converged on the United States Embassy armed with such slogans as 'Stop your filthy rumours' and the time-honoured 'Yankees go home'. An attempt was made to haul down 'Old Glory' from its flag-pole – but was prevented by a particularly resolute Afro-American embassy official.

Anti-American feeling – at a certain level closely associated with the party press – had never been more widely ventilated in Ghana and some of the newspapers made it their daily theme. The US Government made an official protest through the Ghanaian Embassy in Washington, making it clear that they believed the demonstrators were Government-inspired. The Ghanaian Government replied that it disassociated itself entirely from the demonstrations and deeply regretted the incidents.

Edgar Kaiser, with barely three years to go for completion of a £46 million smelter which had not even been started, was now faced with a delicate and difficult situation. On the one hand, the decision had already been taken committing Valco to buy over a 30-year period £70 million worth of Volta current, and without a smelter the current would have been valueless. On the other hand, he felt considerable concern regarding Valco's ability to perform its contracts in Ghana if the present relationship between the two countries continued.

True, however, to his dedicated approach to the Project

Edgar Kaiser flew into Ghana later in the month. His meetings with Nkrumah were warm and personal as always and he tried to believe that the President at least could see the matter in its proper perspective. But my own understanding at the time was that Nkrumah was, in spite of all his protestations, so personally involved in the campaign that it was impossible for him to have discussed the matter frankly.

Apart from politics there were two further complications that were worrying Kaiser. First of all Nkrumah was urging Valco to bring forward their production date for aluminium by at least a year. Secondly he was still pressing for the immediate production of alumina from Ghanaian bauxite. Concerning the first, the decision to start production early in 1967 was based on two factors – the need for an absolutely fault-free and continuous supply of electric power, and the estimated growth of the world aluminium market, which forecasts had indicated would only be favourable by that date. Furthermore, the very magnitude of the construction work involved precluded an earlier start. Kaiser felt strongly too about the proposed alumina plant – a vast additional investment – and went so far as to say, 'Under conditions which exist in Ghana today, I would not finance 10 cents and I simply do not know when conditions will allow the financing of an alumina plant.'

Before he left, Kaiser felt that somehow he must lay the ghost that America is no more than a vast structure of Big Business in which the individual is an anonymous cog, and that he must also convince Nkrumah that smelters are not built in a day and that alumina plants are themselves major undertakings. So he invited a party of influential politicians, industrialists, pressmen and economists from Ghana to visit the United States and to see for themselves not only the vastness of industrial ventures of this kind but also, by way of contrast, the extent to which American industry is made up of thousands of small industries giving free rein to individual enterprise, local skills and personal ambitions.

It seems improbable that the visit in itself could have gone very far towards softening anxiety about the activities of the CIA, but it did generate some necessary goodwill and a greater degree of understanding at a personal level. Writing to me soon after the visit Edgar Kaiser described it as having been 'constructive and worthwhile', whilst, as a solution to the broader problem, he offered as the formula 'constructive leadership and education, with a patient dedication'.

Whilst these developments were taking place, the political crisis was deepening. President Johnson had his own internal political problems to deal with, and therefore despatched that wise and experienced diplomat, Averell Harriman, to inform Nkrumah of the facts of international political life. It so happened – and not by chance – that Harriman and Sir Robert Jackson arrived in Accra from different parts of the world within twenty-four hours of each other. Fortunately for Ghana, they were old friends and were able to decide together how Nkrumah might best be informed of the explosive dangers that now lay in his path; probably at no other time was the Volta Project in greater danger of falling apart. Five separate meetings were held with Nkrumah. Jackson had the first, and afterwards admitted that in his long association with the President, he had never known a harder or more exhausting exchange. Mr Harriman followed, and in the succeeding days Nkrumah realized that his most cherished scheme was in danger of disintegrating. For an adequate period, at least, the Government of Ghana adopted a more responsible attitude in its relations with the United States, and this, the gravest of all crises associated with the Project, was averted.

And so by June of 1964 the rolling acreage two miles north-east of Tema, described as Parcel 5,[1] was in the hands of the heavy earth-moving contractors whose job it was to produce a wholly level site for the smelter. It was about this time that Valco was reminded from an unexpected quarter of the great potential for aluminium consumption in Ghana. As soon as

[1] Parcel 1 is the area of the harbour quay with its twin vacuum cleaner-like suction lifts which extract the alumina from the vessels' holds. Parcel 2 is for the conveyor belt which passes both alumina and coke from the quay to the storage area, as well as accommodating an access road. Parcel 3 contains the alumina storage dome and the coke storage bins. Parcel 4 is the two-mile private road (with overpasses and underpasses) connecting the storage area to the smelter site. Parcel 5 is the smelter site itself and Parcel 6 reserved for future extensions as, for example, an alumina plant. Parcel 7, down by the sea eastwards along the coast, would be for disposal of 'red mud' – the residue from the bauxite after alumina extraction. Parcel 8 is the line for an outfall to the sea.

Parcels 5 and 6 had been levelled they were enclosed with a two-mile long fence of aluminium poles carrying, provisionally, a few strands of wire. To Kaiser, aluminium poles are presumably like bush sticks to a Ghanaian farmer so they were generously spaced at intervals of every ten feet, clipped with their wire and then left for the time being. A while later a Kaiser engineer inspecting the site had the feeling that there was something 'not quite the same' about the fence. He quickly realized that the poles were now at least 20 feet apart and, looking closer, he saw that every other pole had been neatly sawn off at ground level. To anyone else it was still a very serviceable looking fence – but it was only half there. He saw however that the 'treatment' had so far only been given to one section of the fence and the matter was reported to the police.

Meanwhile in the town an observant Kaiser executive noticed in the market some low-priced aluminium saucepans and wondered how they could be marketed at such a figure. Ascertaining who was the supplier he followed the trail to a back-yard factory. On explaining that he was anxious to place quite a large order he was told by the enterprising manufacturer that this would be quite possible but that there would be a short delay as he was awaiting a new consignment of raw materials. A provisional deal was agreed and the Kaiser man, bursting with suspicion, confided in the police. The sad but inevitable ending to the story is that two nights later the embryo industrialist was caught in the act of taking delivery of his bargain-priced raw materials at the next section of the Valco fence.

With Parcel 5 flat, the stage was set for a dramatic little ground-breaking ceremony which Edgar Kaiser had fixed for December 5, 1964. He invited President Nkrumah to join him in cutting the first sod to mark the official start of work on the smelter. Kaiser, as the host, spoke first to the assembly. There were those, he said, who had predicted that 'we would never make it' and that 'we would founder on the rocks of distrust and misunderstanding'. But there are always problems and difficulties in any undertaking that is worth doing and in this particular instance they were solved 'because the people of Ghana were determined to find the solution to those problems'. In President Kennedy's words, he stressed that 'To those new states whom we welcome to the ranks of the free we pledge our word that one form of colonial control shall not have passed away merely to be replaced by a far more iron tyranny. We shall not always expect to find them supporting our view. But we shall always hope to find them strongly supporting their own freedom.' This pledge to help others to help themselves was made for one reason only: 'because it is right'.

Replying, President Nkrumah welcomed the smelter as the last of three inter-related schemes: first Tema Harbour, which had cost the Ghanaian Government £35 million; second the Akosombo dam and power station financed jointly by Ghana, Britain, the United States of America and the World Bank; and now the smelter, owned by American private enterprise with loans and guarantees from the US Government. 'This', he said, 'is an enterprise of international co-operation – a product in the direction of world peace.' He was anxious nonetheless that the remaining stage in aluminium production – that of extracting alumina from bauxite – should be developed in Ghana as early as possible, and announced that Kaiser Engineers had agreed to undertake a feasibility study along these lines. Taking the process a stage further still, he outlined plans for manufacturing a wide variety of aluminium products in Ghana with a view to supplying as large a section of the African market as possible.

Then saying how sorry he was that Henry J. Kaiser himself on his doctor's advice could not be present as he had wished, Nkrumah quoted some lines by Emerson that Henry Kaiser had appended to a photograph of himself and Edgar that they had given to him:

> What makes a nation's pillars high? . . .
> Not Gold, but only men can make
> A people great and strong.
> Men who for truth and honor's sake
> Stand fast and suffer long . . .
> They build a nation's pillars deep
> And lift them to the sky . . .

And Nkrumah had his own words with which to respond:

How inspiring
How significant
These words so profound
From an old American visionary
To a young African Revolutionary.
Such thoughts, so deep,
From him to me.

Aluminium, though the most abundant of all the metals in the earth's crust, is also in usage the newest. A little over a hundred years ago it was classed as a precious metal and was displayed at the Paris Exhibition of 1855 next to the crown jewels. Today its intrinsic value has reduced two thousand times to make it one of the most economical metals of all.

It took scientists a long time to discover the secret of releasing aluminium from its parent minerals; even so, the early chemical process was barely economic. It was not until just before the turn of the century that the electrolytic process was discovered, and with only a few modifications the technique remains unchanged to this day.

The whole process takes place in a large steel bath-tub known in the smelting business as a 'pot', after the earthenware pots in which early copper smelting was done. The pot is lined with carbon material. Inserted into the pot from above is a series of suspended carbon blocks. The bath is then made up from a mixture of chemicals and to this the alumina is added. Alumina, in fact, comprises half oxygen and half aluminium – so tightly locked together that it has taken man all his ingenuity and a vast amount of electric power to tear them apart. The electric power flows by direct current (DC) right through the pot-lines and enters each pot in turn, passes through the chemical bath and leaves it through the carbon lining. It is this 'electric shock' which separates the oxygen from the aluminium – the oxygen rising to the top and burning when it comes into contact with the carbon blocks, and then being discharged through pipes in the form of gas. The molten aluminium settles to the bottom of the bath and is syphoned off every twenty-four hours into crucibles and then moulded into ingots ready for export.

The process is a continuous one, operating twenty-four hours a day and seven days a week, for the business of starting up a pot is difficult, expensive and protracted. The vital importance of a continuous flow of current round the clock is self-evident, as is the importance of the careful timing of the smelter completion – to a date when all four Akosombo generators had been in commission for a year with little fear of a break in current. The amount of current consumed by each pot each day is a staggering figure, a fraction short of 18,000kw – which Valco's ever helpful publicity people have processed for non-technical comprehension as being sufficient to illuminate the average Accra household for 980 years.

Reduced to essentials, these are the ingredients of the Valco smelter – the largest in the world outside North America and probably the largest single factory in Africa. The main structures comprise the three 2,000-foot long pot-lines (space is reserved for a fourth) each of which contains 100 pots. In practice, however, each pot-line is constructed in two parallel halls 1,000-feet long – each containing 50 pots – so that the current runs up one line and returns down the other. An overhead crane traverses the length of each hall, capable of raising the 75-ton weight of each pot. The framework of each hall is constructed from steel; and each pair of halls is encased in some four acres of aluminium sheeting which has the effect of reflecting the sun's rays and leaving the building remarkably cool inside. The foundation and flooring of all the halls is of concrete – the cement being of Tema manufacture – and a total of 120,000 tons of concrete will have been used in the whole structure. Dominating the smelter halls and to the south of them is the 500-foot chimney stack which distributes the waste gas high into the atmosphere.

Even the most modern smelter – and the Tema smelter was designed on an even larger and more economical scale than the newest North American ones – would of course be a mere monument without skilled personnel. Perhaps one of Valco's most demanding tasks has been the creation from scratch of a versatile team of smelter operatives. The total payroll at the smelter during its first few years of operation is reckoned to be about 1,000 Ghanaians and 100 from overseas. Of these, about half work directly on production, a quarter on maintenance and a quarter on services, administration and engineering. The overseas staff are of course almost entirely old hands in the industry. They accept the appointment on the clear understanding that they are as much teachers as production men, so that in a sense the smelter in its early days is a kind of technical college, complete with instructors and earn-as-you-learn students.

John Lowe, the Valco man who has a special responsibility for training schemes, has explained that at first all training is on the job in order for each man to learn quickly how it is done and then settle down to a period of doing it. Later, as a second stage, he has a further opportunity of learning something of the principles that underlie it.

Insofar as the actual process of smelting is concerned three pilot reduction cells were complete and ready by December 1966 – four months before production was due to start – so that a nucleus of staff, under their overseas supervisors, could start their training.

There are also of course attractive openings for Ghanaian engineers, chemists, administrators and accountants at the professional level. At least ten young Ghanaian assistant engineers were employed from the outset, out of a total engineering force of about fifty. Others, with more mature experience in electrical, mechanical and civil engineering, join at a higher level.

The decision that the smelter should be at Tema rather than at Kpong has been an important factor in keeping the overhead costs of the smelter within reasonable bounds. Valco has had to build no living accommodation itself either for its overseas or for its local staff, as it would have been obliged to do at Kpong. Instead it has worked hand in hand with the Tema Development Corporation, assisting where necessary by pre-financing accommodation blocks to meet their requirements, within the framework of the development plan for the fast-growing community. Tema is planned to develop into some twenty separate communities of about 15,000 people each. Each community, of which six have now been completed, is a balanced combination of neighbourhoods catering in each case for a cross-section of the residents according to their income groups. Valco have accommodation in most of these categories, ranging from detached houses and flats to the smaller terrace houses – all within easy reach of the Valco Centre with its club house, shopping facilities, school, sports centre and swimming pool. Even so, with the speed at which demand for accommodation at Tema tends to outstrip supply, there are still many who, for some years at least, have to commute from Accra, sixteen miles away, either by rail or by the motorway, or by the old coastal road with its seaside dormitory towns in between.

23

POWER ON TIME

Let us return to Akosombo in mid-1964 as the dam rises even faster than the lake and as the £10 million worth of integral machinery converges in a crescendo on Tema from Yokohama, from Hamburg, from Middlesbrough and from the St Lawrence Seaway.

Handling this the contractor had a fleet of some of the world's largest road vehicles – including a 120-ton articulated low loader. This particular low-loader was able not only to discharge its own freight without the use of a crane but also to turn sharp corners in stages, a little at a time. This was particularly useful in delivering some of the electrical equipment to the seventeen transmission sub-stations scattered all over southern Ghana. The understandable boast is that over a two-year period some 20,000 tons of equipment were carried without a single mishap.

On the dam itself, work was as disciplined and as precise an operation as war. The enemy, now that the river was in bonds, was time. During this period there were in fact more people working at Akosombo than either before or afterwards. The combined force working at the dam site now totalled about 4,200, of whom 3,500 were Ghanaians and 700 were overseas employees – a ratio of 5 to 1 that did not vary appreciably throughout the contract.

One of the most satisfying features of the close association that existed between Ghanaians and non-Ghanaians throughout the Akosombo construction years was the real friendliness and the sincere personal contact that was the general rule rather than the exception. Ghanaians are perhaps the most welcoming and friendly people in the world. Hotels, clubs, night-spots and other common meeting grounds are a constant delight to nationals and visitors alike as centres of unselfconscious pleasure where everyone shares in Ghana's passion for music, dance and laughter. The Italians, to whom song and laughter come naturally, felt immediately at home with their Ghanaian counterparts and were soon on the sort of friendly terms that spring naturally from a feeling of mutual respect and the comparable experience of men away from their own homes. This was a new and heartening atmosphere for those who had come recently from Kariba where such relationships had just not been possible against the vastly different social background.

Not that life here was in any sense idyllic: Akosombo had its share of human conflict, including the usual petty quarrelling and rough and tumble that attends any construction camp. At first the Ghanaians resented the Italian *Porcodio* – a rather vigorous bit of blasphemy that may well have contained overtones of abuse. Then one day the story circulated that a fellow who was particularly free with the word had been brought before the contractor's joint negotiating committee to explain his habit. The negotiators were surprised to find that the offending word flowed freely in their presence and it was common knowledge that when the man appeared before the management itself he continued to say it without fear or favour. To everyone's satisfaction it was explained that in the particular valley or alp from which he originated this was an everyday word and probably one of the very few with which he was familiar. From then on everyone used it – Ghanaian and Italian alike.

The joint negotiating committee proved to be a very successful solution to what might otherwise have been a source of serious trouble. There had been a stoppage of work at Akosombo early on in the contract just at the time when Impregilo were feeling their way. Though it only lasted ten hours, it involved 1,000 men and repetitions of it could have had a very serious effect on the working schedules. The Minister of Labour paid an immediate visit to Akosombo and, by the evening shift, work had started again. Perhaps the terms of the settlement were more severe than the TUC officials had expected. Firmly but discreetly, it was made known that it was the Government's decision that henceforward union dues would not be collected at Akosombo and that union representation would be replaced by a form of Whitley Council or joint negotiating committee on which both Impregilo management and representatives of the Ghanaian workers would serve. Impregilo appointed their popular Ghanaian personnel manager, Joe Nutsugah, as chairman and from that day until the job was completed some four years later the committee handled, with the minimum of dissatisfaction the thousand and one personal problems that were brought before it.

A notice outside the Impregilo office at Akosombo read as follows: 'From the beginning of this project until now[1] we have lost 20816 working days from accidents. Our last lost time accident occurred 1 day (s) ago. The best previous record was 9 day(s) without lost time accident. Help to improve upon it.' The figures, of course, are changeable. Akosombo's record in this particular field however is good, at least where serious accidents are concerned. Minor accidents inevitably accompany the moving about of a vast quantity of rock. Consequently there were innumerable skinned shins and bruised fingers and toes and, from a study of the evidence, a number of wishful contusions as well. The record of serious and fatal accidents however was for the greater part of the contract 65 per cent lower than the average figures for a 6-year period published for similar dams in the United States. All fatalities at Akosombo, prior to February 15, 1966, were Ghanaian, though one Italian had a permanent disablement. Most of them involved, almost inevitably, heavy machinery of one sort or another. It was a shattering blow when, a few weeks before the end of the contract, the death toll was almost doubled in one day in an explosion that killed ten Ghanaians and two Italians. (See Chapter 25)

Gradually now, through 1964, the dam rose from its eastern foundations at mean sea level to its crest 290 feet above. On December 4th, feast of Santa Barbara, when Italian contractors honour their patron saint, a moving open air service was held on the crest of the dam, which was now almost complete. A simple

[1] November 1965.

high altar and crucifix had been raised on a wooden superstructure crowning a huge yellow Caterpillar scraper. And at this altar mass was being celebrated, before a congregation of a thousand or so, by Impregilo's Father don Betta.

It was appropriate that at this ceremony a machine should have had pride of place. The mighty Haulpaks, the Le Tourneau-Westinghouse dumpers, 40 of which were used to build the dam, are undoubtedly the most remarkable vehicles of their kind today. Weighing over 60 tons when laden they have power-assisted steering and the turning circle of a London taxi. They are equipped with air cushioned suspension which makes the loading of a 10-ton boulder, for example, relatively shock-free, and after that they can move along at an easy 40 miles per hour. At £18,000 each with six 5-foot tyres that cost £117 each and have a round-the-clock life of less than a month, they are not cheap, but the Akosombo Haulpak that tumbled more than 200 feet down the forward slopes of the dam, virtually from top to bottom, and was back in use a few days later (complete with driver who had jumped clear) after only superficial workshop repair, gives some indication of their amazing strength and durability. During the critical days of 1964 when the dam was fast rising ahead of the lake each Haulpak was completing more than 100 trips every 24 hours so that between them they were carrying and placing something like 80,000 tons of material each day, equivalent to the total weight of the *Queen Elizabeth* every 24 hours.

Thus the dam itself was completed, not smooth and white like a concrete dam, but neatly stepped into five terraces of sloped boulders of vast dimensions and from a distance having a grey rough-textured appearance like a plain homespun worsted. On February 8, 1965 before an invited audience which included some of the leading Impregilo backers, Giuseppe Lodigiani and Mario Baldassarrini presided over the final tipping into place of the last load of rock completing the crest of the dam.

Now it was the steel and concrete structures on either wing of the dam that were absorbing the fast arriving equipment. Impregilo had sub-contracted the whole of the electro-mechanical installation of the powerhouse, penstocks, intake structure and spillway to a firm of international specialists in this field –

the South American-Italian Sade-Sadelmi Organization operating for this contract under its Italian name, Sadelmi. This was the same firm that had successfully tendered for the £5 million contract for supplying and installing the eighteen transmission line sub-stations.

Sadelmi's first task on arrival at Akosombo early in 1963 had been to tie in with Impregilo's complex operations all those mechanical bits and pieces that had to be embedded in first stage concreting. That done they set to work erecting their £64,000 derrick, one of the world's largest with a 360-foot mast and 215-foot boom, designed to lift into position the 50-ton penstock sections. This task is usually performed in a less spectacular fashion by the lowering of the sections one by one to their positions. Here, however, this was impossible for physical reasons and the derrick was the only practicable solution.

In appearance the six penstocks were not in fact identical; the two centre ones had been designed to draw in the lake water 20 feet lower than the others which had the effect of making them somewhat shorter at the top. This had been in origin not so much a technical as an economic decision. As far back as 1960 when the long drawn out power rate and loan repayments formulae were being calculated, it had been realized that if some initial power could be generated in 1965, instead of having to wait for the fuller lake level in 1966, there would be some extra revenue that would help to keep costs down. This modification had then been incorporated in the main design. Generators 3 and 4 – the two centre ones – would therefore be the first to be commissioned.

The powerhouse that Kaiser had designed for Akosombo was as simple and functional as the 1956 model was to have been artistic and impressive. Part of the reassessment economy plan had been to cut out frills; an open-air powerhouse was part of the answer. Such powerhouses are now considered to be standard practice in warm and temperate climates where frost, snow and ice are not elements to be reckoned with.

Not dissimilar to the deck of a ship the powerhouse deck has six movable hatch covers, mounted on rails, which can be rolled aside one at a time when direct access from above is required to a particular generator. Each of these is housed, again like a ship, in its own 44 × 44-foot hold. The Waagner-Biro gantry crane, moving on rails astride the holds, has access to each generator as required. Beyond each hatch is a 110-ton transformer which steps up the current from the generator to the adjacent switch yard. The powerhouse's equivalent to the ship's bridge is the central control room where remarkably few panels of dials, knobs and recording graphs control and co-ordinate the whole operation under the expert hand of a roster of key operations men.

In March 1964, from some 20 feet below eventual water level, Sadelmi started the installation of what was to be the first completed generator assembly (No. 3). First to be inserted is the steel tube which serves the purpose of directing the flow of water downwards from the turbine and then inclines it upwards away into the tailrace. More concrete then follows supporting the circular steel scroll case which, like an enormous seashell, actually circulates the flow of water around the turbine. And the scroll case is constructed around a ring of steel vanes which direct the water inwards against the turbine itself. A great deal of welding is involved in all these operations as the 42 sections of the scroll case have all to be welded together in position.

Now the powerhouse itself took shape, as the front buttresses rose and the concrete decking was laid, and soon the first of the rolling hatches was fitted – which was a blessing to the Sadelmi assembly crew who, with an inconvenient number of days lost due to heavy rain, had no love for open-air powerhouses. More concreting and grouting was now necessary in order to embed the whole scroll case assembly into a solid concrete block and all steel work had to be sand blasted and given three coats of vinyl paint. Then the complicated hydraulic system of wicket gates, which automatically control the flow of water from the scroll case into the turbine according to the amount of power that is needed, was fitted and finally on February 15, 1965 the 90-ton turbine runner was lowered carefully into place.

Throughout this operation Sadelmi had been working in close contact with the Hitachi erection engineers and to all intents and purposes the hydraulic part of the installation of this particular plant was now complete. It was now the turn of the electrical people to continue the job and here the Canadian General Electric liaison engineer took over. Already the turbine shaft had been thoroughly aligned with the generator shaft on its way from Japan via Canada so that their final coupling up one above the other at Akosombo in April 1965 was easy. Meanwhile the CGE winders were in and hard at work winding the connections of the four stator segments, whilst the 350-ton rotor was already assembled and stored on one side ready for installation early in May. June and July passed with all the complicated ancillary equipment being fixed and tested so that on that day early in August when the waters of Lake Volta were lapping at the steel gates in the intake channel at the upper end of the penstocks everything was ready.

Simultaneous to work on the powerhouse a parallel operation had been in progress at the upper end of the penstocks. Here a miniature gantry crane that sat on the top of the concrete tower, crowning the intake structure like a small tiara, had successfully installed the mechanism that controls the flow from above. And down in the deep dry cavity from which the powerhouse had risen there was now a massive torrent of water as the solid rock wall that separated the cavity from the river itself was blasted by the biggest single explosion at Akosombo – some 13 tons of gelignite. Quickly the river found its own level as the lower portions of the powerhouse were engulfed for ever.

But the powerhouse tailrace – as it had now become – was not destined to be a backwater for long, for with the debris from the explosion cleared and the stage now set for No 3 generator to be tested the water would shortly be flowing through the first of the turbines. For is there not somewhere in September 1965, a Very Important Date that has to be kept?

It was, quite by chance, on the day that Arthur Bottomley, then Britain's Commonwealth Relations Minister, visited Akosombo that the first of the penstocks was to be filled from the lake. This was the last step to be taken before the turbine itself could turn in the first of many generator tests. At long last the carefully stored water of the great lake was to tumble down to the portals of the waiting powerhouse.

As a layman, I marvelled to see the precision with which this engineering exercise – only one of many comparable events – was carried through. Nothing was being left to chance; all the digested experience of hundreds such earlier exercises was now tabulated in pages of typescript giving a minute-by-minute brief of what had to be done. Geoff Dixon, Kaiser's final phase Resident Manager, had taken me up to the concrete decking of the intake structure where the first of the twin steel sluices was shortly to be raised. There were engineers everywhere. One, like a prompter in the wings of a theatre, held a clip-board in his hand on which he marked off the decreed stages one at a time, at the same time checking, over a walkie-talkie, that the other end of the exercise had also been carried through in the powerhouse, at the receiving end of the penstocks far below. The loudspeaker crackled with voices from time to time like radio commentators at a sporting event.

Now came the moment for the gantry crane to raise, by only two inches, the first of the steel sluices, known as the safety gate. Peering down the 80 feet from where we stood to the intake channel we saw the water move fractionally as it slid through the gate below.

There was more checking off on the clip-board and more crackling over the radio as the exercise progressed. Down in the turbine and generator area there had been an extremely thorough clean-up. Every precaution had been taken to ensure that absolutely nothing had been left lying around, no proverbial spanner in the works, that could conceivably prejudice a successful start.

The suspense and excitement was intense as the time arrived for the penstock gate to be opened. The electrical mechanism for raising this is permanently housed in an aluminium control unit sited immediately above the gate. A large dial-like clock shows exactly how high the gate has lifted. It was 11.22 a.m. exactly when the signal was made for the gate to be opened. An engineer turned a knob and immediately the dial showed that the gate had been raised exactly five inches.

Through an adjacent trap-door in the decking a group of engineers and workers watched the gate rise and at once there followed a rush and a roar as the water surged forward to fall the full 320 feet and into the scroll case at the bottom of the penstock where the system of wicket gates checked it from entering the turbine itself. As we leant forward we could see the water flecked with white as it cascaded past 80 feet below. Waves of hot air were forced upwards from the concrete shaft reminiscent for all the world of the smell of a rather stale Turkish Bath. It took exactly 18 minutes for the penstock to fill. Once it was certain that there were no serious leaks, there followed with the same precision several days of turbine and generator testing and heat runs, when the generator is run but without generating current so that the effect is to dry out the whole giant assembly ready for the real thing.

The real thing came without ceremony on August 27th when, four days ahead of schedule, the first commercial Volta power was fed into the system. Three weeks later, on Friday September 17th, a modest symbolic ceremony took place, so quietly that few knew in advance that it was going to happen. Bearing in mind that September 1965 had now in fact arrived and that, true to the forecasts of five years before and in the face of heavy odds, Volta Power was a reality, many people had expected an important 'switching-on' ceremony with flags, bunting and brass bands. But President Nkrumah had decided that January 22, 1966 – the fourth anniversary of the signing of the Master Agreement and the eve of the official start of work – was to be the formal opening ceremony and that the switching-on was to be almost a family affair between the owner, the engineer and the contractor – and so it happened.

Just two or three dozen people were present when President Nkrumah was greeted outside the powerhouse control room by Nana Kwafo Akoto II, the Omanhene of Akwamu, who poured a solemn libation in which he asked for the blessings of the ancestral spirits on the great power that was now to be unleashed. Frank Dobson, the chief executive, then led his chairman into the brightly lit control centre and in a few impromptu words began the ceremony.

Canadian operations chief, Al Perttula, then stepped forward and showed Nkrumah which knob he had to turn in order to open the sluice gate and set the turbine in motion. Like a good pupil, the President asked with great concentration to be shown once again exactly what to do.

Then slowly he turned the knob from left to right and deep below us we heard and felt the low thunder of the water as it raced through the turbine and then down and out into the tailrace beyond. Someone murmured, 'I think with a little practice we could make a really good Ops man out of him,' and then there were smiles of satisfaction and, without further words, a feeling that something good had been accomplished.

Dials now showed us that 161 kilovolts of Akosombo current were surging down the cables to supply all the needs of Tema and Accra. Within days this would be extended right round the 500-mile grid to take in Takoradi and Kumasi, the heavy power-consuming gold mines at Tarkwa and Obuasi, and all the intermediate stations.

24

INAUGURATION

With the first turbine in motion before September 1965 and the current surging through the cables, the principal target of the Project had in a sense been achieved, although there were still three more generators to be commissioned and a vast amount of tidying-up to be done before ever the whole contract could be declared closed. It was now known that everything was so well in hand that the main contract, not due for completion until the end of August 1966, would in fact be fully wound up three months earlier. It was therefore decided that the celebration to mark the inauguration of the project would be held on the fourth anniversary of the formal start of work, Sunday January 23, 1966. But there was a snag: in Ghana libations, without which no ceremony is customarily sanctified, are not in these days of Christian sensitivity poured on a Sunday. The difficulty was quickly resolved. Saturday being January 22 was selected as an equally appropriate day, being the fourth anniversary of the signing of the Master Agreement. Now Akosombo, the construction camp, had to prepare for the transformation scene and justify its new role as Akosombo, the tourist centre. Dust roads had to be surfaced and tarred, scrap heaps removed, ceremonial sites levelled and prepared, paint work double and treble coated and the whole area dressed for the parade.

But there were still a few technical problems to be overcome. Undoubtedly the trickiest of these was the 'plugging' of the diversion tunnel which, now that the first turbine was discharging water into the tailrace, was scheduled for closure. The gate mechanism for the tunnel had been specially designed so that after the principal inlets had been closed in May 1964 for lake-filling, three smaller hydraulically operated gates would continue to regulate the amount of water flowing through the tunnel. Now that the time had come to close these gates it seemed that something was blocking at least one of them, as a large quantity of water was still flowing through the tunnel. The only practicable solution now lay in the familiar method of dumping large quantities of rock and impervious material over the entrance to the tunnel, which was now, on account of the rise of the lake, some 200 feet below the surface. This was partially effective and the flow was considerably reduced. This made it possible – after the exit of the tunnel had been cofferdammed – for the tunnel to be partially emptied and for a small band of courageous divers to work their way up the tunnel to inspect the gate mechanism and report back on their findings. Amongst their finds were the skulls and skeletons of the two migrant manatees – which caused a sensation at first when they were thought to be human remains. But the principal surprise was the discovery that all three of the hydraulic gates were, in fact, firmly closed. What had happened was that the sheer power of the water had torn up some of the reinforced concrete around the entrance to the tunnel and had forced a by-pass beneath one of the gates. The gap was large enough in fact for one of the divers to pass right beneath the sill of the gate.

Once again contractor, engineer and consultants put their heads together. They agreed that it would be virtually impossible to repair the damage so as to render the tunnel gates totally waterproof. The solution, then, was to reduce the flow even further, and to pass the relatively small remaining flow of water in pipes through the concrete plug itself whilst it was being constructed. This cylindrical plug, about 30-feet long, was sited about half-way down the tunnel at the axis of the dam, and was to be cast in concrete and keyed into the walls of the tunnel. It was itself a major engineering challenge with the continuing flow of water, though reduced, still amounting to over 10 million gallons a day.

The busiest time of all, however, was in the powerhouse, where generators 1, 2 and 4 were nearing completion in rapid succession. And before the contractors left it they had one final item to install: what can only be described as the world's biggest fish kettle, designed to boil the waters of the river. This extraordinary piece of equipment – an outsize rheostat – hung suspended from the front of the powerhouse into the waters of the tailrace. Its purpose was to consume enough extra current to give at least one generator at a time an adequate load for testing purposes. Even with the lake not yet full, and with a consequently reduced head of water, each generator was capable of producing 100,000kw or more, while the maximum demand from the grid was initially no more than 75,000kw and this would not appreciably increase until April 1967 when the smelter would go into action. Hence the need for the 100,000kw kettle.

On January 22, 1966 all roads in southern Ghana seemed to lead to Akosombo; all morning and afternoon the coaches, mammy lorries, tro-tros (light buses), taxis, private cars, cyclists and pedestrians continued to converge on 'Electri-City', as Akosombo was descriptively called that day.

At a ceremony held during the morning, the Paramount Chief, Nana Kwafo Akoto, Omanhene of Akwamu, presided over a short ceremony of purification and consecration when the ancestral spirits were called upon to give their blessings on the now completed Project. Two young steers were duly sacrificed and the necessary libations poured, appropriately enough, in Ghanaian gin.

Invitations to the ceremony had been sent all over the world to many of the people who had played their part in bringing the Project into reality. One element in the success of the scheme was *Nana Osu* – which could be freely translated into English as Old Man Rain. He came rolling off the lake in the middle of the morning and showered his blessings over Akosombo and the neighbourhood for an hour or so, reminding them that everything depended on his own contribution, then departing to leave the place pleasantly cool and overcast for the afternoon gathering.

A handsome dais, hung with red and gold, occupied the centre of the ceremonial ground. To right and left of it long, deep pavilions, draped coolly with canvas and bunting, provided seating accommodation for the 3,000 guests from home and overseas.

From the ceremonial ground there was an exciting panorama

of the whole dam and power station complex. Dominating all else was the grey rough-cast dam itself – a mere 300 yards across the river and towering more than two hundred feet above the heads of the visitors. Away to the right and in the distance was the saddle dam retaining the eastern arm of the lake. Much closer and more massive to the eye was the one visible spillway with its broad surface of solid concrete. To the left of the dam and rising from the tailrace was the powerhouse, now to be seen for the first time in its colourful combination of contrasting shades: the six penstocks a rich red against the light grey of the upper and lower concrete structure and the two gantries standing out vividly in buttercup yellow.

Many guests, anticipating the crush of traffic, had arrived in the middle of the afternoon and had ample time for social exchange before the ceremony which was due to start at 5 p.m. Pope Paul, who had consecrated Akosombo's chapel of Santa Barbara three and a half years earlier, had sent, as his special nuncio, Archbishop Luigi Bellotti. Sir Robert Jackson was there, of course, though disappointingly without Barbara Ward Jackson, who was committed to an inescapable engagement in the United States. From the early days of Halcrows' Volta Basin Survey and site investigations came Peter Scott, still a regular visitor in connection with other Halcrow commitments at Tema harbour and elsewhere. Sir John Howard too was present – the builder of Tema harbour and of the early access roads to Akosombo. Most of the Preparatory Commission's consultants too had been invited and Professor George MacDonald, Dr Worthington and Mr S. Ratnam were present in person. One felt that this was the occasion for them to walk on to the stage in turn and bow to the audience in a grand finale. Representing Ashanti Goldfields, one of the VRA's principal customers for power, was its Chairman, Major-General Sir Edward Spears. Sadly, no representative of the British Government was present, a consequence of the temporary break in diplomatic relations arising from the disagreement over Rhodesia, but present as invited guests were Roy Lewis of *The Times*, Angus McDermot of the BBC and David Williams of the weekly magazine *West Africa*.

The United States Government was represented by its newly

appointed ambassador, Franklin Williams; and also present in their private capacities were two former US ambassadors, Bill Mahoney and Wilson Flake. Needless to say, the Kaiser team came in strength led, of course, by Edgar Kaiser himself and his wife, and supported by Chad Calhoun, Ralph Knight, Louis Oppenheim, Ray Ware, Al Chan, Burt Janes, George Gerdes, Earl Peacock, George Scheer, Warren Schumann, Geoff Dixon, Rob Milton, Mel Alter, Dick Davis, Hal Babbit, Ira May, Dan Duffy – and their wives, none of whom would have missed the occasion for all the bauxite in Ghana. Reynolds Metals were represented by the president of its Mining Corporation, Walter Rice.

The Italian Government deputed Signor G. Lupis, Under-Secretary for Foreign Affairs, as its official representative. Impregilo sent heads of its component parts – Francesco Pennacchioni (Imp-), Giuseppe Recchi (-re-), Cesare Girola (-gi-) and Giuseppe Lodigiani (-lo). Mario Baldassarrini was of course present. Also from Impregilo were Moresco, Cassano, Leto and Danubio – names that will never be forgotten by those who worked at Akosombo. Sadelmi sent a team of directors, and so did Powerlines and Rodio. Each of the major suppliers was represented too – Hitachi, International General Electric, Chicago Bridge and Waagner-Biro.

A *sine qua non* of the Project was its bankers: Governor of the Bank of Ghana, Albert Adomako, came with one of his predecessors, Mr H. Kessels of the Deutsche Bundesbank of Frankfurt. The World Bank was represented by Lester Nurick and John Lithgow, the Moscow Narodny Bank by its London Manager, Mr C. D. Dicks and the Union Bank of Switzerland by Dr A. Hartman.

On the dais was Nana Kwafo Akoto, the Akwamu Paramount Chief and hereditary landlord of Akosombo. Otumfuor, Nana Sir Osei Agyeman Prempeh II, the Asantehene and Ghana's greatest traditional ruler, was amongst the invited guests and so were a colourful array of paramount and lesser chiefs from far and wide, together with Cabinet Ministers, Party luminaries, Members of Parliament, members of the diplomatic corps, High Court judges and hundreds of others from the professions, the business world, the churches and the public. And for everyone in the enclosure there must have been a hundred outside – ranged in vast banks on a series of terraces carved into the natural amphitheatre that backed up behind the enclosure.

Exactly on time there was a whirring overhead and President Nkrumah's personal helicopter broke through the low cloud. Immediately there was order for the first time that afternoon. It had exactly the atmosphere of a great Ghanaian gathering of chiefs, when drums are throbbing, enormous multi-coloured umbrellas twirling and bobbing, horns wailing and hundreds of people milling about – and, suddenly, there is a great silence, and everyone melts into traditional place in a huge hollow semicircle and the ceremony begins.

On arrival from the east-bank heliport via the road traversing the crest of the dam, President Nkrumah and his Egyptian-born wife, Madam Fathia Nkrumah, were received at the dais. A little Italian girl, Ida Milli, on behalf of the Italian community, presented Madam Fathia with a superb bouquet of orchids flown in specially by Alitalia from Rome.

Master-of-ceremonies was Kojo Botsio, then Chairman of Ghana's State Planning Commission, Senior Minister and Nkrumah's close lieutenant from 1948 onwards.

Dr Lodigiani spoke first, making the point that public and private enterprise, when blended together in harmony as they had been at Akosombo, could provide 'an example from which many other initiatives on this continent could and should draw inspiration'. As befitting the contractor he furnished some impressive figures. £4 million worth of equipment and plant had been used on the contract and the 5,000 peak labour force had worked more than 35 million man-hours. Indeed Dr Lodigiani's closing appreciation was to the Ghanaian people at all levels. 'They leave us with the memory of an amazingly warm and happy human relationship throughout our work in Ghana.'

Then Archbishop Bellotti delivered the Papal message. Conveying the cordial greetings of Pope Paul, the Nuncio recalled that 'the Holy Father had the pleasure of visiting the dam when work had recently commenced and rejoices on its successful completion'. In a personal message to the President, His Holiness added, 'We pray that it may bring many advantages to the citizens of Ghana, and contribute to the progress and welfare of the Nation.'

Before Edgar Kaiser spoke he unfolded a telegram addressed to President Nkrumah by his father, Henry J. Kaiser, expressing the old man's regret that he could not be present in person at the dedication ceremonies 'to share the pride of the accomplishment'. Kaiser made the theme of his address the quality of faith which had been the foundation stone from which the whole Project had risen. 'Faith', he said, 'never fails. It's a miracle worker.' He stressed the co-operation among men and nations that had been a feature of the Project, likening these men and nations to the tributaries of a deep river of hope which had flowed throughout this effort. And he quoted a few words written in chalk by a Ghanaian schoolboy on a village blackboard to point the moral, 'If hopes are not, our lives would break.' Addressing the people of Ghana he told them how, in building a better land, they were doing so both for themselves and also for the new generations symbolized by the schoolboy who wrote on the blackboard. 'You are his hope', he said, 'for a better future of opportunity and abundance.'

It was beginning to get dark when President Nkrumah rose to speak. The dais was the focus of attention as the powerful arc-lamps of the film cameramen bathed it in concentrated light. Having welcomed the Papal Nuncio and all the other guests President Nkrumah had a particular word for one invited guest who had not been able to attend: Mrs Jacqueline Kennedy. It is very likely that, for personal reasons, she would have chosen to accept the invitation extended to her to unveil a plaque commemorating the part played by her late husband and by President Eisenhower in the Volta River Project. At the same time there were inarguable political reasons why it would have embarrassed the US Government gravely if she had done so, and she had been obliged to decline the invitation.

Understandably the next to be mentioned were the two Kaisers – father and son. 'Edgar', Nkrumah had said, 'provided the spark that brought the Project to life when the prospects for its continuation were at their lowest ebb.' And the part played by Chad Calhoun, as the Kaiser-Nkrumah go-between, could also not pass without special mention. Then recalling the early days of US participation before the momentum had caught on, Nkrumah told a favourite story of Eisenhower who, not quite sure on the spur of the moment why no actual decisions had been reached, muttered to an aide, 'Then why don't you get on with the damned thing?' And so it had come about that 'the damned thing' was triggered into life.

The Times rightly described the day as 'very much an American-Ghanaian occasion'. As if to explain this strange love-hate relationship Nkrumah said, 'We live in a world of contradictions [which] somehow keep the world going.' Only a few months previously he had published a book under the title *Neo-colonialism* in which he had set out to show that the West's interest in Africa was excessively one-sided and rapacious. 'Hands off Africa' was his warning. The US Government was so incensed by some of the references that it lodged a formal protest through diplomatic channels but later agreed to let the matter drop after a soothing personal letter from Nkrumah to President Johnson. But the concentrated strength of the accusations clearly still rankled and it was generally believed that they, more than anything else, accounted for Mrs Kennedy's absence.

Nkrumah explained that 'a small but very dynamic independent African State' like Ghana 'must attain control of our own economic and political destinies' if higher living standards are to be obtained and 'the legacies and hazards of a colonial past and the encroachments of neo-colonialism' banished. At the same time he conceded that in a world such as this 'we certainly need great friends' and he went on to acknowledge that the United States – 'the leading capitalist power in the world' – is 'like Britain in the hey day of its imperial power . . . and rightly so, adopting a conception of dual mandate in its relations with the developing world'. He added that 'this dual mandate, *if properly applied*, could enable the United States to increase its own prosperity and at the same time assist in increasing the prosperity of the developing countries.'

Edgar Kaiser, President Eisenhower and President Kennedy, he said, recognized in the Volta River Project a scheme with new dimensions of growth and development which they felt could benefit both Ghana and the United States and, within this concept of mutual respect and common advantage, lies the 'living proof that nations and people can co-operate and co-exist peacefully with mutual advantage to themselves despite differences of economic and political opinions'.

Nkrumah then turned to the Project, and spoke of the dam and power project itself, of the smelter at Tema and the transmission network which 'is not for Ghana alone. Indeed I have already offered to share our power resources with our sister African States.'[1] And he paid particular tribute to the 80,000 people who had been called upon to move from their houses in the interests of the nation.

Then looking out into the gathering dusk, President Nkrumah was ready, as he said, to 'turn the switch to shed the full radiance of Volta Power on this scene, symbolizing not only a great achievement of Ghana, but let it also be a light leading us on to our destined and cherished goal – a Union Government for Africa'.

First, however, there were two bronze plaques to be unveiled. President Nkrumah stepped forward and unveiled the powerhouse plaque commemorating the formal inauguration of the power project. At the special request of Mrs Jacqueline Kennedy, Madam Fathia Nkrumah on her behalf unveiled the second plaque commemorating the part played in the Project by Presidents Eisenhower and Kennedy.

Now that the twilight had almost gone the arc-lights were extinguished one by one in readiness for the ceremonial switching-on. Flanked by Edgar Kaiser, the US Ambassador and Frank Dobson, President Nkrumah released the switchboard handle, producing an effect that was instantly beautiful. The vast wall of the dam itself was bathed in a soft green light evenly spread over its gently sloping surface from a battery of 180 lights mounted high above our heads at the overlook point. The crest of the dam and of the intake structure and the spillway was fringed with an amber necklace of permanently placed standard lamps whilst for several minutes the last deep turquoise hues of the setting sun added to the delicate confluence of pastel shades.

But if the floodlighting was beautiful and breathtaking the

[1] Regrettably, however, Nkrumah's strained political relationship with his neighbour states had made it impracticable for such an offer to be accepted.

fireworks display that followed was wholly entrancing and made a fairy-land of the whole arena. The London firm of Brocks, who have been designing gigantic fireworks displays for two hundred and fifty years for every conceivable occasion from Royal Coronations to school festivals, had arranged the programme in two consecutive parts – the first to tell the story of Akosombo in fireworks and the second to be a colossal display worthy of the enormous setting. In this display two thousand fireworks – maroons, Roman candles, shells, mines and rockets in the most gorgeous display of crimson streamers, green raindrops, showers of rubies, lace-wing moths, falling curtains of gold lace, screeching parakeets, glittering orchids, rainbow fantasies and golden scarabs – came to a climax with the Weird White Waterfall in which the whole of the adjacent spillway burst into immense torrents of cascading fire, lighting up the vicinity with intense brilliance and 'rending the night air with loud reports and eerie whistles', the programme advised us. Four hundred and fifty rockets were then fired together from the dam itself, followed by a magnificent Grand Finale of every species of firework discharged simultaneously.

Though this concluded the formal celebrations, revelry continued through the night all over Akosombo. At a splendid, Italianate banquet the directors of Impregilo entertained hundreds of guests and presented each with a commemorative bronze medal depicting the dam. And at four o'clock in the morning in the Akosombo Community Centre, as the climax to a crowded, night-long Celebration Ball, I found myself crowning a remarkably lovely Miss Akosombo as Queen of the Volta. There could not have been a happier ending.

25

THE PRICE IS PAID

On the morning of Tuesday February 15, 1966 a tremendous explosion shook the dam site. They said afterwards that Nkrumah was so certain it was the direct result of a botched sacrifice by Nana Kwafo Akoto, on the morning of inauguration, that Nana's name had been added to the growing list of citizens who were to be put into preventive detention just as soon as Nkrumah had returned from his (never-to-be-completed) peace mission to Hanoi.

It is true that the downstream end of the diversion tunnel where the explosion took place is within a few yards of the ancient cave where, for as long as man and his traditions can recall, the high priest of Deh-Sekyi, the river god of the lower Volta, has received tribute from all travellers passing up and down the river. There was no escaping this tribute, which might be as little as a penny or a single banana or, if you really had nothing, a little symbolic dance wobbled in your canoe to show that you really respected the deity in the cave. But there are plenty of witnesses to testify to the fact that the Paramount Chief did well and truly perform his sacrifice, in full view of the site of the ancient Deh-Sekyi shrine. A fully grown ox was despatched, prayers were offered and the symbolic thirsts of the ancestors assuaged with copious libations of best Ghanaian gin.

The explosion occurred during the very last stages of the extremely complicated process of casting in solid concrete the plug 30-foot long and 30-foot in diameter in the middle of the diversion tunnel. And millions of gallons of water were flowing through the tunnel each day as work continued.

The plug of course was vital to the completion of the job, since no leakage whatever through the dam or its surrounds was permissible, and the ingenious method which they had devised in order to tackle the problem stage by stage must be explained. At the point where the plug was to be cast – about the middle of the tunnel – the contractor had, during construction, left two wide recesses around the circumference of the tunnel, which would enable the concrete plug to be integrated solidly into the tunnel lining.

The plug itself was now being built up in four equal layers each of about 7 foot 6 inches in height – and through the lowest of these had been passed three 20-inch diameter pipes which would allow the passage of the full amount of leakage, 23 cusecs (12 million gallons a day), at which level it had remained constant for several weeks.

One by one the concrete masses were placed, with provision being made in the middle ones for a hollow centre from which liquid 'grout' could, in the last stage, be pumped downwards in order to fill and seal the 20-inch pipes, when they were no longer needed, and upwards in order to make a firm bond between the top of the plug and the crown of the tunnel.

In actual fact it was decided, from experience, that the topmost layer should itself be divided into two separate stages, the final and fifth one being to fill the last 3 feet between the top of the fourth stage and the crown of the tunnel. This fourth layer had in fact been placed on February 13th so that during the following two days the final preparations were being made for the last of the concrete pouring to take place on February 16th.

At this stage several sequences had to be followed, as once the plug was completed there would be no further access to that part of the tunnel upstream of the plug. Whatever needed to be done had to be done now. A wall or bulkhead of cement blocks was built at the upstream end of the plug in order to act as a solid 'form' for the concrete placing which was to be done under pressure. However, so as to allow continued access to the upstream part of the tunnel, a 2-foot square aperture was left in the bulkhead which would be sealed off with a wooden cover at the last moment.

Meanwhile two of the three 20-inch pipes that were still carrying the leakage through the plug had to be blocked, before

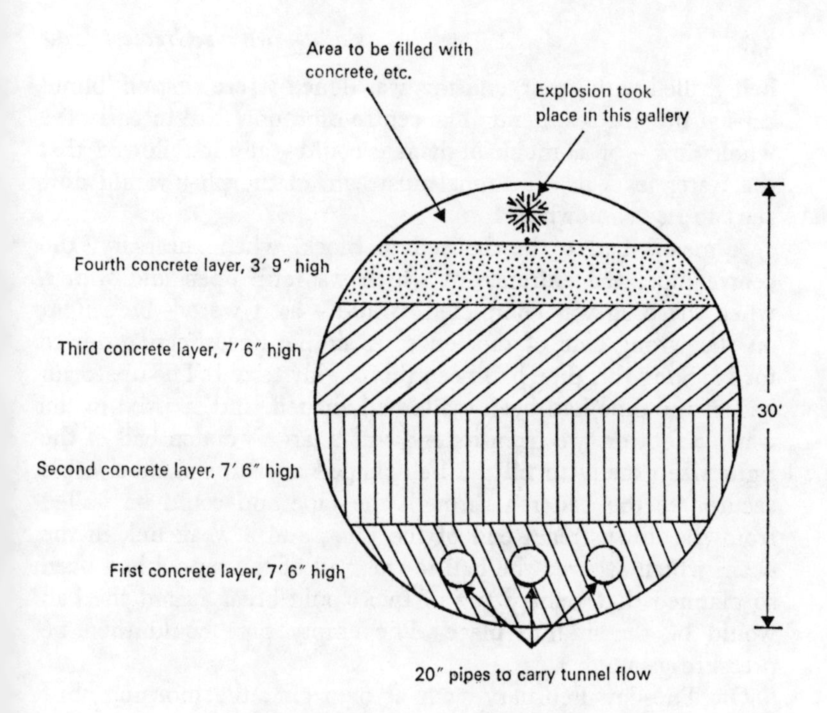
Area to be filled with
concrete, etc.
Explosion took
place in this gallery
Fourth concrete layer, 3′ 9″ high
Third concrete layer, 7′ 6″ high
30′
Second concrete layer, 7′ 6″ high
First concrete layer, 7′ 6″ high
20″ pipes to carry tunnel flow

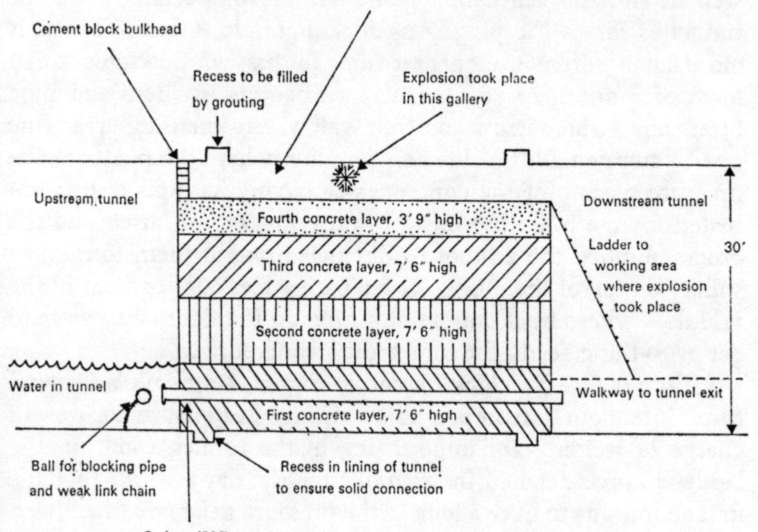
Area to be filled the following day with concrete pumped under pressure
(3′ 9″ at highest point)
Cement block bulkhead
Recess to be filled
by grouting
Explosion took place
in this gallery
Upstream tunnel
Downstream tunnel
Fourth concrete layer, 3′ 9″ high
30′
Third concrete layer, 7′ 6″ high
Ladder to
working area
where explosion
took place
Second concrete layer, 7′ 6″ high
Water in tunnel
Walkway to tunnel exit
First concrete layer, 7′ 6″ high
Ball for blocking pipe
and weak link chain
Recess in lining of tunnel
to ensure solid connection
3 pipes (20″) to carry tunnel flow during period of construction

being filled with grout, and this was done by screwing on 'blind' caps at the upstream end. The centre pipe now had to carry the whole flow – or as much of it as it could – and it followed that the water level in the tunnel upstream of the plug would now start to rise somewhat.

A means had to be devised to block, when necessary, the centre pipe, the entrance of which was still open and which, when the plug was completed, would – as it were – be caught on the wrong side of the fence. A simple but effective device for blocking this pipe had been thoroughly tested. The upstream end of the pipe had been made bell-shaped, and secured in the water a foot or two from its end was a large wooden ball of the right size exactly to fill the bell-shaped aperture. A steel cable secured to the ball ran through the pipe and could be pulled from the downstream end of the plug, and a weak link in the chain which secured the ball to the wall of the tunnel had been so planned that a sharp tug or two would break it and the ball would be drawn into place. The empty pipe could then be pressure-grouted.

On Tuesday February 15th at 6.30 a.m. the morning shift started to arrive on duty. As always the 30-foot wide tunnel was well lit and the ventilation plant was blowing fresh air up the tunnel as far as the plug. Angelo Zangrando, a forty-four year old Italian foreman-carpenter was in first and led his small team of a dozen or so Ghanaian carpenters, welders and pipe fitters along the narrow 500-foot walkway to the plug area. One or two stopped a little short of the plug, where the plant for the pressure placing of the concrete was having its pipe system adjusted for the following day's work. Zangrando himself and the others climbed the 20-foot ladder that brought them to the low gallery on top of the plug – with a bare 3 feet of headroom in the middle – where bent double or sitting on the floor, they were to get everything ready for tomorrow's concreting.

A little before 7 o'clock Ferruccio Bigoni, Impregilo's General Superintendent, accompanied by Carlo Bertona, who was in charge of welding and pipe fitting in the tunnel, came up the ladder to give detailed instructions for the day's work. Bigoni's first action was to have a look at the pressure gauge that had been installed in the wooden bulkhead that now closed the aperture in the concrete wall. It had already been noted that there was a slight tendency for the air pressure to build up upstream of the plug and he therefore instructed Zangrando to release whatever little pressure there was by means of a valve, and then remove the timber bulkhead so that he could check the upstream water level. Bertona in the meantime had been explaining to his Ghanaian welders their part of the operation.

Then the two Italians had gone back down the ladder and had turned their attention to the work being done on the concrete placing plant. Soon afterwards Bertona noticed two of his welders carrying up the walkway a fresh bottle of oxygen and they explained as they passed that the one they had been using the previous day was empty. Having deposited the oxygen bottle at the foot of the plug and connected it up to the hose serving the work area above, they were then all ready to start.

The explosion that took place at 7.15, was felt as a tremor as far away as the Impregilo offices on the opposite bank and was seen by many in the form of a large cloud of white smoke billowing out from the downstream end of the diversion tunnel. One eye-witness who was at the powerhouse saw a water jet and white smoke *above* the dam, which can only be explained as the effect of the explosion at the upstream end of the tunnel, where a vent pipe serving the tunnel must have projected an extremely powerful jet of water and smoke a hundred feet or more into the air.

No one is alive today who can say what exactly it was that sparked off the explosion. It is certain that something ignited a heavy and totally unexpected build-up of methane or natural gas inside the tunnel and it seems probable that it was the routine lighting of a welding torch that set the gas alight. No one who was working on the top of the plug where the explosion took place survived; all were killed instantly including Zangrando.

Bigoni and Bertona were still standing by the concreting plant when what Bertona later described as ' loud rumbling, gradually increasing in intensity' exploded into a vast cloud of blue smoke. The lights went off and they were all hit by a violent blast of hot air and thrown into the water below the walkway with their skin scorched by terrible burns. Bigoni had lost his bearings and made his way in the darkness at first towards the plug only to realize, on reaching it, that he had to turn back and wade on through the debris-filled watercourse to the tunnel outlet. Bertona too, stuck to the watercourse, keeping mostly under water all the way to the outlet, in order to avoid flying timber wreckage.

M. A. Quaye, a foreman-carpenter who had been working up at the plug with Zangrando half an hour before the explosion, had been sent to take some timber that was no longer required out of the tunnel and was nearer the outlet than most of the others when the explosion occurred. But he too was seriously burned; so was Klee Kwabla, an attendant on the pump pontoon immediately outside the tunnel, who caught the full blast of the explosion as it emerged.

Within minutes of the explosion rescuers started to arrive from all over the site, and the Akosombo Fire Brigade, who normally have nothing more serious to extinguish than a short-circuited air conditioner or at most a small forest fire, lost no time in plunging into the pitch black tunnel and in bringing out the dead and injured.

Igor Leto, the Impregilo Project Manager, arrived shortly afterwards and assumed control of rescue operations. He made his way at once by torchlight to the scene of the explosion at the plug area and satisfied himself that there was no further immediate danger. Meanwhile Geoff Dixon, the Kaiser resident manager, was having detailed examinations made of the eastern end of the dam and in the vicinity of the spillways to be sure that no incidental damage had sprung from the explosion. It was unlikely in the extreme, but someone was bound to ask. None was found, and someone did ask very quickly. For when Frank Dobson, in Accra, went to report the explosion to his chairman, the first thing that Nkrumah asked was, 'Is the dam damaged?' and then 'Was it sabotage?' Within two or three hours he had a three-man investigation team from his personal security service on the site at Akosombo making their own detailed enquiry. A more devastating aspect of Nkrumah's reaction to the accident was his apparent lack of concern for the casualties and their families after whom he never enquired. Indeed his feelings must have communicated themselves to the Authority itself, which did not pass on to him a draft message of condolence that had been prepared for his signature. Edgar Kaiser sent him a very warmhearted message of sympathy from California, and so did Dr Lodigiani from Milan – but neither of them was made public.

The casualties, in fact, had been very heavy by any standards and, more particularly, by standards at Akosombo. There had been eighteen people in the tunnel when the explosion occurred and by mid-afternoon ten of these had died, five of them instantly. Two had died on arrival at Akosombo Hospital, and three others who had been transferred by ambulance to hospital in Accra had either died en route or on arrival. In each case the skin had been burnt completely away by the heat of the blast and the shock to the system had been too great to survive.

Of the eight others five had not been burnt too seriously and recovered after treatment. Bertona too was well enough to fly home within a month. Bigoni however died at Akosombo Hospital a week later on the same day as the twelfth victim – a young carpenter named Joseph Afum whose contract Bigoni had only recently extended on account of his good work. And so they died together.

That the explosion had been caused by a build-up of gas there was little doubt, but what gas, and where did it come from?

Leto had read some time before that during the closure of the diversion tunnel at Furnas in Brazil a similar explosion had taken place, and that this had later been attributed to methane deriving from rotting vegetation and fish. Foreseeing the possibility of a similar condition occurring at Akosombo he had asked for and obtained from the jointly owned Ghanaian-Italian petrol refinery at Tema an explosion meter which had been used to take readings in various parts of the tunnel, at intervals of a few days, from the end of October 1965 onwards. Readings taken on twenty-two separate days – the last, three days before the explosion – had all shown a negative result.

Yet two hours after the explosion, when a test was made in the plug area, there was a reading of 40 per cent on the instrument's scale; by 10 a.m. this had risen to 60 per cent, which is the dividing line between safe and dangerous conditions. By midday the reading was 75 per cent and all further work was suspended in the tunnel except for the installation of an additional ventilating pipe. Still the gas, which was evidently surging over the top of the plug from the upstream end of the tunnel, continued to build up, and by 1.30 p.m., when Leto and Dixon entered the tunnel with Frank Dobson, who had arrived from Accra, it had risen to the highly dangerous level of 90 per cent. At this stage the tunnel was completely evacuated, all lights turned off and the entrance barricaded. Thus the unexpected had happened: a tunnel that had been wholly gas-free throughout the operation had suddenly been made into a death trap.

A team of six British mining engineers and ventilation experts with special knowledge in this field travelled 250 miles overnight from the Ashanti Goldfields Corporation mines at Obuasi with a vast amount of rescue and other equipment in order to supply a completely independent opinion of the accident and to help in any other way they could. As it happened the gas had departed as unexpectedly as it had arrived: exactly twenty-four hours after the 90 per cent reading on the afternoon of the explosion further readings on an identical instrument showed negative results. The British miners confirmed this verdict; using a Davis lamp they could find no trace of combustible gas, even inside the drainage cavities in the tunnel lining through which it might have been expected that the gas could have leaked. Speaking for the group Mr G. Thomas, the chief ventilation engineer said: 'We talked this over between ourselves for a long time last night and we are all of the opinion that you have had what we miners call an "act of god" type of explosion. I have had almost thirty years' underground experience and with a short, large-diameter close-to-the-surface tunnel like this which has been checked for gas over a three-month period I would not have hesitated to treat it as an open-cast operation.'

In view of the circumstances, however, it was now agreed that from this time onwards[1] the work should be treated as a mining operation: no welding or naked lights or even electric lights other than miners' safety lamps. And ventilation was to be stepped up four times. Knowing what was now known, no risks could be taken.

What was still not known – and may never be known – was

[1] The task of plugging the diversion tunnel was successfully completed on March 17, 1966 without further mishaps.

where exactly the gas came from. Samples taken of the water in the tunnel and of the water at the bottom of the lake upstream of the tunnel showed a methane content of 2 per cent – which is fairly high. No other types of gas trace were found in the water. Another theory – that gas was forced out of the adjacent black shale area and into the tunnel through its 'weep holes' by the steadily growing pressure of the lake – is also perfectly possible. But no one can be sure and it is a fact that, during the low river season, the lake pressure, far from rising, had been constant – had even dropped a fraction – since November 1965.

That it was indeed an 'act of god' seems to be unquestionable. But which god? Deh-Sekyi is not likely, in the circumstances, to tolerate any suggestion of a rival.

26

FOR THE FUTURE

Accra awoke on February 24, 1966 to the crack of rifle fire and an early morning radio announcement that 'the myth of Kwame Nkrumah is broken for ever'.

Nkrumah himself was arriving in Peking at the time, paying a state visit to China and en route for Hanoi where he had planned to hold peace talks with the North Vietnamese Government. The irony of the situation at this particular moment was that Nkrumah's image at an international level seemed to be glossier than his standing at home. Accustomed to lionizing their rulers while in office, Ghanaians are equally eager to taunt the mighty when they fall from grace and there was little doubt that on that day the military take-over was a popular move. The National Liberation Council, which was the name adopted by the new military-cum-police government, immediately assumed responsibility for the Volta Project and appointed one of their number, Mr J. W. K. Harlley – their Vice-Chairman and Inspector-General of the Ghana Police Force – as the new Chairman of the Board of the Volta River Authority.

The power project, as initially planned, was now virtually complete and both the Kaiser and Impregilo staff were fast withdrawing from Akosombo. Viewing it however as a multi-purpose project, it was clear that the new government and its economic advisers would be obliged to trim down expenditure on anything that was not directly connected with the manufacture of electric power. One of their first discoveries was that Ghana had to face some £300 million worth of foreign debts with reserves virtually reduced to nothing.[1] There was now no alternative but for a

[1] At the time of Ghana's independence in March 1957 the country had hard currency reserves of some £250 million.

period of several years' stringent economy while the country itself recovered from this critical position.

One immediate result was the postponement, for an initial period of two years, of the schemes for irrigation on the Accra Plains. Less serious was the decision to abandon for the present any further work on the Bui Hydro-electric Project on the Black Volta.

Bui, the only other deep gorge within Ghana where a major hydro-electric scheme would be possible, had been earmarked for further investigation by Sir Albert Kitson fifty years previously. Nkrumah for his part appears to have used Bui cleverly to maintain some kind of political balance between West and East. Whilst the United States had been so deeply involved in the main power project at Akosombo, the Soviet Union had been following through the earlier Bui investigations with a comprehensive survey of the area as the site for a further hydro-electric project. The survey had been thorough and wholly favourable and the Russians had formally recommended that a dam be built there – at an overall estimated cost of £47.7 million. It seems likely, however, that knowing as well as anyone the state of Ghana's economy the Russians would not have been impatient to match the deed to the word. In any case there would be no pressing need for this particular source of electric power for at least a further fifteen or twenty years; the Bui project could be shelved indefinitely.

But in spite of the plentiful current from Akosombo constant power cuts in the capital suggested that all was not well. Ironically, the first of these black-outs had occurred half-way through the gala banquet held in Accra to celebrate the inauguration of the dam. By the flickering light of Edgar Kaiser's cigarette lighter it was possible to see Nkrumah's security men hemming him in, and only a swift wise-crack from Edgar Kaiser relieved the inevitable tension. 'Where's Dobson?' – (the VRA's chief executive) he called out, peering into the darkness.

What had happened was a case of new wine surging into ancient bottles; the distribution system in Accra and elsewhere was overdue for replacement, but the country's weakening economy, even before Nkrumah's departure, had made it impossible to implement a new scheme, fully planned though it was.

One source of aid, however, still appeared to be available:

the British Government's £5 million share in the capital cost of the Project itself. Partly because of the considerable economies made during tendering and construction and partly because of the relatively few supply contracts that had gone to Britain the greater part of this £5 million was unspent.[1] But then a frustrated and very needy Ghanaian Government found itself faced with the British reply that, without a vast amount of parliamentary and administrative reconsideration, it was not feasible to switch a loan negotiated to help build a dam and power plant into one to renovate the power distribution system in the country's principal cities. Even *The Times* added its avuncular advice:

> Possibly the balance of the British £5 million could be released to improve the electricity supply to industrial areas, although so far Britain has declined, perhaps pettishly, to extend the uses to which the British contribution could be put.

Whatever Britain's reasons for shilly-shallying, the fact remains that British industry lost a valuable and continuing order for electrical equipment which she, as well as anyone, was in a position to supply. Indeed, for this reason the order had been reserved for Britain.

Now, however, it went to Germany, who made sufficient funds available for German equipment to be bought without delay and the needs of the capital city satisfied; further loans negotiated with the World Bank will have enabled the remainder of the city lights to be constant by 1970.

By far the most significant outcome of Nkrumah's departure from the scene was the immediate interest now shown in Ghana's abundant and inexpensive power by her French-speaking neighbours.

Except for the Atlantic seaboard, Ghana, which is about the area of the United Kingdom, is surrounded by former French colonial territories, and language alone is a constant barrier to easy communications. Add to this the fact that, for the greater part of the Second World War, French West Africa was under Vichy control and the borders were virtually closed, and that

[1] The residue of Britain's £5 million loan, which amounted to £3.7 million, was subsequently released by the Government as part of another exercise to assist Ghana's balance of payments.

they were closed again during the latter period of Nkrumah's government because of mutual suspicion and mistrust, and the country's tendency towards isolation becomes evident.

The new government, however, lost no time in proffering the hand of goodwill to Togo, Niger, Upper Volta and the Ivory Coast – the immediate neighbours – and to Dahomey, 50 miles away through Togo. As a result, agreement in principle has been reached with the governments of Togo and Dahomey for Ghana to sell them power from Akosombo.[1] This will bring one stage nearer reality the prospect of a fully integrated West African grid – with Dahomey linked the 70 miles to Nigeria's supply at Lagos and Ghana linked the 85 miles to the Ivory Coast's nearest power centre. Further inland a return arm of the grid could then link the Ivory Coast's Bandama scheme with Nigeria's Kainji, serving in a vast sweep Upper Volta and Niger and the northern parts of Ghana, Togo and Dahomey. If ever politicians were looking for a practical means of binding fragmented West Africa into some sort of effective economic community this surely would help to furnish part of the frame that future generations could nourish and develop.

Thus, within two years of inauguration, the prospect of exporting power combined with the booming sales to industry and public alike of current from Ghana's own grid, had made completion of the Akosombo power station a necessity. Had the VRA been blessed with second sight there is little doubt that from the savings made they would have installed all six turbines and generators in the first instance and saved again, against the inevitable rise in the cost of repeat orders, perhaps with less competition. Big business however is not directed by the crystal ball. However the new Board has put in hand the financing of the two remaining turbines and generators and there is every prospect of completion by 1972. Detailed planning of the subsequent Kpong Barrier scheme downstream is also being undertaken.

Valco, the aluminium smelter at Tema, will continue to be the largest single customer for power. Ahead of original planning they have resolved to complete the smelter to its limit of 4 pot lines so as to coincide with the additional power available in 1972.

[1] During 1968 the financing for this development was completed and, with Canadian technical assistance, work was expected to start in 1969.

So far, so good: by 1968 the Volta River Project had more than justified itself economically, commercially and industrially. Slowly, in the face of the country's recent economic problems, new industries are being attracted to Ghana – power-consuming industries, moreover. In all these respects the Project is already an outstanding tribute to its architects, its financiers and its builders.

But what of the lake? And what of the 80,000? Inevitably there can be no such clear-cut conclusions or complacent judgements, for here we are dealing with the evolution of nature and with the personal problems of human beings, and who can be certain that they are better or worse off than before the lake was formed?

1968 was in fact the year in which the lake rose for the first time to its peak level so that it is still too early for it to have settled characteristics or for the marine biologists to have drawn serious conclusions. Under the chairmanship of the Authority's first Ghanaian Chief Executive, Mr E. L. Quartey, a distinguished electrical engineer, the Volta Lake Research Project has co-ordinated the multiplicity of long- and short-term studies of lake conditions formerly being made by the University of Ghana, the Academy of Science, and international and local health, food and fishery authorities. This in itself should help to speed up and co-ordinate nature's own efforts to adjust to the new lake conditions.

Even at this stage, however, some factors appear to emerge clearly. First of all, the lake is abundant in edible fish and this is a matter of considerable importance to all those living in the vicinity of the lake. Secondly, the lake is capable of being a source of ill-health to its communities unless constant care is taken to guard against water-borne or water-bred diseases and infections. There appear, for instance, to be some parasites which are capable of growing immune to the chemicals or drugs which at first controlled them, and constant research will be necessary to maintain health measures at a satisfactorily level. Thirdly, water weeds do not yet appear to represent a major problem on Lake Volta as they do elsewhere in Africa. Fourthly, it is not as simple to refashion the lives of 80,000 people as might appear from a social planner's blue-print. It is a noble design to try to give to the resettled people in their larger communities the economic advantages of cash crop and livestock farming, but in the time available and in the circumstances that prevailed it was bound to lead often to disappointment, disillusionment and hardship. Many of those resettled were bound to move back to the relatively simple surroundings in which they could pursue the type of subsistence farming that was the basis of their old way of life. The Authority, aided considerably by a £1 million World Food Programme scheme, has adapted its policy accordingly and is encouraging subsistence farming and ensuring that each settler has clear legal title to his new land so that there is at last the essential feeling of belonging once and for all to the new community.

Lastly there is Lake Volta itself. While being the largest man-made lake in the world, it could also be described as the least visible. From the air, of course, one can see it stretching northwards for its full 250 miles, with mighty tentacles stretching east and west along its tributary valleys; but from ground level it is not easy to see the lake in its true proportions except from a few vantage points to the east. From Akosombo itself one only sees the first twelve miles of narrow gorge as it passes through the Akwapim-Togo mountain range. Only from a few points on this range – at Anum or at Kpandu or, from a distance, from Amedzofe – does one gain an impression of its vast extent. For this reason few Ghanaians have yet been able to accustom themselves to the presence in the heart of their country of this enormous stretch of water, now there to stay and destined to reshape the pattern of living and movement in the country.

In spite of its anonymity, however, Lake Volta is slowly beginning to play its part in the communications of the country – especially between north and south. Gone, for the present, is Kaiser's dream of a mighty water/road or water/rail transport complex using interchangeable freight containers, switching swiftly from land to water transport. In its place a variety of small craft now ply up and down the lake – some with passengers, some with freight and some with both – so with little capital outlay the lake is daily being used by an ever-growing number of travellers and transporters. There is no luxury and the minimum of facilities, but the movement is there and it is growing. A new cadre of technocrat is emerging – the lake waterman – who is coming to know the varying moods of the lake season by season, and whose experience is laying the foundations of lake craft and lore.

Volta has come a long way since Sir Albert Kitson, during his 1915 canoe trip, first recognized at 'Akonsomo' a pre-eminent site for a dam; since Duncan Rose read Kitson's report in the Johannesburg public library and immediately made tracks for the Gold Coast to satisfy himself that it was feasible; and since President Kennedy had the courage to say in 1961 that, in the true interests of Africa, the Project must go forward and the necessary loans be made. In the years ahead it will come to be taken for granted, will appear always to have been there. The loans will have been repaid from revenue, according to plan, and Ghana will have not only the advantages of the lake itself but also perpetual power from its flowing waters. This is a legacy indeed from the old age to the new, from the Gold Coast to Ghana, from the twentieth century to the future.

Part Three

INTRODUCTION TO PART THREE

This book now goes into a fourth impression inasmuch as Parts One and Two, which first appeared in 1969, remain the standard work on Ghana's Volta River Project. Some years earlier this had become North America's first entrée into newly independent Black Africa in a major industrial investment. And the Kaiser-Reynolds aluminium smelter at Tema is still the largest plant of its kind in Africa and one of the largest outside North America.

Part Three endeavours to carry the story to 1983 showing how Ghana, whilst flying in the teeth of a terrible storm of economic recession and unstable government, was nevertheless able to extend its hydro-electric generating capacity according to plan in a valiant attempt to keep abreast of the growing demand for electric power. It also tells the story of the remarkable 'rapport' that blossomed between the two immediate architects of the Volta River Project – Kwame Nkrumah and Edgar Kaiser – both of whom died during the fifteen-year interval and to whose memory this new edition is dedicated, along with the project's original pioneers, Sir Alfred Kitson and Duncan Rose.

And the story would not be complete without an analysis of the strained relations which have progressively developed, due to conflicting basic interests, between the Kaiser group on the one side and the people of Ghana on the other. It is a conflict which, at this moment of writing, remains unresolved. It is my belief that, in spite of its formidable contemporary problems and some rumbling ideological conflicts, Ghana has never forfeited its role – pioneered by Kwame Nkrumah – as the first pilot of Black African aspirations.

In this context I quote from an article[1] written by the late Lord

[1] 'The Wind of Change Myth', Lord Egremont, *The Sunday Times*, May 10, 1964.

Egremont in 1964 (as John Wyndham he accompanied the British Prime Minister on his 'Wind of Change' tour of Africa four years earlier) who recalls a visit to Akosombo when the new dam was nearing completion. Sitting on a wooded hill top with John Osei (still the VRA publicity man at Akosombo) and surveying the ant-like activity of 3,400 workers below, he recalled his earlier visit with Harold Macmillan when only two sticks, one on each bank of the river, showed where the massive dam would soon take shape.

Commenting on some of Nkrumah's despotic tendencies he drily remarked, 'I suppose that in a country like Ghana we should not have expected only a little totalitarianism – just as well expect a little pregnancy.'

And then he wrote, 'Next to Lady Egremont and taking the stuffing out of the stuffed shirts my passion in life could well be Ghana. . . . Whatever happens I shall never abandon my love for Ghana, dark, distant African princess.'

And just as Whistler commented on Oscar Wilde's 'I wish I had said that' – 'You will, Oscar, you will' – I would gladly usurp John Egremont's sentiments. And not simply because they were made by a most acute observer and a remarkably sensitive Englishman.

In acknowledging the immense help that I have been given in preparing this new edition of *Volta* I am bound to be selective, which does not mean that I am not deeply grateful to all those others who have given me of their time and knowledge.

My first thanks go to the VRA and especially to Louis Casely Hayford and Kobla Kalitsi. My second to the late Len Allen of Acres, the consultants for the Kpong project, who not only during the constructional period but just before he died in May 1983, gave me immense help and advice in commenting wisely and with authority on my draft manuscript. To the Managing Trustees of the Valco Fund I owe a great debt – first for helping me to research on the spot the Caribbean and US bauxite and alumina industry – and secondly for generous help in the publication of this new edition. In this same context I have also to thank my immensely patient and sympathetic publisher, André Deutsch. To the Kaiser organization both in the US and, as Valco in Ghana, I am deeply grateful for their co-operation, friendship and kindness. I pray that they will read with understanding my observations on the long drawn out Valco–Ghana dispute. The First Presbyterian Church of Atlanta, Georgia, whose 1981 seminar I attended when, hand in hand with the Christian Council of Ghana, they analysed the suffering of the people displaced by Lake Volta, helped to open my eyes to the anxiety of Christians all over the world to the human problems caused by the creation of the world's largest man-made lake.

My nephew Philip Hobson has applied his mathematical skills to some of my more bizarre calculations. And Alex Tordzroh, my loyal amanuensis, has transcribed every word with skill and good humour.

James Moxon
June 1983

27

FIFTEEN YEARS LATER

Much water has flowed through the penstocks and over the spillways of Akosombo since the lake reached its peak level in 1968 and since the previous chapter was written in the same year. One hundred trillion[1] gallons to be precise – or, in current metric parlance, four hundred and fifty trillion litres.[2]

And how does one visualize this astonishing quantity of water? Enough to flood the whole of a flattened Ghana or United Kingdom to an inconvenient depth of six feet (2 metres) or so. Enough to fill Lake Ontario to the brim or Lake Geneva many times over. In any event a tidy amount of captive water!

That these early years of Ghana's development as an independent nation were not easy ones is already a matter of contemporary history. The military government that unseated Kwame Nkrumah in 1966 gave way gracefully three years later to the Second Republic, with Dr K. A. Busia,[3] one of Nkrumah's bitterest opponents, as Prime Minister. A second military coup d'état swept away his government in 1972 and opened up the rapacious regime of Colonel (later General, cut down to Mr) I. K. Acheampong. The first Rawlings 'cleaning-up operation' followed in 1979 ushering

[1] In using the word trillion we are adopting the current international usage, i.e. 10^{12} (a million million) rather than the OED definition which is 10^{18} (a million million million).

[2] In Chapters 1–26, which are reprinted in the unaltered text of the 1969 edition of this book, the pre-metric formula is used. For consistency's sake the same formula is used in Part Three (Chapters 27–30) but with metric equivalents where necessary. New international contract figures are shown in US dollars, except where a specific currency is mentioned. But references to earlier figures are made in £ sterling. Power generation in these concluding chapters is now shown in megawatts (mw).

[3] K. A. Busia (1913–79) who had been one of the Gold Coast's first two African District Commissioners, was my predecessor in 1946 in charge of the Volta River District and passed on to me the top security WAFAL file (see p. 55).

in the Third Republic under Dr Hilla Limann. Disillusioned however by what he saw as this betrayal of his campaign to sweep out the Augean Stables of contemporary maladministration, Flight Lieutenant Jerry Rawlings returned to power on December 31, 1981, leading his Provisional National Defence Council (PNDC) with its declared policy of 'participatory democracy' and with the power of decision both in the public and private sectors being tilted in favour of the working rather than the managerial man. Being a revolution it suffers from the basic drawback of a self-imposed and not an elected regime and though many believe it is motivated by high moral values at a time when these are much needed, it tends to be torn asunder by divergent policies and is consequently faced with the gravest economic, administrative and social problems.[1]

Meanwhile in the face of these obstacles to the ordered process of development the Volta River Authority has over the years stuck firmly to its purpose of planning ahead a series of reservoirs that are designed to keep Ghana firmly abreast of her power needs for decades to come. Ten or more have been surveyed. A combination of circumstances however has complicated the pattern. Akosombo itself is currently 1,000gw.h per annum lower than its regulated energy output[2] due in part to the Sahelian drought of the 1970/80s and also, as it has now emerged, on account of a serious overcalculation arising from inadequate hydrographic data available to the dam consultants thirty years ago.

The fact that the completion in 1981/2 of the second hydroelectric project at Kpong (described more fully in this chapter) has added a further 1,000gw.h of energy per annum merely means that Ghana's long term capability hasn't changed. Kpong was intended to raise it to keep pace with development.

A third power project at Bui (on the Ghana/Ivory Coast border) which would have been needed by 1985 had Ghana's normal

[1] In November 1983 the PNDC's 1984–6 Recovery Programme and investment plan, drawn up by Dr K. Botchwey, Secretary for Finance and Economic Planning, earned cautious approval at a meeting in Paris, chaired by the World Bank, of some twenty donor countries and lending agencies which are directly concerned with Ghana's aid requirements. The programme was described as 'feasible and pragmatic' and not over-ambitious in relation to existing ruling factors. The PNDC itself received praise for its political courage and steadfastness in pursuing the programme. The donors' pledges for aid are to be reviewed on an annual basis. The target set for 1984 was in fact exceeded.

[2] 5,625 gw.h per annum. One gigowatt (gw) = 1 billion watts.

economic growth continued, and which has been fully designed to the point of contract letting, is currently in mothballs until the economic climate improves. The hard fact that new power plants have risen in cost as much as twenty times since Akosombo was built makes it that much more difficult for the necessary funding by the international lending agencies to be arranged.

THE KPONG PROJECT

Nevertheless a decade earlier, just before world oil prices rocketed, the VRA set in motion the Kpong Hydro-Electric Project which takes the form of a 15-mile lake immediately below the Akosombo Dam, flooding the Kpong and Senchi rapids, and creating a new dam and powerhouse at Akuse, 60 navigable miles from the sea at Ada. On July 1, 1982 – Republic Day – the $260 million Kpong project, financed in 1977 by the Volta River Authority and by eight international lending agencies, was officially inaugurated by the new Head of State. To simplify this extremely complicated financing, which involved eight different currencies, it was decided to apply the loans of particular investment groups to defined activities. Thus the Kuwait Fund, the Arab Fund for African Development, and the Saudi Fund, who jointly loaned $92 million, became responsible for the main civil works – the dam, the powerhouse and dykes, camp facilities and resettlement villages. The contractor for these works was Ghana's trusty friend who built the Akosombo dam, Impregilo-Recchi of Italy.

Another group comprising the World Bank, the European Development Fund and the European Investment Bank, applied their joint $60 million to the 'works' in the shape of the turbines, generators and powerhouse crane (Toshiba of Japan and Boving of the UK), the transformers (by Stronberg of Finland), mechanical and electrical services and transmission lines (another Akosombo friend, Sadelmi of Italy) and switchyard equipment (Merlin Gerin of France). The seventh lending body, the Canadian International Development Agency (CIDA) whose Canadian $39 million were interest free, with repayment spread over forty years and ten years of grace, devoted it to the engineering studies and supervision, and to the supply of the spillway and powerhouse gates (Dominion Bridge Company and Canron – both of Canada).

And the OPEC Fund joined them in financing the installation by Sadelmi of these spillway and powerhouse gates ($3.7 million) in addition to other maintenance work at Akosombo.

This total of some US $200 million in hard currency would be misleading if it were not understood that the Volta River Authority – from its own considerable resources, carefully saved from its local power sales over the years and from the sale of bonds – contributed a further ¢170 million (equivalent to a further $60 million) to cover purely local costs in Ghana's own currency. Thus, of all the nine sources of financing for the Kpong Project, the VRA's was by far and away the largest.

Back in 1973, when the second stage of the Akosombo Dam Project was completed with the addition of the fifth and sixth generating units as planned (p. 247), the VRA then turned its attention to being ahead of the demand for power generation. Everything seemed to point to the proposed Kpong Project as the next in line, but first it was necessary to have every alternative option re-examined and it was in these circumstances that the VRA, encouraged by the Government of Canada, made its approach to the Canadian International Development Agency (CIDA) for aid. With funds provided by CIDA the Volta River Authority engaged the well-known Canadian firm of hydro-electric consultants, Acres International Ltd, together with the Shawinigan Engineering Company Ltd (SECO) to undertake the feasibility study.

The Acres–Seco feasibility report was ready by mid-1975 and, on the basis that Akosombo power would be fully committed by 1980/1 or earlier, recommended immediate action in view of the urgency. The report confirmed that the Kpong Project was the most economical choice of the options available (including possible alternative oil fired plants) with Bui (a larger project) next, and others on the Oti and the Black and White Volta tributaries, as well as the Pra and Tano Rivers in the south-west of Ghana, to follow. The total generating capacity of these projects (including Akosombo) was estimated to be almost 2,000mw, of which Akosombo and Kpong between them would account for rather more than half. So the Acres-Seco study confirmed previous findings that Ghana still has substantial hydro-electric potential and a programme for developing these sites was prepared.

The man chosen by Acres–Seco to be their Resident Manager

for the Kpong project and to supervise the work from start to finish was fifty-five-year-old Len Allen, who possibly knew as much of the Volta background as anyone else alive. He had lived in a tent on its banks as far back as 1952 when, as a young engineer, he spent three years on the Volta as one of the Halcrow team that examined all seven possible sites for the dam between Misikrom and Akosombo and which set the pattern for the future Volta River Authority (pages 62–6). Len Allen, who died in May 1983, was a veritable father, mother and midwife; he succeeded, with his team of skilled specialists, in completing the project on schedule and within the budget. Once again Ghana (VRA) and her overseas friends (consultants and contractors) have shown that they know how to perform miracles together. And full recognition was given to Len Allen's personal contribution when, at the official inauguration of the Kpong Project, the Head of State, Flight Lieutenant Jerry Rawlings, invested him with Ghana's most prestigious award, The Grand Medal of Ghana (GM).

In the space at my disposal I must trip lightly over the principal features of the Kpong Project – in effect Akosombo's kid brother. The lake, or the headpond as it is called, extends from the dam itself which is just on the outskirts of Akuse, as far as the toe of the Akosombo Dam, 15 miles (25km) to the north. As there is no natural gorge in which to dam the river the lake is contained on either side of the dam by three miles (5.6km) of rock and clay dykes. A feature of the lake is that it totally submerges the Senchi and the Kpong rapids[1] which together lowered the river level at this point by 35 feet (11.75), thus giving the river its potential for hydro power. The four generating units that combine to create 148mw of power at Kpong are housed in a very impressive enclosed powerhouse – 500 feet long, 170 feet wide and 200 feet high (146m × 44m × 64m) – which, with its discreetly encased machinery and lit by day from a great wall of light-filtering stained glass blocks that dominate the west of the structure, presents much of the splendour of a great cathedral dedicated to all that is best in this age of science and technology. Akosombo's open air powerhouse continues to hold its own with its sheer simplicity. Kpong's elegant Temple complements it appropriately.

The extra power generated at Kpong (equivalent to one addi-

[1] Redolent of Paget Jones and Mary Gaunt (pages 41 and 46).

tional unit at Akosombo) is in fact fed into the national grid system and has the effect of taking some of the pressure off Akosombo, which since 1980 has been adversely affected by the progressively falling lake level. The well-worn criticism of Akosombo, that it has supplied too much (over 60 per cent) of its output to the Valco aluminium smelter (albeit for essential loan-repayment dollars), can now be softened a little because of the inclusion of grid extensions to the Sefwi-Wiawso area of the Western Region and to the Volta Region. It is very much the VRA's policy to speed up rural electrification where possible and as evidence of this the VRA commissioned a feasibility study into anticipating, in part, the proposed Bui project by extending the national grid into the north, via Bui.

The disappearance of the Senchi and Kpong rapids successfully eliminates the principal breeding grounds of one of the great scourges of this neighbourhood, the simulium fly, which flourishes in fast running water. The devastating effect of this fly, the bite of which causes river blindness (onchocerciasis) has already been told in Chapter 16 (pages 156–7). Nature however is a fickle mistress and, if the experience of Lake Volta over the past fifteen years is to be taken as a guide, the very waters that drive away the simulium fly may breed even greater trouble in the form of bilharzia (schistosomiasis) and hookworm. In spite of planning precautions to site new townships away from the lakeside, the Tongu fishermen did what fishermen the world over do – they settled at the water's edge and, ignoring elementary health measures, have created a problem of major proportions by progressively infecting the water-snail vector in the vicinity of human habitation with bilharzia, and in return infecting themselves.

At Kpong the health authorities claim that the very smallness of the new lake perimeter will enable them to prevent this by strict patrolling and other special precautions. One hopes they are right. My own early observation was of people bathing in the new lake at Kpong, alongside the busy new waterfront. How, in a relaxed tropical society, do you stop them?

Many lessons learnt the hard way by the failures that emerged from the 1960s' resettlement of the 80,000 people and by the actual emergence of several 'ghost towns' (page 179)[1] have proved to be

[1] But it is only fair to state that in spite of obvious failures the overall exercise achieved a measure of success.

the very bricks with which the Kpong Resettlement Scheme has been developed. Call this latest exercise in fashioning new lives for an age-old people a cross between the ancestral and the avant-garde and you will have the key to its character. The concrete and timber, the roads, the hygiene of fresh water and good drains, the schools and electricity – all these are in the newest style. But the traditional courtyard shape of the houses, the number of rooms, the relative siting of families and neighbours, the general approach to farming – these have been very carefully patterned on the past and on the expressed wishes of the settlers. But because settlers do not all come from one mould there is ample scope for individual expression; in irrigated farming for example as against pure subsistence, in fishing, in property development and in small industry. In this, as in many other fields of activity, Kpong has gained much from the earlier lessons and aims to play the role of something of a showpiece.

A FRESH APPROACH TO IRRIGATION

A glance back to the opening pages of Chapter 20 will recall the ambitious plans of the early 1960s for harnessing at least some of the headwaters of Lake Volta to the task of irrigating substantial areas of the Accra Plains for agriculture. Not all these pilot projects fell immediately victim to the post-1966 period of growing recession. The University of Ghana's 200-acres experimental project has done much in twenty years to introduce the principles of irrigation to local farmers with no such experience. Of steadily diminishing output were the much heralded sugar factory and adjacent cane plantations at Assuchuari, which never managed to achieve even a tenth of their aims and are now earmarked for a major rehabilitation exercise. A little more successful were the results of the downstream Japanese rice experiments where smallholders working on a co-operative basis have been producing steady if rather low yielding, crops twice a year.

By the time construction work started on the Kpong Project in 1977 it was evident that a fresh approach to harnessing the freely available Volta waters to food production was a priority matter. Many studies had already pointed in this direction and, though originally there was no provision for irrigation outlets in the Kpong barrier designs, the VRA thought it wise to provide those facilities at Kpong which had never materialized at Akosombo. It is my understanding that at this point it was the persistence of Len Allen of Acres that won the day. He was a dedicated irrigation man and, when the break-through finally came, Acres lost no time in incorporating the necessary irrigation sluices and outlets into the east and west dyke designs, following which the VRA set in motion the additional irrigation studies for the land below the dam. Indeed by the time (1981) that the power project was nearing completion, work had actually started on canal construction and levelling for this important gravity-fed irrigation development.

Eighteen months later the VRA can already point to an extremely successful pilot agricultural project of 250 acres (100 hectares) where 100 acres of paddy rice, 20 acres of fish ponds and extensive fields of deep purple aubergines, pungent red peppers, onions, okras and tropical vegetables are a modest curtain raiser to the infinitely more extensive KADCO (Kpong Agricultural Development Company) project which is planned to follow. Indeed the gravity-fed canals from the Kpong reservoir are capable of extending right through the east and west bank KADCO project into the existing sugar cane and rice plantations downstream at Assuchuari, which hitherto have been dependent on mechanical pumping from the river. And though Len Allen – after a thirty-year association with Ghana – did not live to reap his own harvest, Acres, on contract to the VRA, continues to put all its skill into teaching young University-trained Ghanaians to plan and manage the irrigated farms of the future.

Meanwhile on a broader footing, the Volta River Authority was looking again at prospects of irrigating further portions of the Accra Plains. In July 1980 Kaiser Engineers were invited to review and up-date their comprehensive 1965 proposals. Within four months they presented an interim report pin-pointing five areas they considered most suitable for near-term development. Gone was the long-term (fifty-three-years) approach of 1965 with its dream of a market-gardener's paradise the size of Worcestershire, and in its place the choice of five areas no more than 9 or 10 miles square. Of these the VRA selected two on either bank of the Angaw Creek, which lies on the west bank of the Volta between the lower Volta bridge at Tefle and the river mouth at Ada.

The general idea was that, though sponsored and supported by the government, these irrigated farming areas should be largely operated by local smallholders on a labour intensive basis. In 1981 Kaiser Engineers came up with their final report indicating that each 6,000-acre (2,500 hectare) project should be capable of producing annually 23,000 tonnes of farm produce and 400 tonnes of fish from controlled fish ponds. The farm produce would be principally rice, maize, groundnut, cowpeas, vegetables and cassava and the annual yield should in each case be worth some $55 million. Broken down this ought to yield to a five-person family holding about $30,000 a year. At the time of writing the theory has yet to be translated into practice but there are clear signs that given the opportunity (for so many local ventures founder through poor administration) the rich soils of the plains – well watered from the Volta and its tributaries – can supply much of the foodstuffs that the nation needs.

TRANSPORT ON THE LAKE

The 1964 vision (described in Chapter 16) of Lake Volta fast developing into a water highway, serving not only northern Ghana, but her five French-speaking neighbours as well, proved to be £9 million[1] too optimistic, as the investment funds were simply not available. The VRA had its hands full generating the essential electricity and doing its best to solve the problems of the 80,000 displaced Volta settlers. Many very desirable multi-purpose aspects of the Project such as lake transport and agricultural irrigation, though not abandoned, were obliged to accept a far lower priority. Meanwhile the 1965 pioneer pontoons continued to ply up and down the lake, soon to be augmented by the 350-ton freight craft, the *Yapei Queen* and then the 50-ton passenger vessel, the *Akosombo Queen* which was a present from the Netherlands government. Indeed, within its strict limitations the VRA pursued first a pilot project to gain more experience of lake conditions, and then in 1972 a more definitive technical and economic study using Danish technical assistance. This in turn led to the whole issue of the charting of navigational lines, the preparation of the Lake Traffic regulations, the licensing and control of all crafts on the lake and

[1] Then equivalent to US $25 million.

the provision of adequate shore facilities being tackled. For these the Marine Division of the Authority was responsible, with assistance from Dutch technical aid.

The commercial operation was handled by a new venture known as the Volta Lake Transport Company Ltd with, at first, a 51 per cent government and a 49 per cent commercial shareholding. This partnership expired in 1975. The company proved to be under-capitalized and, by the time of the withdrawal of the commercial partners, the nation's steadily declining economic situation had itself compounded the company's problems.

At this critical moment Ghana invited the Federal Republic of Germany to develop the water transport scheme within the context of bilateral agreements that existed between the two countries. This led to a feasibility study which promised to be the most hopeful solution to the lake's recurrent anxieties of the past fifteen years. Broadly speaking it is estimated that by 1986 almost a half of the cargo traffic that is normally carried in what is known as 'the lake influence areas' will be carried by improved lake transportation. This is in contrast to the mere 5 per cent that was being carried on the lake when these figures were prepared in 1977.

To enable a sound start to be made the West German government has made available a loan of DM 88 million which, as near as matters, is the equivalent of US $37.3 million. The Ghana government will provide ¢59 million (equivalent to US $22 million) but both the German and the Ghanaian contributions would have been worth a mere US $11 million in 1964, so it can be seen as a much more modest approach than its predecessor. Yet it appears to have its feet on the ground or, perhaps more appropriately, its keel in the water.

In fact only Phase One of the overall plan, drawn up by West German consultants, GOPA, is covered by this particular loan – the development of cargo services and the necessary ports, harbours, navigational aids and equipment to maintain such a system. Phase Two, which is the bulk transportation of petroleum products to the north and a very important sector of potential lake transport, must await a further injection of financing. Passengers for the present will continue to be carried on the existing vessels. Lake Volta is at last about to start to come into its own as the nation's No. 1 Highway.

While the benefits are essentially directed at Ghana and Ghanaians, they will clearly overflow into adjacent territories, and it is anticipated that the spin-off advantages will go deep into the nation's economy. The savings in foreign exchange for road transport inputs (estimated in 1977–8 as 25 per cent of the total national imports), will be considerable when the heavy north–south traffic has been relieved by lake transport. The benefits to northern farmers (as well as southern consumers) arising from cheaper transport for produce coming south and for fertilizers and equipment going north should help to reduce the cost of living and provide greater incentives. Indeed the number of enterprising young people who are likely to find new openings and opportunities on and around the lake may be surprisingly great. I have always believed, since my first lake journey in 1965, that Lake Volta – so little known to Ghanaians themselves – is destined to play a most significant and as yet unforeseen part in the nation's future.

TOWARDS AN INTEGRATED ALUMINIUM INDUSTRY

Ghana's long-term programme to fit the aluminium smelter at Tema into what is known as a vertically integrated aluminium industry, i.e. designed to produce from top to bottom, bauxite, alumina, ingot and rolled sheet for manufacturing purposes – led to the creation in 1972 of the Aluminium Industries Commission (AIC) to oversee the interest of the government in the venture, first as a shareholder, and second as the custodian of the people.

Almost immediately a prospecting licence was issued to the Bauxite Alumina Study Company Ltd (BASCOL), a group comprising the Kaiser Corporation and a number of Japanese aluminium companies. Their common interest was to mine bauxite in the Atewa mountains near Kibi and to process it into alumina for use in their smelters at Tema and, for this purpose, the Japanese companies intended to construct a small (50,000 tons p.a.) smelter and to feed it with Akosombo power. Indeed, without the smelter, the Japanese group was not interested. The venture fell through when Valco decided to take up its existing option to add a fifth pot-line (opened in 1977) and the government accepted this firm commitment in lieu of the unconfirmed Japanese offer. Kaiser declared himself not ready to go it alone with the alumina plant plant and no alternative partner could be found,

Meanwhile a comprehensive BASCOL report had been submitted in 1975. This was more recently up-dated by AIC. Though Kaiser stated that there are distinct advantages to Valco in using locally produced alumina, according to Kaiser these are at present outweighed by negative economic factors. The BASCOL report claims that the project would be unprofitable for the first seven years and only marginally profitable thereafter. Kaiser also claims that Ghana has not yet spelt out its terms in the matter of partnership and that there are many undecided factors such as whether the plant should be near the bauxite at Kibi or near the smelter at Tema. Meanwhile other groups – one Hungarian – have also submitted studies, some more optimistic than BASCOL, but even if an early start could be made there is little chance of Ghana alumina being available before the end of the decade.[1]

Working vertically downwards the AIC has been more successful, for work has already started on a government owned sheet-casting and rolling plant at Tema to use Valco-made primary aluminium. Aluworks Ltd should start production in 1984, with an initial output of 10,000 tonnes per annum in sheet for roofing material and for the manufacture of cooking pots and utensils. A later development is likely to be the all-important plant for making beer and mineral and food-packing cans. However a clause in the aluminium supply contract precludes the raw material from being taken out of Ghana, which is designed to prevent Valco's product finding its way surrepticiously to competitive markets elsewhere in West Africa.

The $33.7 million plant – financed by fourteen overseas banks – is to be managed for two years by Fata Industrial SPA of Italy, with the installation of the equipment and the design and construction of buildings in Ghanaian hands. AIC and possibly some Ghana banks are to be joint shareholders. This a bold challenge to Ghanaian ability and integrity. If it succeeds it will be a major step forward.

[1] A further positive step forward was taken in mid 1983 by the Rawlings government which financed from domestic sources through AIC an internationally backed feasibility study to assess the viability of an 800,000 tonne capacity alumina plant and bauxite mine at Sajumasi near Kibi. The working consortium includes US, Swedish and Swiss mining interests.

28

THE NKRUMAH-KAISER 'RAPPORT'

Some time after Kwame Nkrumah's fall from grace in 1966 his friend Edgar Kaiser was reported as saying, 'Nkrumah and I achieved a good rapport, but it wasn't so much the cut of my hair he liked. He liked our money.'[1] This was a surprising thing for Edgar Kaiser to say – not because it was unkind (I fear that after Nkrumah's disgrace he was subject to a lot of calumny, not least from Ghanaians themselves who lampooned him mercilessly until death restored to him the dignity and respect due to the Founder of the Nation) but because it was basically untrue. There is no doubt that Nkrumah desperately needed President Kennedy's support in 1961 to trigger off the international loans that made the Volta River Project a reality. But it was not Edgar Kaiser's money that made it possible.

Nkrumah invested £35 million ($100 million) of Ghanaian funds in the Volta Dam and Kaiser only £12 million ($34 million) of his money in the smelter. Everything else was borrowed both by Ghana and by Kaiser. Furthermore Kaiser was very adequately compensated by Ghana for his many and diverse consultancies.[2] It was a coming together of mutual interests and not, as Edgar Kaiser seems to have been hinting, a cap-in-hand relationship.

One of Kwame Nkrumah's most memorable traits was his immense personal charm which seemed to spring from an almost childlike simplicity of character. There was little or no weakness in this characteristic – indeed one sometimes suspects that he played his charm like a trump card when necessity arose – but it was a natural and not a contrived asset.

[1] *Forbes Magazine* 101, No. 8, 1968.
[2] Twenty-one in number between 1959 and 1974 (R. Graham).

An instance of this easy relationship with his peers was the miniature 'toy fair' that became an annual event between him and General Spears, the veteran chairman of Ashanti Goldfields, who made it a habit to winter at the goldmine each year where he played the traditional role of squire and father figure. Sir Edward Spears, renowned during the war as Churchill's man in the Middle East, scented out Nkrumah's fondness for working models and mechanical toys and made an arrangement with Hamleys of Regent Street to supply him every Christmas with their most fascinating toy of the season. From his Accra pad, the Villa Rose, the General would call to pay his official respects to Osagyefo Dr Kwame Nkrumah at Flagstaff House and, while the conventional greetings were being exchanged, the chauffeur would be struggling in with the strangely shaped tinsel-wrapped parcels.

And then they would be left to themselves – crawling, puffing and blowing around the floor – shunting engines, launching Space Rockets or otherwise manipulating whatever had caught the toy connoisseurs' fancy that season. Thus the world's richest goldmine did its loyal obeisance year by year . . . and duly prospered.

Nkrumah's personal relationship with Edgar Kaiser was not dissimilar. I have frolicked with them in the Flagstaff House private zoo – riding camels, feeding the crocs and the pythons and chortling at the antics of the chimpanzees. Haile Selassie's present of a young lion cub, a junior Lion of Judah, was always a great attraction. These informal get-togethers were inevitably a laugh-a-minute and there can be no doubt that the human fun was mutual. It was however a necessary yeast with which to leaven deadly serious issues. *Forbes Magazine* put it this way: 'Edgar Kaiser himself has become so good in dealing with prickly foreigners that for a time, in 1961, he served as the only link between the US and Ghanaian governments during the critical period when Nkrumah refused to receive the American Ambassador.'

This indeed was that nerve-racking year (featured in Chapter 11) when Nkrumah was frantically trying to shake off his feelings of total subordination to the West with a stimulatingly successful two month visit to Khrushchev and Mao Tse-tung, whilst at the same time being warmly welcomed at the White House by the Kennedy family as their first visiting Head of State and hosting Queen Elizabeth and Prince Philip in Accra on a memorable visit.

And the year ended with full agreement being given to the US loans for the Volta River Project and by contrast the departure into voluntary exile of K. A. Gbedemah who had done so much to help Nkrumah to bring the Project to life.

Edgar Kaiser, more than anyone else, had a common interest with Nkrumah to make the Project a success – albeit for totally different reasons – and was able over a period of almost eight years to participate in this astonishing friendship. It was only in 1963[1] that one sensed that Edgar Kaiser was near to doubting his own convictions in the wake of emotional anti-American demonstrations in the streets of Accra, but his interests and his business sense persuaded him not to give in and he went straight ahead with building his smelter. Ten months later at the ground-breaking ceremony Kaiser and Nkrumah were again flattering each other, this time in blank verse, with an additional quote from the late President Kennedy who had said of 'the new states whom we welcome to the land of the free . . . we shall not always expect to find them supporting our view. But we shall always hope to find them strongly supporting their own freedom.'

And that in a sense is just the line that Nkrumah took in his book *Neo-colonialism – the Last Stage of Imperialism* which he published the following year and in which he made explicit accusations of US subversion in Africa by every possible means from Jehovah's Witnesses, the Peace Corps and USIS, to coups, and assassinations and even slanted Hollywood wild-west films. These charges, like Robert Southey's chickens and curses, soon came home to roost when in the words of *The New York Times*, commenting on the coup that caught Nkrumah nodding in Peking, 'the CIA advised and supported the Ghanaian Army and Police Officers who took over the Government.'

With the completion of the Akosombo Dam the safe-keeping of Valco's embryo smelter became a top priority to the US government, and Edgar Kaiser himself was assured from more than one quarter that before his smelter was in operation Kwame Nkrumah would not be there to covet it. As a man with so much capacity for good relations this must surely have saddened him. But as a remarkably clear-headed businessman no doubt he welcomed it as a cautious insurance premium.

[1] Pages 205–8.

The relationship between Edgar Kaiser and Kwame Nkrumah has often seemed to me to have much in common with the life cycle of a Jumbo Jet. For the first two years – the fabricating years – the firm foundations of common interests and mutual understanding were laid. This gave the friendship its durability. From 1960 onwards however, when they were truly airborne, they had to alternate between smooth flying with happy landings for the most part, punctuated by sudden turbulance and fearful storms – sometimes falling into deep pockets of depression, as the economic, the Cold War and the basic ideological disparities tested them to the brink of the safety margins. But the true strength of their relationship kept them aloft. That is, until the useful life of the Jumbo Jet had been spent and by February 1966 it could fly no more and this remarkable association came to an end.

Edgar Kaiser saw in the fantastically cheap electric power that he alone, with his dual expertise as a dam builder and as an aluminium producer, could extract from Ghana, the opportunity to bring untold riches to his family business. And at the same time Kwame Nkrumah knew, after a number of grim disappointments, that it was only the unique power of American capital backing the skills and enthusiasm of the Kaiser consortium that would give him the entrée to a new industrial economy that was his cherished goal for Ghana. And, even though he disliked intensely the ideology of US capitalism and, later on believed that it had cheated him of the wider industrial economy that he had set his heart on, in favour of a single American-owned enclave which was essentially self-prospering, he too pulled out every stop to fulfil his dreams.

Thus the Nkrumah-Kaiser 'rapport' was born and indeed flourished and if, in truth, it was more in the nature of cupboard love than a fusion of hearts it was nevertheless a very real force and, most certainly, changed the course of Ghana history.

29

ONE PERSON CAN MAKE A DIFFERENCE!

Kaiser's first public appearance on the Ghana scene was in 1958 as consultant called in to find a cure for the prematurely ailing Project. Having prescribed a remedy which was to ensure life for the Project in its barest essentials – a hydro-electric generating complex providing primarily for an aluminium smelter which would itself over a period of years pay for the power installation – Kaiser next designed and supervised construction of the dam and powerhouse itself. This done he then, in a remarkable turnabout from engineer to entrepreneur, put together the smelter project, designed it, found finance for it, and proceeded to build it and run it.

Next he turned his attention to exploring Ghana for some of the multipurpose aspects of the project, principally the use of Lake Volta water for large scale agricultural irrigation and the development of the 250-mile long lake into a major highway into the interior. Difficulties in international financing however coupled with low government priority made it impossible for these VRA-sponsored research proposals to be implemented.

There were other Kaiser consultancies during this period which probed the possibilities of further expansion. The first of several studies into the establishment of a rolling mill at Tema, to convert Valco ingot into household articles and building materials, proved to be uneconomic. And in 1971 Kaiser Engineers made a comprehensive re-appraisal of Ghana's whole power potential: Akosombo, Kpong, Bui and half-a-dozen other sites.

Kaiser next re-addressed himself to one of the major drawbacks of the 1958/9 re-assessment report, which had been to feed the smelter with imported alumina rather than to manufacture alumina in Ghana from locally-mined bauxite. This apparent economic necessity (it cut more than £60 million[1] from the original capital cost) seemed from the outset to favour Kaiser – with his existing alumina facilities elsewhere and his fleet of ore-carrying vessels – and to be a severe blow to Ghana which urgently needed to develop her own bauxite and alumina resources. So it was a further blow when the 1975 BASCOL report (a joint Kaiser and Japanese study) concluded that there was still no immediate economic prospect of utilizing Ghana bauxite and alumina for the Valco smelter. Meanwhile Valco had twice expanded its capacity – first in 1972 to its original limit of 160,000 tons per annum. This has variously been interpreted as either major job satisfaction or a successful bid to hog the local smelting field.

When Edgard Kaiser died in December 1981 Ghana's normally divided Parliament, in the last Parliamentary debate of the Third Republic (for Parliament was abolished a fortnight later), united to pay tribute to the man who made such an immense contribution to Ghana's development. The consensus of opinion was that nothing less than an Edgar Kaiser Memorial Hospital would do justice to the greatness of the man and the Kaiser humanitarian legacy.

It will be recalled that as far back as 1960, Kaiser complained to Nkrumah (p. 106) that some of the Ghanaian negotiations in the power talks gave the impression that he (Kaiser) was driving too hard a bargain for Valco. In preparing his figures in the first place (2.5 mills as against the World Bank's 4.5 mills) Kaiser worked on the assumption that the future VRA would earn considerable revenue not only from the sale of power but also from a flourishing lake transport system, from large-scale irrigation, from tourism and from food supplies from the lake and vicinity. Little indeed of this materialized, so it could be said that Kaiser's calculations were founded on premature and in many cases unattainable factors. He also argued (which was true at the time) that there was a grave aluminium recession and that, unless the power rates were attractive enough, the Valco shareholders simply would not invest.

This is seen today by many observers of the Valco–Ghana power rate negotiations as having been a gigantic bluff at Nkrumah's expense by the Kaiser–Reynolds team.

[1] $180 m.

Fortified by the still unexplained volte-face of the World Bank who, in place of their hard-line support for an economic power rate, suddenly fell in line with the meagre Kaiser figure, the skilled Valco negotiators unquestionably outwitted the less experienced Ghanaian team, banking on Nkrumah's anxiety not to forfeit his objective. Whereas in truth there was no way in which Edgar Kaiser, backed by the State Department, would have withdrawn from this golden opportunity. It is for this reason that today Ghana views with some cynicism Valco's plausible claim to a watertight legality for their bargain-basement power rate. Legality is not the real issue. Edgar Kaiser himself liked to insist that such joint investment returns should be measured in terms of people – their aspirations, hopes and ideals – as surely as they are expressed in balance sheets. And it is precisely in this field that the people of Ghana, in contrast to the shareholders of Valco, continue to hold what has to be described as the dirty end of the stick.

So Valco got its attractive terms, unchangeable for thirty years, which, if not in fact too hard a bargain (for there were indeed lower power rates existing both in the USA and elsewhere), was nevertheless both a very favourable and an unrealistic one. In spite of the thirty years clause, which most observers would say gave too little allowance for changing circumstances, Valco has in fact bowed to the inevitable and has agreed to several interim power rate increases. And at the time of writing, the pressure on Valco to accept a major increase and indeed to re-negotiate the whole 1962 Master Agreement is very much on.

In fact this is far more than a domestic matter between Ghana and Valco, for the international aluminium industry is currently having to face up to facts which may shake one of its basic precepts, viz. that aluminium smelters must be sited where cheap power rates prevail. This was certainly the case twenty years ago, but the growing dependence on more expensive forms of power generation – coal-fired and nuclear – is creating a world-wide trend towards equalizing the price of energy from various sources. Twenty mills is now quoted as being an average power rate for smelters, with instances of fifty or more. It is in Valco's and in Ghana's interests that a rate acceptable to both, and in line with changing world rates, will emerge.

Kaiser's critics, who in recent years have been as outspoken in the USA as in Ghana itself, point out that the 1962 Master Agreement has had just as crippling an effect on the future of Ghana's bauxite and alumina processing industries as it has had on the application of the power rates. For whereas a combination of pressures has made at least minor power rate increases inevitable, Kaiser contrived to circumvent in the Master Agreement any future obligations whatever to use Ghana-made alumina in the smelter. True – there were ultimate incentives, but they only compensated Ghana with modest tax increases. It may be argued that, in ducking any obligations in this matter, Kaiser, in the light of events, has again proved himself to be the master negotiator for he still claims that – in present circumstances – the alumina venture would be unprofitable and therefore an unwelcome bride for the affluent smelter. But he goes on record as stating that 'ultimately there will be a plant in Ghana which will utilize this resource and will supply the Valco smelter with local alumina. But when this will occur is difficult to predict.'

Indeed it has always been difficult to predict. In 1969 in a review of the first edition of this book the magazine *West Africa* joined issue with me claiming to 'disagree profoundly' with my statement that 'for the time being' the smelter would continue to depend on imported alumina. 'Happily', the reviewer said 'there is now plenty of evidence that Valco is interested in developing Ghana's bauxite and establishing a refinery.' This was during the short-lived Second Republic under Dr Busia's ill-fated Premiership. Busia who, when in opposition, had tried his utmost to try to ditch the Volta River Project by appealing to the US government to withdraw the loans, had curiously when in office almost lured Edgar Kaiser to invest in an alumina plant. Possibly Kaiser reckoned that Busia was not the bouncing sort and that he could safely invest. But the euphoria did not last and it was not long before Kaiser was again pleading the 'negative economic factor'. And there the case has since rested, blowing sometimes hot and sometimes cold. Kaiser himself insists that a future decision depends on economic and not political factors. Assuming this to be the case Ghana's de facto devaluation of May 1983 may prove to be one of the economic factors that could cast a decision in favour of the local industry but Kaiser is likely to base any future decision on very long-term rather than short-term factors. Meanwhile Valco continues to import American alumina processed from Jamaica bauxite.

By 1980 the 'Hang the Kaiser' lobby in the United States was being firmly pushed along by Ralph Nader's *Multinational Monitor* and by Lindsay Mattison's Center for Development Policy – both immensely active pressure groups. Having worked successfully enough on a section of the US press and on African student movements they turned in 1981 to the Presbyterian Church in the United States whose Atlanta Presbytery was already involved with the Christian Council of Ghana in a project to relieve the suffering of people displaced by the Akosombo Dam. In its chosen absence from the one-day public discussion held in Atlanta in May, the Kaiser Corporation came in for severe attacks and was held largely responsible for many of the misfortunes of the 80,000 displaced people. Indeed very shortly afterwards the 121st General Assembly of the Presbyterian Church in the United States passed a resolution calling for a re-negotiation of the 1962 Master Agreement 'on a basis more equitable to the people of Ghana and more consistent with genuine human development'.

Much emphasis was placed at the discussion on the nightmare proportions of the new lake's capacity for spreading disease and death at a speed that was almost as fast as the lake flow itself. Within the space of four years – between 1960 and 1964 – the dread bilharzia (urinary schistosomiasis) spread from a mere 5 per cent incidence in riparian children to an outrageous 90 per cent amongst lakeside children, and today virtually the whole 4,000-mile shoreline is infected wherever there are people. The incidence of river blindness (onchocarciasis), the lake's other devastating disease, is not nearly so widespread, as the offending simulium fly only breeds in fast running water and these areas are limited to tributary locations. But where they do exist the result is equally devastating and here again the infection today in some of these areas is more than 90 per cent in children over fifteen years old. This obviously was not what Kaiser foresaw when he reserved his share of Lake Volta (considerably more than half of it) with which to energize his smelter and one wonders whether his actuaries, who were at such pains to calculate the earning capacity of Lake Volta when pressing their 2.5 mills power rate claim in 1960, had done equivalent homework into the *cost* potential of maintaining the lake.

Valco does acknowledge some responsibility for the lake's terrible health record and is spending money on research at Johns Hopkins University in Baltimore, Maryland. No figure is mentioned. In Valco's own words, 'This School of Tropical Medicine has been testing a new drug for the treatment of schistosomiasis. The animal tests indicate that all varieties of schistosomiasis can be effectively treated with this new drug which is easy to administer, effective, inexpensive and with no known adverse side effects. We are helping to fund extensions from animal tests to treatment of human beings and if the results of human testing are satisfactory, we would expect to assist in field tests in Ghana. Such a drug may be a more practical way to control the effects of bilharzia than either attempting to eliminate the snail vector or persuading the lakeside dwellers to adopt the sanitary standards needed to eliminate the problem.'

This is a welcome development with, it is hoped, beneficial potential, but in the meantime it has been tabbed in responsible quarters as 'chicken feed'.

Another severe critic of the Ghana/Valco relationship is a former Edinburgh University student, David Hart, who in 1973 became interested in the Volta River Project as part of a wider study at that university of major river projects around the world. In 1980 he published his findings,[1] having spent six months in Ghana researching his subject. He concludes that Ghana has emerged a very second best with Valco the clear winner; he does not ascribe this unsatisfactory state of affairs to 'intentional exploitation'. Indeed he states, 'I have come across no avowed desire on the part of anyone to exploit Ghana' (presumably he is writing in the VRP context). But he does believe that Ghana has been the victim of 'unintentional exploitation resulting from narrow self-interest'.

Inevitably we return to the divergent roles which Kaiser chose to play. The culmination of the power rate struggle of 1960 was that the figure agreed was not only an incentive to the smelter shareholders at a time of crisis in the industry but was also acceptable to the World Bank for repayment of long-term loans from which the dam and power plant were built; Ghana accepted the inevitable,

[1] *The Volta River Project.* A case study in Politics and Technology. Edinburgh University Press.

content that the much sought-after project would go ahead.

What concerns Hart and other analysts today is that in order to achieve this guaranteed security for the all-powerful aluminium industry, something else had to snap. And what noone at the time was apparently far-sighted enough to see was that it was the very people who were hurriedly leaving their homes to escape the energy-committed waters who were doomed to bear the full brunt of what must be seen as a grave miscalculation. And it was nothing to do with the skeleton houses that they were obliged to occupy, nor with the over-complicated new farming techniques that they simply could not absorb. These transitional misfortunes were part and parcel of a great experiment which had no precedents. It was the explosion within Lake Volta – largely through unpremeditated settlement on the lake shore – of those dense pockets of infection that has shocked the world. Hart's conclusion that such appalling conditions do arise in part from 'unintentional exploitation' is difficult to question.

Endeavouring to point some constructive remedies from his critical case study he firmly recommends a better price for electricity sold to Valco and a revision of the Master Agreement to oblige Valco to pay the normal company tax instead of its concessionary rates. The extra money he believes should be spent on improved health care for the lake people and for more adequate lake transport but, as he cannily hints, this would depend on Ghana's internal political situation. He also develops the idea often ventilated over the years that, in order to hasten the advent of an integrated aluminium industry in West Africa, Ghana's smelter could use Guinea's existing alumina and could possibly supply a rolling mill in Nigeria, so furnishing all West Africa's needs, perhaps under the ECOWAS[1] umbrella. Since however a number of aluminium companies would be seriously affected by such a scheme he foresees a vast amount of opposition and even the risk of international boycott.

An even more recent and very keenly researched study of the complicated relationship over twenty-five years between Kaiser and Ghana is the backbone of Ronnie Graham's outspoken book,[2]

[1] The Economic Community of West African States (ECOWAS) comprises all sixteen West African nations.
[2] *The Aluminium Industry and the Third World.* Zed Press, London.

published in 1982, which he dedicates 'to the aluminium workers at Tema and the bauxite miners at Awaso in whose hands the future of Ghana's aluminium industry lies'. Graham, who describes his book as a work of Marxist history, had a close relationship with the University of Ghana in the 1970s and the philosophies that had been steadily developing there in the decade after the downfall of Nkrumah's government. Underlying this new approach was the determination of thinking Ghanaians to help to point their country positively in the direction of economic recovery and growth, against the apalling mismanagement and inconsistencies of successive regimes. Inevitably this radical approach had to impinge upon the interests of others already in the field. And Graham's book with detailed annotation, takes readers through the story of how the West's industrialists in their ever-growing need for raw materials (all too often one fears for instruments of destruction), comb the world for the best possible bargains and, having cornered them, in close association with their parent governments and interlocking banking systems, hang on to them like the muscular clams of the Volta River. In Ghana's case the basic raw material is cheap (extremely cheap) electric power and that at a time when all over the world the cost of alternative power supplies is rising astronomically. Small wonder that Valco's shareholders, Kaiser and Reynolds, feel outraged – even alarmed – at being asked to sacrifice their one trump card they fought so hard and successfully to capture. It seems to be little different from asking the Ghana Black Stars – when victorious in the Africa Cup Final – voluntarily to relinquish the Trophy. But some would see it differently of course for they would assume that the Trophy had been fairly won.

Graham's point is that in the circumstances that prevailed in 1961 Nkrumah stood no chance of securing a fair deal, having been indeed fortunate to have secured a deal at all. He ends his carefully argued 250-page study with the conclusion that the nation should start to move in the direction of a general withdrawal from the international capitalist system with consequent nationalization of foreign enterprises, and localization of management. This he feels would enable an ensuing vertically integrated aluminium industry to become the catalyst for future industrial development, thus fulfilling Kwame Nkrumah's cherished aims for the Volta River Project.

Of course it is pure political theory but, just as one of Edgar Kaiser's biographers describes him as 'a dreamer and a doer who envisioned what could be done and then set about doing it,'[1] so may such theories as these take root and grow.

Only the briefest reference is made in previous pages (p. 203) to what was at first known as the Special Fund and is now firmly established as the Valco Fund. In effect it is a profit-sharing agreement in which Valco and Ghana (the Fund) share equally the net annual profit (above the cost of investment and management) of the smelter. At one stage there was the suggestion that Ghana and the aluminium companies should share the equity of Valco on an equal basis. It was clear however that the aluminium companies did not favour the concept of mixing business and government capital. It was in these circumstances that the idea of the Valco Special Fund came to life on January 22, 1962, when it was jointly signed by Edgar Kaiser and Kwame Nkrumah.

There has since emerged a definable impression that the Valco Fund is some kind of charitable offering in which Ghana is favoured with largesse from a generous godmother. Nothing could be further from the truth. Nkrumah, who had been keen on the 50/50 shared equity basis, accepted the Valco Fund solution as Ghana's absolute right in lieu of the sacrificed opportunity for business participation, and there is a strong body of opinion in Ghana that this right of participation in Valco's dividends also confers on Ghana, as the equal partner, the additional right to participate in Valco decision making and, as a business formality and safeguard, in the drawing up of Valco's annual balance sheet.

The Valco Fund by its nature took, like a good fruit tree, some ten years to achieve maturity. The $100 million smelter, built largely from loans, has had to service its debts, it has had to cover the capital cost of expansion in 1972 and 1977, and it had to carry the annual cost of management and maintenance. Furthermore three power cuts (two of them very serious) had an adverse effect on profits in 1973, 1977 and 1978. By 1979 a useful $1.7 million had been paid into the Fund which enabled it to establish itself. By 1980 however the true value of the Valco Fund materialized when $9 million was paid in, followed by a further $11.3 million in 1981. Thus – were it not for growing inflation making serious

[1] Valco 1981 Annual Report.

inroads on profits[1] – the Valco Fund would be playing an expanding part each year in meeting some of the nation's medical, educational, social and cultural needs. The Trustees of the Valco Fund, who are all Ghanaians appointed by the Volta River Authority which administers the Fund, have already, to their credit, given a most diverse spread of grants which go deep into the nation's needs. A grant to help fill the vacuum in schools and colleges from years of severe text book shortages has started to succeed. Also of special interest was the grant in 1980 of ¢687,500 to Ghana's Ministry of Health to pay Ghana's share of a multinational effort combating river blindness in the Volta basin. 1979/80 may then be seen as a significant point in Valco's history when its level of profitability enabled not only the Valco Fund to come of age but, so we are told, for its own two shareholders, Kaiser and Reynolds, to draw their first dividends.

Kaiser as a corporation is very conscious – and rightly so – of its public image.

It needs to be since, as one of the top 100 public companies in the US, it is never far from the headlines and, like most of its contemporaries, has had its share of bright and gloomy patches.

Supporting Ghana's 'hard luck' case the fierce anti-Kaiser lobby even achieved the Jack Anderson column in the *Washington Post*. Not this, of course, but the corporation's understandable yen for a strong bond of corporate brotherhood must have triggered off Kaiser's 1981 nationwide TV jingle campaign 'ONE person CAN make a difference – YOU can!' The slogan, reproduced on mammoth hoardings, seemed to follow you around – in Jamaica, Louisiana, in West Virginia, in Ghana and even in Australia.

I believe that if the government of Ghana was to re-invest some of the VRA's hard-won dollar earnings in effective international public relations there would be a better chance that Ghana's powerful claim for a fairer deal from the Kaiser Corporation would be understood. Kwame Nkrumah would certainly have done so, as he fully appreciated the value of strong public relations.

The Kaiser Corporation has been described as patriarchal and patrilineal and it is true that both Henry J. and Edgar F. tended to play the role of father figures with plenty of good homely advice on 'giving yourself to the needs of others' and of 'investment of

[1] The 1982 payment, based on 1981 profits, fell to $2,175,000.

heart and soul'. Hart describes Henry J.'s homily (p. 93) as 'a piece of humbug' and claims that, having identified its aims in Ghana, the Kaiser Corporation did not sacrifice them or itself for the benefit of the people of Ghana.

Edgar F. in his letter to Nkrumah (p. 106) states that his company placed a bid to build the dam and was obliged to withdraw because, at Ghana's request, they are now sponsoring Valco. This is clearly intended to imply both a professional and a financial sacrifice, but to me it has the same minty flavour as Papa Henry J.'s homily that Hart refers to. And possibly Nkrumah was not aware that, for two whole years, forming the smelter consortium was Kaiser's principal interest in Ghana – as one of the 'top four' US aluminium companies. Ever since Vice-President Nixon's much publicized visit to the new nation and reports of his government's official interest in the Volta River Project, Kaiser had been lobbying the State Department by offering his services as a dam builder, as an entrée to the even more attractive smelter possibilities.

For here was a unique opportunity for one single industrial consortium to design and build – at no expense to themselves – a dam and power plant with the principal aim of providing a guaranteed source of very cheap electric power for the consortium's own aluminium smelter. For Kaiser there had been no sacrifice whatever – only a heaven-sent shower of blessings.

But history will relate – and it will be right – that Nkrumah and Kaiser (with a little help from their friends) made the Volta River Project a reality and, in so doing have conferred upon the nation an untold benefit which could last forever. That there are grave problems still to be resolved is without question and the negotiations will undoubtedly continue. Edgar Kaiser's death in 1981 removed the key figure from the negotiating table – though he had in fact retired the previous year – and his place was taken by his successor as chairman of the board of Kaiser Aluminum and Chemical Corporation, Mr Cornell C. Maier. In the talks[1] that may still bond the close historic association between Ghana and Kaiser, ONE person CAN make a difference. YOU can, Mr Maier!

[1] The negotiations between the government of Ghana and Valco to discuss various aspects of the Master Agreement opened in Accra in February 1983 but, after three rounds of meetings, reached an apparent deadlock in May when the government of Ghana felt obliged to break off negotiations. The talks were resumed in January 1984.

30

THE CHALLENGE

It is indeed a long cry from the days in 1966 when the VRA was obliged to 'boil' the waters of the Volta (page 227) because, prior to the opening of the Valco Smelter in 1967 and to supplying the mines, a single generator at Akosombo yielded more power than the nation's demand of 75mw.

Five years later, when Akosombo was operating five of its six generators full-time, the nation's consumption had more than doubled, Valco had stepped up its demand by one-third and Ghana was exporting (also for foreign currency) 25mw to the Communauté Electrique du Benin (CEB) in Togo and Dahomey (now Benin). Another five years and Valco was taking its permitted total of 400mw, CEB had doubled to 50mw and Ghana's own consumption, including the mines, had risen to 260mw. Akosombo power had virtually reached its limit.

It was now that the VRA, using its own financial resources as a base, went out to raise the necessary loans with which to construct its 'mini-Akosombo' dam, downstream at Kpong. And in another five years the VRA was again thought to be 'ahead of the game' with enough surplus current to enable overworked Akosombo to enjoy some well earned relief. But as we have already noted, the drastic fall in the level of the Lake Volta effectively counter-balanced the potential Kpong advantage.

The CEB story however well illustrates the VRA's growing inter-territorial role. When, in 1964, Togo and Dahomey asked the United Nations to help them develop the hydraulic resources of their frontier river, the Mono, both for energy and for irrigation, they were disappointed to find that the venture was unlikely to be economic. Further investigation however showed that their energy requirements could be satisfied by importing the current either from Nigeria or from Ghana. This scheme proved attractive when relations had eased between Ghana and her neighbours following Nkrumah's overthrow in 1966 and, with generous help from Canada, which made the scheme practicable, an agreement was signed in 1969 between the VRA and the CEB. The line, which extends 188 miles (300 kilometers) from Akosombo via Lome to Cotonou was commissioned in 1972 with a contractual limit of 50mw, which was reached by stages over a period of five years.[1]

A further move towards an integrated power system for the entire West African Region (outlined on page 247) occurred in 1981 when steps were taken to link Ghana to the Ivory Coast with an 85-mile (140 kilometer) power line extending from Prestea to Abidjan. The Ivory Coast has 648mw of power, derived partly from its hydro project at Kossou and partly from the thermal (oil powered) unit in Abidjan. By joining the two countries' systems there will be a great savings in standby reserve. For example if the time comes for the proposed Bui reservoir to fill, over a period of eighteen months, the corresponding flow of water entering Lake Volta would be reduced and electricity generation would fall. This would be an opportunity for Ivory Coast power to be 'borrowed'.

But on completion of Bui there would for a time be a surplus of power in Ghana, some of which could be used to advantage in the Ivory Coast. If indeed, as is the plan, the Bui project was also to supply part of the needs of Upper Volta, then that country too would be connected indirectly to Ivory Coast power whilst, to the east, Benin may wish to link with Nigeria's adjacent power resources.[2] Thus would the combined electrical energy of Nigeria, Ghana and the Ivory Coast be available for shared use by themselves and by their neighbours.

With the commissioning of the Ghana–Ivory Coast inter-tie project before the close of 1983 the first step will indeed have been taken towards the realisation of a trans West African power grid. Fifty-eight per cent of the Volta basin lies outside Ghana and it is

[1] During a second five-year period the limit was again increased and in 1982 CEB consumption had reached 85mw.

[2] A study for this was indeed made in 1971. At the time of writing a further joint study is being made for the interconnection of the electrical systems of Nigeria, Benin, Togo and Ghana.

understandable that the five 'shareholders' notably Upper Volta, the senior member,[1] would wish to enjoy their respective water resource dividends for agricultural, industrial and social uses. The VRA's role, as Ghana's representative in a regional planning body for water resources as a whole, becomes clear.

Meanwhile having successfully launched the Kpong Project with its key auxiliary and compensating benefits to Ghana's power needs the VRA is bringing its next project to life – the $500 million (half a billion)[2] Bui Project on the Black Volta, which borders the Ivory Coast. First recognized by Kitson in 1925 as a potential hydro-electric development, Bui was subsequently studied by Halcrow (1954), Hydroproject of USSR (1964), Kaiser (1971) and finally by the Snowy Mountains Engineering Corporation (SMEC) of Australia in 1976. With minor variations all concluded that Bui will be the second largest hydro-electric project in Ghana after Akosombo, with a clay core rockfill dam of nearly the same height as Akosombo – 426 feet (130 M) to Akosombo's 438 feet (134 M). Capable of generating about half of Akosombo's 882mw, it would carry three units, each capable of generating 150mw, i.e. thrice the Kpong generating power. A lake of some 40 miles in length up the Black Volta, backing up the dam, will in fact cross the Ivory Coast border at three points for a short distance, which is one of the items – including the future supply of power – covered by the 1980 agreement between the governments of Ghana, Ivory Coast and Upper Volta. SMEC duly completed all the preliminary engineering for the project and, early in 1982, everything stood ready for the contract to be advertised.

Bui is planned as a five-year construction and reservoir filling job so that, if power were needed in 1988, work should have been started in 1983. But if Akosombo/Kpong power (with possible Ivory Coast supplements) can be made to spin out till 1990, then 1985 would not be too late to start. Meanwhile the VRA is keeping in touch with lending agencies, many of whom have expressed their provisional agreement to help to finance Bui.

And what should follow? Recent studies by SMEC into the potential of the River Oti which supplies Lake Volta with one

[1] Upper Volta 43 per cent of the basin area. Ghana 41.5 per cent, Togo 6.5 per cent, Benin 3.5 per cent, Mali 3 per cent, Ivory Coast 2.5 per cent.

[2] At 1980 prices (equivalent to £250 m).

third of its water, suggest that a dam at or near the town of Juale, near to Bimbila in the Northern Region, could be capable of generating a further 200mw. Lake Oti would stretch 100 miles northwards from Lake Volta almost as far as Sansanne Mango, with the upper part of the lake forming part of the Togo border. Here again regional planning is an essential ingredient.

And it is this regional aspect of such projects as Bui and Oti which complicates their progress for, as major contributors to a West African power grid, they are bound, so far as the international lending agencies are concerned, to be considered alongside other comparable projects in neighbouring West Africa territories. So whilst the VRA can and does continue to plan for the future, the ultimate decision 'to be or not to be' will inevitably depend on much wider regional considerations.

But this does not prevent the VRA from exploring the potential of Ghana's much smaller hydro-electric sources, such as the centrally located Pra River which has the added advantage of drawing its water supply from catchment areas that do not supply Volta. And this the VRA is now doing, perhaps concentrating on the need for comparatively small generating plants fed solely by the seasonal river flow rather than from a major lake or reservoir. For several months each year power may be fed into the national grid, thereby taking some of the load off Akosombo, which could then progressively restore its sadly depleted reserves of water.

If Ghana's plans for its macro-economy are able to include some selected industrial projects – for example a ferro-manganese plant using locally mined minerals – in addition to the urgent need for major agricultural investment and development, then some additional power generation will soon become necessary quite independent of the broader regional projects. And other possible solutions to Ghana's short-term power needs which the VRA is exploring include conservation of existing power, such as necessary restrictions on existing consumers;[1] studying the potential of available sources of natural gas; and the best use of the new inter-tie systems.

[1] Indeed Valco was asked by VRA to close down its pot lines by June 15, 1983, until the level of Lake Volta had risen, in order to prevent damage to generating equipment. It was hoped that the level would start to recover during the second half of the year, but that this did not happen – and the immediate consequences – is made clear in the Postscript on p. 290.

But perhaps the most important decision that Ghana will be obliged to make, once the VRA's generating capacity has been fully restored, is how to market this valuable commodity to best national advantage. Valco's traditional role as the major power consumer – so vital to Akosombo's economic well-being in its formative years – may well have to give way to competitive claims both from within Ghana and from its inter-tied neighbours from consumers who are anxious to pay the full market value. This could even downgrade the whole concept of an integrated aluminium industry as an economic goal for Ghana if it was found that the non-availability of cheap electric power had pulled the rug from underneath the aluminium smelting sector of the industry.

Who then in the year 1983 constitutes the VRA? In 1981 Louis Casely Hayford, a distinguished engineer, whose father and grandfather were great nationalist figures in the fifty years after the First World War, succeeded Dr E. L. Quartey, Chief Exeuctive of the Volta River Authority from 1966. One of the original Akosombo powerhouse engineers, Casely Hayford rose to be VRA's Chief Engineer before succeeding to the top job. His deputy Kobla Kalitsi, who features much in these pages as the 'father' of Akosombo resettlement, is another founder member of the VRA team and has played a leading role in its financial planning and administration for over twenty years. Backing them up is a formidable team of engineering, administrative, legal, financial, medical, personnel, public relations and archival specialists each of whom is a long-standing component of the greater VRA family – for it undoubtedly carries a recognizable cognate quality.

The VRA has been responsibly described as unique amongst Ghana's public corporations in being untouched by scandal and with a clear reputation for straight dealing. It is a record for which it deserves to be proud.

It was born late in 1961 from the womb of the Volta River Project Secretariat, which guided the negotiations on behalf of Ghana for the previous two years. Staffed by experienced civil service administrators and strengthened by international specialists, the secretariat, led by Nkrumah and his supporting Ministers, did a sterling job in handling Ghana's part in the complicated international negotiations. But whether, as with hindsight we can see it today, they were wholly equal to countering the sophisticated know-how and actuarial skills of some of the cream of America's business negotiators, is now questioned. The Master Agreement[1] that appeared at that time to be fair, still frozen for thirty years against all equitable adjustment, cannot be said to have been in Ghana's long-term interest. In this lies the basis of Ghana's current claim for a serious review of the Master Agreement and its provisions.

The VRA inherited this legacy from its parent body. But though bound absolutely by the terms of the agreement, the VRA has not been content to accept the status quo without regular calls for power rate revision. And these, by mutual agreement and based on inflationary pressures which increased the cost of electricity generation at Akosombo, were twice increased in the 1972–3 period from 2.625 mills to 2.75 mills and later to 3.25 mills. In 1977 a new basis, involving an annual escalation clause, was agreed, with the rate rising from 4.5 mills in 1976 to 5.00 mills in 1981 and thereafter.

At this point Valco feels it has voluntarily done all that is necessary to temper the terms of its thirty-year agreement with the recognition of the effects of basic inflation. It is still buying at Akosombo some of the cheapest non-subsidized power in the world and its justification is that this accords with the letter and spirit of the 1962 Power Contract.

The VRA's contention is that the 1962 Power Contract was agreed against the background of a world aluminium recession and the need to offer the aluminium companies an incentive but, in all fairness and in light of changing world conditions, the incentive didn't have to hold good for thirty years. Furthermore the 1962 rates, paid in dollars, were considered to be just sufficient to enable VRA to service its long-term constructional debts – but with very little to spare, calculated to cover generating costs only.

What seems clear today is that the generating costs are only a part of the VRA's obligatory outgoings to provide Valco with power. What was not taken into account when the Power Contract was signed was the cost of replacements, under inflationary conditions, for maintaining the lake itself (two-thirds of it is there specifically for Valco's needs) and of combating wholly unforeseen levels of disease and of continuing scientific research. Furthermore the

[1] See Sir Robert Jackson's remarks, pages 16 and 17.

recent study by Acres, which reveals a decrease of 20 per cent in the long-term power generation capability of Akosombo when compared with Kaiser's evaluation twenty-five years ago, is very significant.

All these factors, and many others, strengthen the VRA's belief that a major review of the Master Agreement and its Power Contract is now fully justified. Perhaps it will require a build-up of public opinion to persuade Valco but it might be more in keeping with the declared Kaiser tradition of the fair sharing of mutually earned benefits if the initiative were seen to come from the shareholders themselves.

It has been said[1] that Nkrumah 'looked at the VRA in much the same way as Roosevelt and his New Deal planners looked at the Tennessee Valley Authority in relation to the development of the US South.'

Today the TVA has thirty-six dams under its control with sixty-seven power stations. Within a generation or two the Volta and its basin tributaries could have as many as twelve separate generating dams and lakes, and an inland waterway of rivers and lakes extending perhaps 750 miles (1.200 kms) from south to north of Ghana and well into neighbouring countries. Combined with this would be power sales and exchange on a West African grid basis and agricultural irrigation and re-afforestation projects for human and industrial use.

It may be argued that this type of thinking is idealistic in the current West African context. And it is a fact that Ghana is obliged to import $300 million worth of food each year; this in itself suggests that money invested in agriculture today is more important to the Ghanaian householder than dreams of inland waterways and an abundance of electric power. Indeed the VRA would be the first to accept this view and, by its own example of irrigated agriculture, has already shown that it has a thoroughly pragmatic approach to the nation's priorities. But the dreams should not be forgotten, for a nation as rich in natural resources and in skilled manpower as it is Ghana's pride and privilege to boast can well afford to look into the future whilst it struggles to salvage the present.

The VRA inherited from its founder-chairman Kwame Nkrumah

[1] *The Structure of the Volta River Authority*, A. B. Futa, VRA, 1981.

a degree of autonomy as an international agency which it has largely retained. It is inspired by a healthy and financially buoyant spirit of independence, which enables it to negotiate international borrowing for project construction, to take the initiative in regional planning on a West African scale and to enjoy an enviable international reputation.

This is a solid foundation that Ghana can build on. The nation which plunged headlong in the early 1960s into some of the most controversial problems of the age, fired by age-long pride and spirit and a wholly understandable – if over-ambitious – determination to 'show the way' in newly independent Africa, has not in the event been able to derive much real satisfaction from the passage of its first twenty-five years.

But, dark as the hungry days of 1983 were, it was not difficult to detect a new spirit of self-help in the air. No longer would or could the government alone be the panacea for the nation's ills. Today Kofi Countryman intends to share the load and is well on the way to doing so. And if, with the example of the VRA and its skill and facility for regional planning and co-operation, Kofi – having gone some way to solving his immediate problems – can then start to look further afield to his ECOWAS neighbours, and if perhaps they can exchange a working knowledge of each other's languages, there is reason to hope that Ghana's second twenty-five years of Independence will prove to be the nation's turning point.

This surely is the immediate challenge for Ghana.

POSTSCRIPT – DECEMBER 1983

The dry cycle which has enveloped West Africa since 1971, and has contributed so much to suffering in the Sahelian zone in particular, has led to the inflow of water to Lake Volta falling below average in nine out of twelve years.

1982 proved to be the lowest influx for 47 years and 1983 lower still.

In spite of a well above average intake in 1979 and an average one in 1980 the level of the lake had dropped by the end of 1982 from 270 to 249 feet which is close to the minimum operational level.

Early in 1983 a policy of power cuts was introduced and the Valco smelter, as the major consumer, was required to reduce its consumption by stages so that by June 1983 only a token quantity of power was being supplied to Valco. Production at the smelter came to a halt in November.

Had the 1983 inflow proved to be normal it would have been possible to modify the policy of power cuts but, in the extreme circumstances of continuing drought conditions, it became necessary in November for Mr Louis Casely-Hayford, the Chief Executive of the Volta River Authority, in making public these facts, to announce the introduction of scheduled national power cuts throughout the country with effect from December 1st.

He explained that, with average river flow conditions in 1984, it should be possible to restore domestic supplies to normal levels in the second half of the year, with supply to major consumers following later in the year.

A further bad drought however would mean power cuts continuing for another year.

The Chief Executive believed that this calculated strategy would minimize the risks of a total collapse of the power system and furthermore enable the Akosombo Reservoir progressively to recover its normal level.

A visit to Ghana and to Akosombo during the first week of December 1983 by Mr A. W. Clausen, President of the World Bank, was seen to reflect – *inter alia* – a deep concern in the overall effects of Lake Volta's problems on the project as a whole. On the day of Mr Clausen's visit the lake level stood at 240 feet – 8 feet below the normal lake minimum, and having the effect of halving approximately both the rated lake area and volume.

BIBLIOGRAPHY

Though no attempt has been made to prepare a detailed bibliography of all the source material which has contributed to the preparation of this book the following references may be of assistance to those wishing to study further various aspects of the subject:

Chapter 1

W. E. F. WARD, *A Short History of Ghana*. 7th ed., 1957.

J. D. FAGE, *Ghana: A historical interpretation*. Madison, 1959.

A. A. BOAHEN, *Topics in West African History*. Longmans, 1966. (The origins of the Akan, etc.)

OLIVER DAVIES, 'Archaeological Exploration in the Volta Basin'. *Ghana Geographical Association Bulletin*, June 1964.

IVOR WILKS, *The Rise of the Akwamu Empire*. Transactions of the Historical Society of Ghana, 1957.

Chapter 2

H. M. STANLEY, *Coomassie and Magdala*. Sampson, Low, 1874.

G. A. HENTY, *The March to Coomassie*. Tinsley, 1874.

A. B. ELLIS, *A History of the Gold Coast of West Africa*. Chapman and Hall, 1893.

C. REINDORF, *A History of the Gold Coast and Asante*. Basel, 1895.

Chapter 3

M. GAUNT, *Alone in West Africa*. Warne, 1911.

Records in the National Archives of Ghana.

R. P. GOULD, *The Development of the Transportation Pattern in Ghana*. Evanston, Northwestern University, 1960.

Chapter 4

The Diaries of A. E. Kitson (1913–1927). Ghana Dept. of Geological Survey.

A. E. KITSON, *Geological Survey Bulletin*, 1925. 'Outline of the mineral resources of the Gold Coast.'

C. ST JOHN BIRD, *et. al.*, *Volta River Scheme*, Vols. 1–3. WAFAL, 1949.

Power from the Volta. Focus Group, Accra.

Aluminium Ingot production. Report of Joint Mission, B.A.C. Ltd. and Alcan Ltd., 1951.

Chapter 5

Report of the Commission of Enquiry into Disturbances in the Gold Coast, 1948. London, H.M.S.O., 1948 (Watson Report).

British West Africa Rice Mission Report, 1948.

Preliminary Report on development of the Volta River Basin. Sir William Halcrow and Partners, 1950.

Report on development of the Volta River Basin. Sir William Halcrow and Partners, 1950.

Chapter 6

Volta River Aluminium Scheme (White Paper, Colonial Office, London.) London, H.M.S.O., 1952.

Chapter 7
Volta River Project Preparatory Commission Report. Vols. 1–3. London, H.M.S.O., 1956.

Chapter 8
R. G. A. JACKSON, 'The Volta River Project.' *Progress*. Unilever, No. 4, 1964.
PRESIDENT EISENHOWER AND PRIME MINISTER NKRUMAH: *Joint Statement*. White House, Washington, July 1958.

Chapter 9
Publications of Kaiser Engineers Inc., Oakland, California. *Reassessment Report on the Volta River Project for the Government of Ghana*. Kaizer Engineering Inc., 1959

Chapter 10
Master Agreement between the Government of Ghana and Volta Aluminium Co. Ltd., 17th November, 1960.

Chapter 11
Ghana: The Volta River Project. Statement by the Government of Ghana. White Paper, 20th February, 1961.

Chapter 12
Publications of Impregilo, Milan.
Reports from the Volta River Authority, Kaiser Engineers Inc. and Impregilo.

Chapters 13 and 14
Reports from the Volta River Authority, Kaiser Engineers Inc. and Impregilo.

Chapter 15
Volta River Development Act, 1961. Government of Ghana.

Chapter 16
G. W. LAWSON *et. al.*, *Publications of Volta Basin Research Project*. University of Ghana.

Chapter 17
Volta River Project Preparatory Commission Report. Vol. I. London, H.M.S.O., 1956.

Chapter 18
MARION JOHNSON, *Ashanti East of the Volta*. Transactions of the Historical Society of Ghana. Vol. 3, 1965.
K. AMEYAW, *Akan oral traditions*. Volta Basin Research Project.

Chapter 19
Ed. R. CHAMBERS, *Volta Resettlement Symposium Papers*. V.R.A. and University of Science and Technology, Kumasi, 1965.
Report of W.F.P. Mission on the appraisal of the Volta River Resettlement in Ghana. F.A.O. (Food and Agriculture Organization of the United Nations), Rome, 1967.

Chapter 20
Irrigation of the Accra Plains. Kaiser Engineers Inc., 1965.

Report on survey of the lower Volta River flood plain. Vols. 1–5, F.A.O., Rome, 1963.

ROWENA LAWSON: Reports on structure, migration and resettlement of Ewe fishing units and on the *Egeria* (clam) fishing industry on the Lower Volta. University of Ghana, 1958 and 1963.

Chapter 21

Records furnished by Kaiser Engineers Inc. and the individual supply contractors.

Chapter 22

Records furnished by Kaiser Engineers Inc. and by Valco.

Chapters 23, 24 and 25

Reports from V.R.A., Kaiser Engineers Inc. and Impregilo.

Chapter 26

Volta River Authority Records.

Chapters 27, 28, 29 and 30

Reports from Volta River Authority, Acres International Ltd, The Shawinigan Engineering Co. Ltd and the Canadian International Development Agency.

A. B. FUTA, *The Volta Lake Transport System in Ghana*, German Agency for Technical Co-operation (GTZ), Munich, 1982 (mimeo paper).

A. B. FUTA, *The Structure of the Volta River Authority*, U.N. Inter-regional meeting of International River/Lake organisations, Dakar, Senegal, May 1981 (mimeo paper).

Valco Annual Reports 1979, 1980, 1981.

RONALD GRAHAM, *The Aluminium Industry and the Third World*, Zed Press, London, 1982 (including bibliography).

E. L. QUARTEY and L. ALLEN, 'Hydroelectric Power in Ghana', Parts 1 and 2, *Water Power and Dam Construction* (December 1980, February 1981).

DAVID HART, 'The Volta River Project', *A Case Study in Politics and Technology*, Edinburgh University Press, 1980 (including bibliography.

For a more detailed study of the subject, attention is drawn to two comprehensive bibliographies:

T. W. COCHRANE: *A Bibliography of the Volta River Authority Programme.* Volta River Authority, Accra, 1968. Mr Cochrane is Librarian of the V.R.A.

ROBERT CHAMBERS, *A Bibliography of the V.R.A. Resettlement Programme*, 1968.

Further information concerning any of this source material may be obtained from The Atlas Bookshop, P.O. Box M.160, Accra, Ghana.

INDEX

Index for Part 3

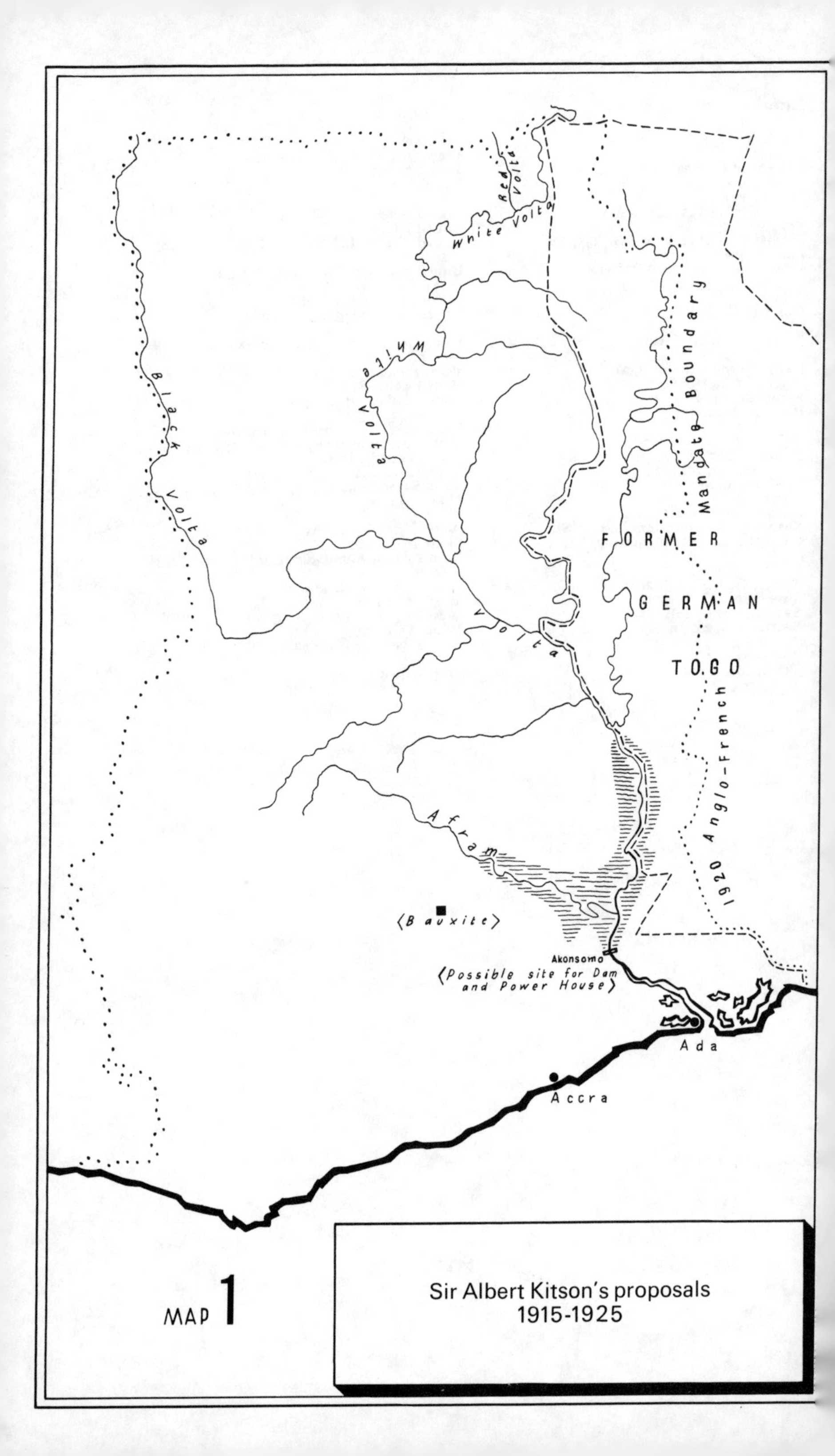

Sir Albert Kitson's proposals 1915-1925

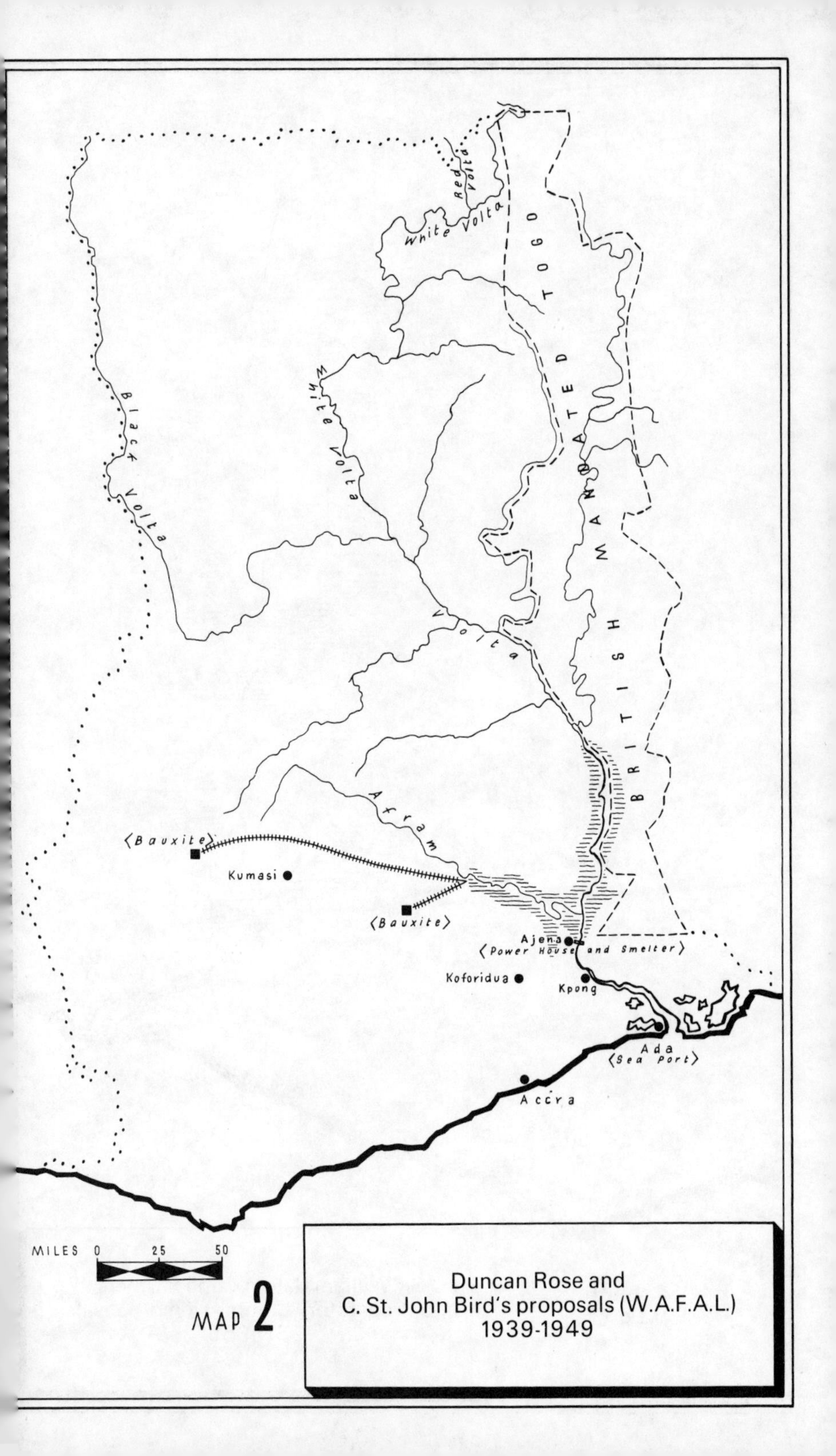
Red Volta
White Volta
White Volta
Black Volta
Volta
TOGO
BRITISH MANDATED
Afram
<Bauxite>
Kumasi
<Bauxite>
Ajena
<Power House and Smelter>
Koforidua
Kpong
Ada
<Sea Port>
Accra
MILES 0 25 50
MAP 2
Duncan Rose and
C. St. John Bird's proposals (W.A.F.A.L.)
1939-1949

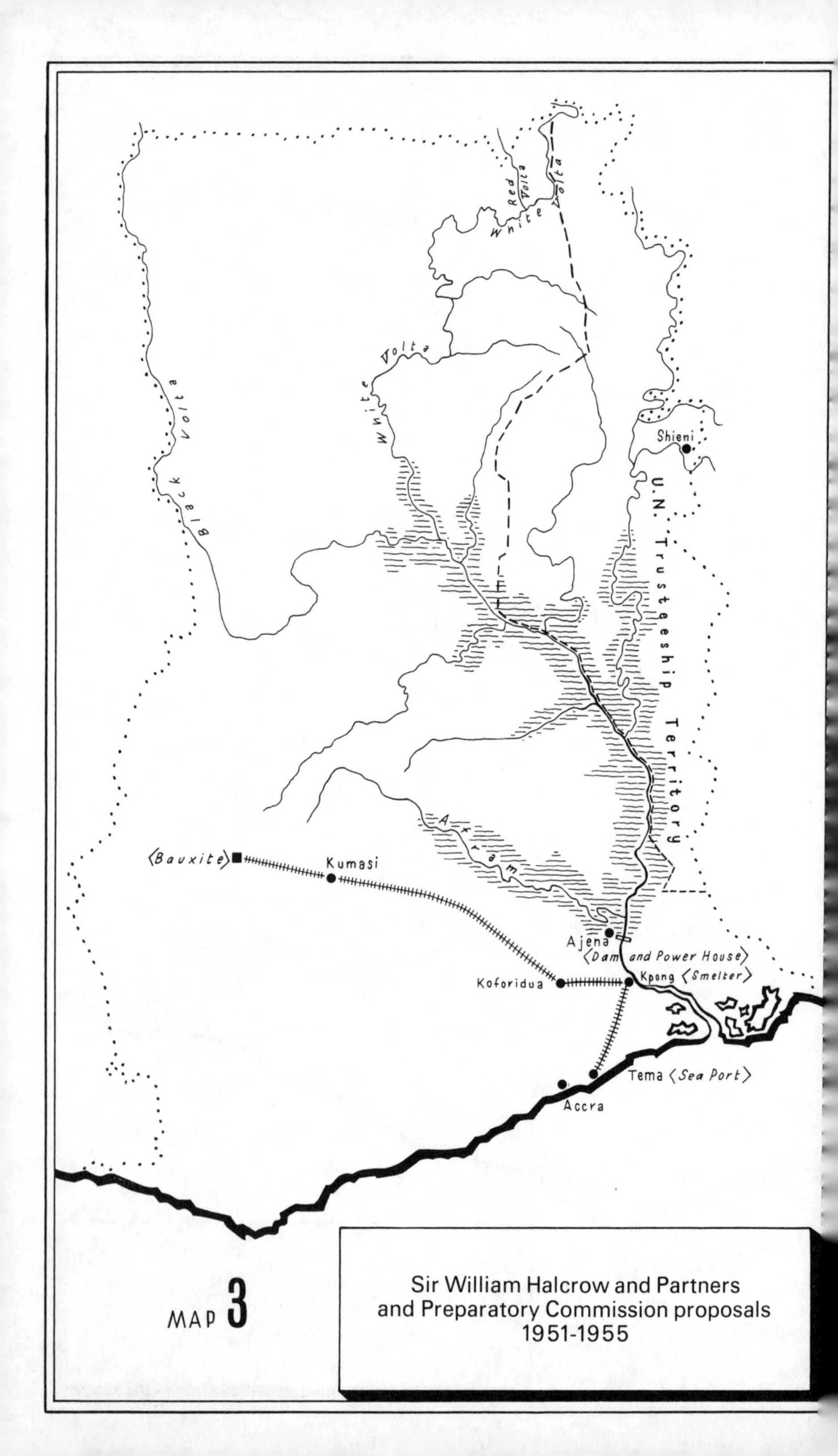

Sir William Halcrow and Partners and Preparatory Commission proposals 1951-1955

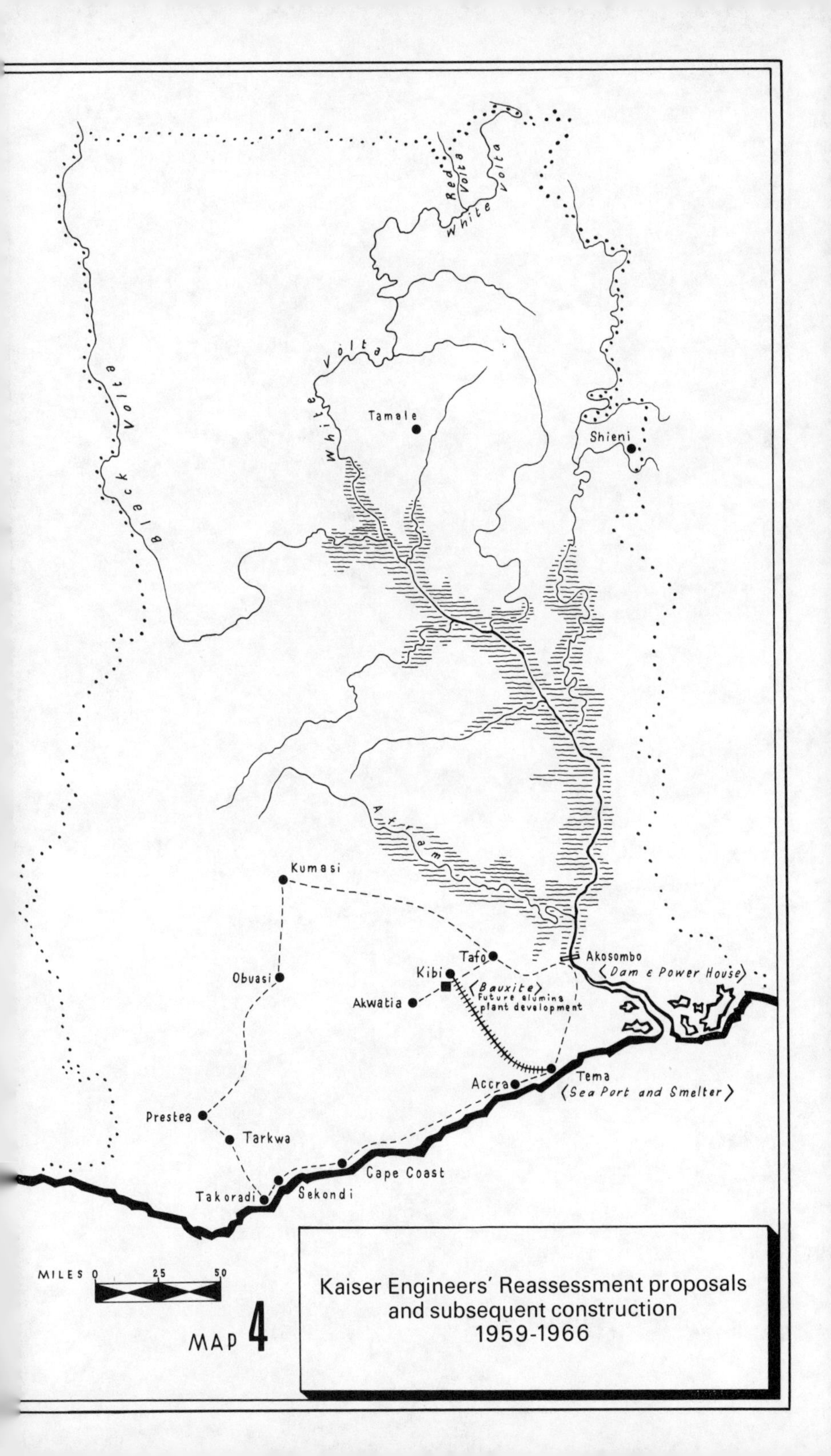

Kaiser Engineers' Reassessment proposals and subsequent construction 1959-1966